SARTON

ON THE HISTORY
OF SCIENCE

SARTON
ON THE HISTORY
OF SCIENCE

Essays By
George Sarton

Selected and Edited By
DOROTHY STIMSON

HARVARD UNIVERSITY PRESS
Cambridge, Massachusetts

1 9 6 2

Preface

For forty years the name of George Sarton has been practically synonymous with the history of science. He was its most tireless spokesman in this country. He demonstrated its possibilities in literally hundreds of articles and in many books. He founded and edited a quarterly journal with international circulation that other scholars might have a hearing. In his monumental *Introduction to the History of Science* he provided a veritable encyclopedia of facts and references from ancient times through the fourteenth century. And at Harvard he helped train students as leaders and teachers for universities across the land. Before he came to the United States in 1915 there was no such subject in university curricula — histories of mathematics, of chemistry, of medicine, yes, but none of science. Forty years later students were earning their doctorates in that field at half a dozen university centers.

How was all this possible, aside from the passionate enthusiasm of one man? One reason was that interest had already been awakened in this country from several different sources. A group of strong professors at Columbia University, notable among them James Harvey Robinson the historian and James H. Breasted the Egyptologist (later at the University of Chicago) were emphasizing what Robinson called "the New History" of culture and ideas rather than the old one of politics and wars. History was rapidly shifting from kings, battles, and dates to trends and influences, helped on by the new-style textbooks the two men wrote separately and together, as well as by their powerful influence in their crowded lecture rooms. Professor Robinson's course on the History of the Intellectual Class in Western Europe was an eye-opening experience for scores of graduate students year after year. Out of that course came his *Mind in the Making* (1921).

In that same period before the first World War, a new movement was stirring in philosophy classrooms, notably at the Johns Hopkins University. Under the guidance of Professor Arthur O. Lovejoy and his colleagues, especially George Boas, philosophy was swinging from a preoccupation with philology to a deep concern with ideas. The influence of Lovejoy's seminars for graduate students was later spread far and wide through his *Great Chain of Being* (1936).

The rapid advance of science in the latter part of the nineteenth century had kept alive the old struggle between science and religion, so-called. Andrew D. White's scholarly volumes on *A History of the Warfare of Science with Theology in Christendom* (1896) were widely read and his library of rare books helped to make Cornell University another center for further studies, such as those of George L. Burr on witchcraft. Professor Lynn Thorndike at Western Reserve University (later at Columbia) had already started on his many-volumed *History of Magic and Experimental Science* (1923–1958). Another lover of history and of rare books, Dr. William Osler, was infecting his students in the Hopkins Medical School with his own enthusiasms, continued by his lectures at Yale in 1913 that became his *Evolution of Modern Medicine* (1921). These enthusiasms his colleague Dr. William Welch shared to the fullest extent. And Dr. Welch became in the final stage of his long and varied career the founder and first director of the Institute for the History of Medicine at the Hopkins University.

Consequently there was already a good deal of interest in the history of science when the young Belgian scholar, George Sarton, came to Cambridge to work at Harvard as a research associate of the Carnegie Institution of Washington. Following a meeting of the American Historical Association in Boston, December 1923, David Eugene Smith, historian of mathematics, Lynn Thorndike, and a group of other members organized the History of Science Society, incorporating it in January 1924. Its main purpose was to further that subject and at the same time to support Dr. Sarton's work, especially his journal, *Isis*, again in publication after the interruption of the four war years. During the succeeding years the membership of the Society represented a wide range of interest, from scientists in many fields to historians, philosophers, journalists, publishers, and bibliophiles. When Dr. Sarton finally resigned the editorship of the journal and the Society in 1953 took over full responsibility for its publication, it had the support of some fifteen hundred members and an established place nationally and internationally.

Many of Dr. Sarton's articles appeared in *Isis*, often as prefaces to volumes. Before his death he had drawn up a list of some of these, with others printed elsewhere, which he considered worth republishing. From that list, with three exceptions, this collection has been made. Its intent is to present the importance of the history of science as he understood it, as the unifying factor underlying all knowledge and forming its very core of truth. To him it was also the bridge that would bring science and the humanities together. This theme runs throughout his work. He presented it in articles, in biographical studies, in lectures, and in books. Intensely as this conviction was held, it was inseparable from the man himself, for he gave it all his energies and thought as well as his time and money, to the exclusion of much else except music and art. A scientist by training, he had made himself a historian, a medievalist, a linguist, an Arabic scholar, and an Orientalist as he followed his major interest. His writing thus became an expression of his personality in a fashion unusual in scholarship. He did not hesitate to use the first person singular or to note the parallels between his own experiences and that of the man whose life he was describing. Even his footnotes on occasion are personal. His mind ranging over wide fields of knowledge was quick to see comparisons and contrasts in illustrations drawn from different civilizations and literatures, and some of his biographical articles, though with one name in the title, may deal with one or more other men almost as fully. The essay on Bonpland, for instance, reprinted here, is on Alexander von Humboldt as well. Again and again these analogies impress one with the range and depth of his knowledge.

To make this selection of Dr. Sarton's writings adequately representative, they are divided into three groups with a certain amount of overlapping: to present Dr. Sarton (I) as propagandist, so to speak, for the history of science; (II) as historian demonstrating its possibilities; and (III) as writer and editor explaining his methods and procedures. The first group of essays is roughly in logical order; the second, in the chronological order of the men discussed. The third proceeds from the reasons for the choice of English for the language of his journal through a discussion of some of the problems arising out of his work and of suggestions of work needing to be done, concluding with a summing up of what he himself had accomplished.

In the leading article, apparently the last important one he wrote, the general reader will find a masterly summary of the history of science, succinct, concise, and far less personal and discursive than was usual for him. It is the epitome of his fifty years of thought and study on the history of science. Comparing it with his statement twenty years or so earlier giving the guiding principles in all his work, one finds unchanged his emphasis on the unity of all knowledge — the symbol of the tree with roots and branches constantly recurs — on the search for truth as its goal and on the importance of the history of science as the very core of the tree of knowledge connecting all its branches. With his advancing years and the gradual acceptance of his views, his writing became less dogmatic, more tolerant, and more insistent on the brotherhood of all men, East and West, who should together pursue ultimate truth in universal peace. Science is above political, racial, and geographical boundaries and is the creation not of a few but of the many, each adding his bit to that of others. Therefore its history should both humble the student and also impress him with the supreme importance of the search for truth regardless of the searcher's race, creed, or color. Dr. Sarton's own studies in Arabic deepened his convictions on this point, as did his interest in Chinese, Japanese, and Indian cultures.

The essays on Avicenna and Maimonides are important representatives of these principles and of the author's erudition. They also contain much material difficult to find elsewhere and they appeared originally in publications not generally available. The summary of the Renaissance period, "The Quest for Truth," valuable for its concise comprehensiveness, is another such example. "Simon Stevin of Bruges" is a thoroughgoing historical study of an important but somewhat ignored scientist — as well as, perhaps, an unconscious tribute to the author's native land. Some of these articles were originally lectures to which the author added technical material before publication. Others, like those on Montucla and Quetelet, are fully developed studies. Still others, like "Notes on the Reviewing of Learned Books," are in the nature of an editorial prefacing a volume of his quarterly.

PREFACE

Most of Dr. Sarton's work centers around men; for whatever their theories, human beings do the work. He therefore studies men, seeking to determine the influences upon and through them, always relating them to their own era. Thus his first scholarly love, Leonardo da Vinci, could not properly be studied until he knew what had gone before. Out of that search grew his many-volumed *Introduction to the History of Science* which after twenty years' labor he had to end fifty years before he had reached da Vinci. No collection of his writings would be adequately representative without some word on Leonardo; hence a hitherto unpublished article is given here. It, like many of the other articles, exemplifies the author's own personality as well. His warmheartedness touches all his subjects. He seems to share their trials and to rejoice with them over their triumphs. "Rumphius," "Bonpland," and "Moseley" are illustrative of that and also of his generosity in wishing to give well-earned credit to workers perhaps not too well known. This markedly personal character of his style runs throughout his work, even the drily technical parts. What would be egoism and antiquarianism in another are in his case the product of a simple, whole-souled absorption of the man in his work.

Scholar that he was, his articles are a student's great resource. They fairly bristle with bibliographical detail. Lists of publications, editions, and dates are given meticulously, accompanied often by a careful comment on which books he himself has handled and which he has not seen. He sought for portraits to illustrate his biographies, for seeing to him was worth many words. And the authenticity of these portraits was a matter as important as the authenticity of a manuscript. His "Iconographic Honesty" makes that very clear.

Obviously this collection is just a sample of Dr. Sarton's productiveness. However, the editor hopes that through the presentation of some of the author's views on the history of science, some illustrations of his historical and biographical studies, and some accounts of his scholarly procedures evolved out of his rich experience the author himself will become a personnage to the reader. For, encyclopedic scholar that he was, he was also a warm, compassionate, gentle human being, humble in his own eyes, intense in his devotion to his chosen subject, but ever ready to help others. Internationally known and admired, he was greatly loved for himself by student and colleague alike. If the reader

PREFACE

becomes interested in the history of science, well and good. If he becomes interested in George Sarton himself and wants to know more of his work, then this compilation will have accomplished its purpose.

At the suggestion of Miss May Sarton and Professor I. Bernard Cohen, Dr. Sarton's literary executors, the Director of Harvard University Press, Mr. Thomas J. Wilson, asked me to select and edit some of Dr. Sarton's writings on the history of science for republication. With their support and encouragement and with that of Mr. Joseph D. Elder, science editor of the Press, whose help along the way has been invaluable, it has been both a pleasure and a privilege to work on this material.

For permission to use copyright material, grateful acknowledgment is made to the Americana Corporation, publishers of the *Encylopedia Americana* for "Science, History of"; to the Carnegie Institution of Washington for excerpts from *Introduction to the History of Science*, Monograph No. 501 (1938), and Year Book No. 48; to the Metropolitan Museum of Art for "The Quest for Truth" from *Symposium on the Renaissance*; to the New York Academy of Medicine for "Avicenna"; to the Cleveland Medical Library Association for "Maimonides"; to the Académie Internationale d'Histoire des Sciences for "Acta atque Agenda."

D. S.

CONTENTS

CONTENTS

CONTENTS

Biographical Note

George Sarton was born August 31, 1884, in Ghent, Belgium. Two years after graduation from the University of Ghent in 1906, he won for a paper in chemistry a gold medal offered by the four Belgian universities. He received his doctorate in mathematics (his thesis was on Newtonian mechanics) in 1911, and in that year married Mabel Eleanor Elwes, an English artist; their daughter, Eleanor May, the poet and novelist, was born the next year. Forced to flee by the invasion of Belgium, he came to the United States in 1915 by way of Holland and England, becoming a naturalized citizen in 1924. He lectured on the history of science at George Washington University and at the University of Illinois in 1915, then at Harvard in 1916–1918. In 1919 he was appointed research associate of the Carnegie Institution of Washington, a position he held till 1948. Moving to Cambridge in 1920, where he lived thereafter, he made his headquarters in Widener Library, and lectured on the history of science at Harvard. In 1940 he was appointed professor of the history of science.

In 1912 he founded *Isis*, a quarterly journal in the history of science, and edited it for forty years. In 1936 he founded and edited *Osiris* as an occasional journal for long articles. His major work, *Introduction to the History of Science* (three volumes in five parts, 1927, 1931, 1947, and 1948), was the outgrowth of his desire to make a thorough study of Leonardo da Vinci's background. The author of a dozen other books and many scores of articles, at the time of his death he was working on a nine-volume history of science of which he had completed but two. For a full bibliography of his writings, prepared by Katharine Strelsky, see *Isis 48*, 336–346 (1957).

Dr. Sarton received many honors in his later years, including seven honorary degrees, and election to membership in learned societies in America, Europe, and the Near and Far East. From 1950 to his death he was president of the International Union of the History of Science. He died in Cambridge, Massachusetts, on March 22, 1956.

D. S.

NOTE: In this book the technical and bibliographical material is printed ordinarily in small type to help the general reader to do some judicious skipping, yet preserving much of value for the student. Iconographical notes and most appendices are omitted, as are also the illustrations of title pages and the references to them. These specific page references are omitted without noting that fact; all other deletions are indicated by . . . ; editorial additions and translations are enclosed in square brackets. Punctuation and paragraph and sentence structure have been left unchanged, thus providing an interesting illustration of the author's rapid increase in facility in the use of his adopted language.

History of Science

If ONE DEFINES science as systematized positive knowledge (or what has been taken as such at different ages and in different places), then the history of science is the description and explanation of the development of that knowledge. For example, considering all that we know today in astronomy, how did we obtain that knowledge? It is a very long story which takes us back to prehistoric times when men began to observe the sun, moon, stars, planets — and wondered. Our knowledge of today has been reached only after taking an infinity of steps and false steps.

If one bears in mind that the acquisition and systematization of positive knowledge is the only human activity which is truly cumulative and progressive, one realizes at once the importance of these studies. Should one wish to account for the progress of mankind, one must focus one's explanation upon that activity, and the history of science in this broad sense becomes the keystone of all historical investigations.

The definition will be clarified if we illustrate it with an outline of the way the scientific experience of mankind was gradually developed until it reached its present depth and complexity. The reader must be warned, however, that this is not a history of science but simply a general view of it, enough to give him some awareness of the many kinds of investigations which are involved.

Any history must begin with an account of the dawn of science. This is a part of anthropology and prehistory. How did early men invent and fashion their tools? How did they domesticate animals and learn the tricks of husbandry? How did they obtain the rudiments of arithmetic, geometry, astronomy? How did they find the best foods

1

for health and the best drugs for sickness? How did they learn to navigate the waters, to hunt and fish, to lift and transport heavy stones, to dig for ores and smelt them, to make bronze implements and later iron ones? How did they discover the ways of social life in families and tribes, the methods of economy and government? How did they develop a language and means of recording it? Did they achieve a kind of social or historical consciousness, and if so, how did they gratify it? How were artistic and religious needs awakened in them and what did they do to obey them?

These are but a few of the innumerable questions which must be answered in order to understand the level of knowledge which man had attained before the curtain of recorded history rises. The earliest cultures represented by written documents occurred in Egypt, Mesopotamia, India, and China, and an account of these cultures cannot be given without the collaboration of orientalists able to decipher and to interpret those documents. Historians of science must manage to extract from the studies of orientalists all the data pertinent to their own quest and to explain them.

After many vicissitudes and the violent upheaval caused by the discovery and use of iron weapons, a gifted nation, the Greeks, tried to explain the universe and themselves in a deeper way. The earliest of those Greeks were settled along the western coast of Asia Minor, in Sicily and south Italy. We owe them the elements of mathematics, astronomy, mechanics, physics, geography, medicine. Few of their writings have been preserved and what we know is derived from fragments and indirect quotations.

The golden age of Greek science coincided with the golden age of Greek literature and art. Its main center was Athens; the language, Greek; the time, 5th and 4th centuries B.C. The 5th century witnessed great philosophers such as Democritus and Leucippus, who invented the atomic theory, mathematicians like Hippocrates of Chios, astronomers like Philolaus, and physicians like Hippocrates of Cos, "the father of medicine." That golden century was brought to a close by the political murder of Socrates in 399 B.C.

The 4th century was even richer in scientific achievements and it was dominated by two philosophers, two of the greatest personalities of their kind in the whole past: the first half of the century was dominated by Plato, founder of the Academy of Athens; the second half by Aristotle, founder of the Lyceum in the same city. So far-reaching was the influence of these men that to this day every thinking man, every scientist, may be said to be either a Platonist or an Aristotelian.

The political ruin of Greece caused such deep changes all around that scholars are agreed in using a new name to designate the new culture which developed chiefly from the 3d century B.C. on. The center was no longer in Athens but in Alexandria and other Greek cities outside of Europe. The new culture was no longer called Hellenic but Hellenistic. It is immortalized by the deeds of 3d century anatomists like Herophilus and Erasistratus and of mathematicians and astronomers like Euclid, Aristarchus, Archimedes, Eratosthenes, and Apollonius, the last three flourishing in the second half of that century, and Hipparchus in the late 2d century B.C. The end of the Hellenistic age merged with the Roman age because Rome had become the political master of the Greek world just before the Christian era began. Roman science was but a reflection of the Greek; a few scientific books were written in Latin, however, by Lucretius, and Cicero, in the 1st century B.C., and in the succeeding 1st century A.D. by Celsus, Pliny, and Frontinus. Yet, until the 7th century, all the outstanding names are Greek, the two greatest of all being the 2d century astronomer and geographer Ptolemy and the physician Galen — two giants dominating the golden age of the Roman Empire with Greek writings. Later appear more mathematicians and astronomers like Diophantus and Pappus (3d century), Theon of Alexandria in the 4th, and in the 5th his daughter Hypatia, and Proclus; philosophers like Philoponus and Simplicius (6th century); physicians like Oribasius (4th century), Aetios and Alexander of Tralles in the 6th, and Paulus Aegineta in the 7th century. This has brought us to the time of the Moslem conquest of a great part of the Mediterranean world.

It is impossible to describe here even in briefest manner all the vicissitudes of medieval history. From the 9th century to the 11th, all of Greek knowledge was translated into Arabic and the best new scientific books were written in Arabic. After the 11th century, the whole was gradually retranslated into Latin, and to a smaller extent into Hebrew. The greatest physician of the early Middle Ages was the 11th century ibn-Sina (Avicenna) and the most original scientist was

3

his contemporary al-Biruni. The leading mathematicians and astronomers of that period (9th to 11th century) were all writing in Arabic — al-Khwarizmi, al-Farghani, and al-Battani in the 9th century, Abul-Wefa in the 10th, Omar Khayyám and al Zarqali in the 11th — as were the leading philosophers, the 9th century al-Kindi, al-Farabi (10th), and ibn-Sina and al-Ghazzali, both 11th century. Arabic culture was international, extending from the far west (Spain and Morocco) to India; it was interracial and interreligious, for it included not only Moslems but also Jews and Christians. The common features were the Arabic language and the Islamic culture it served to express.

Later medieval thought was dominated by three giants, the Moslem ibn-Rushd (Averroes), the Jew Maimonides (both 12th century), and the 13th century Christian, St. Thomas Aquinas.

The greatest events of the 15th century were the invention of typography about the middle of it and the geographical discoveries initiated by Henry the Navigator and reaching a climax at the end of the century with Columbus and others. These geographical discoveries continued during the 16th century and increased immeasurably human experience in many directions.

The discovery of printing did not mean simply a far greater diffusion of ideas than had been possible before, but also the production of *standard* texts and a little later *standard* illustrations. For the first time the progress of knowledge could be registered forever as soon as it was made, standardized and transmitted to every corner of the civilized world. Until that period East and West had worked together, but the Moslem East, increasingly inhibited by religious obscurantism, rejected printing and ceased to cooperate with the Western world.

The discovery of printing was so pregnant that it is well to consider it the beginning of a new period, the so-called Renaissance, almost exclusively Western (as far as science is concerned). If we define the Renaissance as the period 1450 to 1600, we find that one of its main characteristics was the recovery of the texts of the Greek classics, most of which had been known only through Latin translations of Arabic translations. In other respects the Renaissance was essentially the continuation of the Middle Ages. There were a few giants like Leonardo da Vinci, Nicolaus Copernicus and Andreas Vesalius, Vannoccio Biringuccio and Rodolphus Agricola, Ambroise Paré and Pierre

4

Belon, Konrad von Gesner, Tycho Brahe, William Gilbert and Simon Stevin, and rebels like Philippus Aureolus Paracelsus and Bernard Palissy, but modern science cannot be said to begin in earnest until the 17th century with such men as Francis Bacon, Galileo Galilei, Johannes Kepler, and René Descartes.

During the Renaissance printing shops had become very numerous and the number of printed books had increased immeasurably. The steady accumulation of knowledge was guaranteed. Another powerful means of controlling and recording the progress of science was the establishment of academies. The first academies of science date from the 17th century, the Accademia dei Lincei in Rome (1603–1630), the Accademia del Cimento in Florence (1657–1667), the Royal Society in London (1662), the Académie des Sciences in Paris (1666). The books and journals sponsored by those academies and a few other journals such as the *Journal des savants* of Paris (1665) and the *Acta eruditorum* of Leipzig (1682) guided the activities of men of science wherever they were working.

Almost all the leading scientists were fellows of at least one of these academies, and it would be possible to describe the development of science in innumerable directions on the basis of the academic publications. The main monuments of modern science, however, are the great treatises such as the *Principia mathematica* of Sir Isaac Newton (1687); the *Traité de la lumière* of Christian Huygens (1690), and a great many others, too many to be listed.

In the 17th and 18th centuries the number of distinguished men of science is so great that an enumeration of them would be impossible. It is more interesting to point out that they were distributed all over Europe. It became clearer than ever that scientific activities are international; the history of science in any one country, however great, is very incomplete, because some of the essential work was done in other countries. Even such a small country as Switzerland produced its full share of scientific heroes: Paracelsus, Gesner, the Bernoullis, Albrecht von Haller, Leonhard Euler, Lambert, Steiner, and others. Young America started making her own gifts with Benjamin Franklin, John Winthrop, Benjamin Thompson (Count Rumford).

During the 19th century, science developed so fast and in so many directions, with almost incredible luxuriance, and yet with so much steadiness that even the best observers were deceived and became a little too optimistic. They believed that science was approaching a stage of perfection. Further progress would simply consist in obtaining an infinity of new data to complete the schemes of the naturalists, or in making physical measurements with greater precision and expressing results with more decimals. That peaceful and optimistic climate was upset toward the end of the century, when there began a series of inventions which changed radically the material conditions of life and caused the 20th century to be so completely different from the preceding ones that the whole past tends to be unified in our remembrance. Many people seem to believe that an entirely new world began in the 20th century, and they are not quite wrong.

Many of these fundamental inventions were not fully developed until the end of the 19th century, but then their growth was so rapid and their diffusion so intense that they have become essential parts of 20th century environment: dynamos, electric motors, telegraphs and telephones, internal combustion engines, phonographs, aviation, cinema, wireless, radio, television, methods of refrigeration, plastics (each of these words could easily be amplified into many volumes). The purely scientific discoveries have been equally revolutionary; they have upset many sciences as deeply as inventions have upset the ways of life. It will suffice to refer to the discovery of X-rays (Wilhelm Konrad Roentgen, 1895), radioactivity (Antoine Henri Becquerel, 1896), and psychoanalysis (Sigmund Freud, 1900 and after), to the rediscovery of Mendelism (1900), to the discovery of the theory of quanta (Max Karl Ernst Planck, 1901), theory of mutations (Hugo De Vries, 1901–1903), radium (Pierre and Marie Curie, 1903), special and general theories of relativity (Albert Einstein, 1905, 1916), and disintegration of the atom (Sir Ernest Rutherford, 1919).

Men of science and technicians want to know the latest results; they consider previous ones as obsolete and disregard them. The historian of science, however, is interested not only in the newest results but in the whole evolution which has led to them and made them possible. The latest results are like the new fruits of a tree; the fruits serve our immediate needs, yet without the tree the fruits could not come into being. The historian of science wants to know the tree of knowledge with all its roots and branches; he appreciates the fruits of today but not more so than those of the past and the future.

Since the 18th century at least, that is, since the time of Giovanni Battista Vico, Montesquieu, and Voltaire, the concept of history has become more and more comprehensive. At first, historians were concerned mainly with political and military history; they learned gradually to attach more attention to arts and letters, religion, and economics. Thus the old political history was transformed into something much broader which might be called the history of culture.

The historical field was extended also in a geographical way. Early historians (like the Jewish ones) were concerned only with the history of their own people; under Greek and Roman influence the geographical field was increased; but a great many centuries were to elapse before historians obtained a sufficient knowledge of all the nations (East and West) and included all of them in their conception of mankind or the scope of their own studies.

It was only in relatively recent times that the importance and centrality of the history of science was realized, and even today the great majority of historians do not realize it fully. There were a few pioneers beginning with the end of the 17th century (not to go back any further).

Witness such men as the Swiss, Daniel LeClerc (1652–1722) and Albrecht von Haller (1708–1777); the Germans, J. C. Barkhausen (1666–1723), J. C. Heilbronner (1706–c.1747), Johann Beckmann (1739–1811), A. F. Hecker (1795–1850), Abraham Gotthelf Kästner (1719–1800), Johann Friedrich Gmelin (1748–1804); the English, John Freind (1675–1728), Joseph Priestley (1733–1804), Adam Smith (1723–1790); the Swedish, Olaf Celsius (1670–1756); the French, Jean Etienne Montucla (1725–1799) and Jean Sylvain Bailly (1736–1793).

But the first man to introduce this theme in a broader context and to increase its circulation was the French philosopher, Auguste Comte, who developed it in his *Cours de philosophie positive* (1830–1842). His views were discussed by another French philosopher, Antoine Augustin Cournot, in 1861, but the real inheritor of Comte's thought and the first great teacher of the history of science was Paul Tannery (1843–1904). During the 20th century his example has been followed by many scholars in the leading countries. The history of science has become a full-fledged discipline; yet the number of men who can devote their whole time to it is still very small.

One would expect philosophers to be specially interested in the history of science, because the philosophical implications of scientific work are not clear until one considers science in its growth. In order to understand a function, it does not suffice to consider only the last points in the curve which represents it; one must take into account the whole curve. On the other hand, the historian of science cannot accomplish his task satisfactorily unless he understands the philosophical implications of science. Many men of science were primarily inventors and technicians, avoiding philosophy; yet none grew up in a philosophical vacuum. Every scientist is influenced by the religious and philosophical conceptions of his time, whether he is aware of it or not.

The methods which the historian of science uses are necessarily the same as those used by other historians, but as they must be applied to scientific facts and theories, the historians of science must receive a scientific preparation as well as a purely historical one. It is impossible to understand and to appreciate scientific documents without adequate scientific knowledge. All the difficulties of the history of science stem from the necessity of a double education. Much bad work has been done by historians who did not know science and also by men of science who had no idea of historical methods, and did not even realize that such methods existed.

The main point is that knowledge of any kind is worthless unless it be as accurate as conditions permit. It is here that the conflict of methods appears. A physicist fully aware of all the difficulties of physical measurements may be trusted to do his best to overcome these difficulties; the same man is not aware of historical difficulties and of the need of historical precision.

The historian like the scientist must try to be as accurate as possible, yet must remember that the same degree of precision is not required in every case. For example, when the length of an object is mentioned, the unit varies with the needs; it may be expressed in microns, millimeters, yards, or miles; in the same way, it may be necessary to give the time and date of an event very exactly, say 9 A.M., March 21, 1591 (Gregorian); in other cases, it may suffice to say March 1591, or 1591, or "toward the end of the 16th century." All those expressions are accurate, though their degrees of accuracy vary considerably. To use a higher degree of precision than the circumstances warrant is a form of pedantry. On the other hand, when the historian is investigating any subject he should note the dates and other facts with as much precision as possible; it will be easy enough to diminish the precision in his account if needed, while the reverse procedure is impossible.

Historical methods are on the whole less tangible and more delicate than physical methods, and therefore more difficult to set forth. This is due to the fact that the subject matter of history is human and therefore capricious, even when we are dealing with the development of science. The reactions of a man of science are infinitely more complex than those of the objects he is studying. The methods required to investigate ancient, medieval, or oriental science are, of course, more complex than those needed to explain modern events. In the case of contemporary events, described in our own language, it is hardly necessary to study the background, which we know well enough, or to consider linguistic difficulties. On the other hand, when one tries to appreciate the trigonometrical facts included in Arabic books written in Baghdad in the 9th century, one must be able to evoke the culture of that place and period, understand the Arabic language and Islamic religion, and so forth. That kind of work is not simply historical but philological. The basis of it is always what the philologists call "the establishment of the text." That is (in this case), one must determine as exactly as possible what was written by al-Khwarizmi, by Habash al-Hasib, by al-Battani; one must establish the text of their very words (either as written by themselves or quoted by others), and it is only after that has been done that their trigonometry ideas can be safely investigated. To assume that al-Battani may have written this or that is worthless and perverse.

The establishment of a text implies a very special and complex training. Philological and historical methods can be learned only through personal experience in their use, and that process of learning is never completed.

As the history of science is a new discipline, the teaching of it is very recent. The first professorship was established at the Collège de

France in 1892, but the appointment of unqualified professors defeated the grand aim. Today, over 60 years later, in the writer's opinion university administrators have yet to appreciate (1) the importance of such studies; (2) the need of entrusting them to competent scholars equipped with the necessary training (scientific, historical, philosophical); (3) that such work, being difficult and still in the experimental stage, must be a full-time occupation. Too often that teaching has been entrusted, as a kind of side job, to men who, however eminent in other science fields, were not qualified to teach the history of science.

The teaching of the history of science is organized fairly well, though in different ways, in various European and Asiatic universities, as London, Paris, Frankfurt-am-Main, Moscow, and Ankara, and in a few American universities as Harvard, Wisconsin, Cornell, Yale, Johns Hopkins, and Brown. It is possible in those universities to continue these studies up to the degree of Ph.D. Professional historians of science are still exceedingly rare.

It should be noted that the history of science as defined by Comte, Tannery, and the author of this article is essentially different from the history of particular sciences or of particular techniques. To consider technology first, the explanation of its development implies a large amount of economic or sociologic research. Inventions are made to answer definite needs, and each new invention of any importance creates new needs and causes an endless chain of other inventions. For example, the discovery of the first steam engine opened up an enormous branch of technology. Not only were those engines and their accessories gradually improved but their availability suggested new technical departures, such as railways, steamships, and an infinity of other machines. The historian of any branch of technology must be familiar with patent literature and with all kinds of industrial and commercial ramifications, even with legal problems with which the historian of science would hardly concern himself.

On the other hand, the historian of science must try to take into account every branch of science, and investigate their interrelationships which are frequent and complex. Indeed, his main purpose is to explain the development of the whole tree of science, a tree which never ceases to grow in its roots, trunk, and innumerable branches and twigs.

10

He must explain how the progress of one science affected the progress of other branches. For example, the development of microscopes and telescopes implied the solution of physical and chemical problems and other technical difficulties; better microscopes influenced the progress of natural sciences, better telescopes accelerated astronomical progress and enabled us to conceive a universe (or universes) immeasurably larger than the universe of our ancestors.

As the historian of science is writing for scientists and learned men of every kind, he can never assume that the scientific knowledge of his readers is sufficient to understand the intricacies of any problem, and therefore his account should never be too technical. The historian of chemistry expects his readers to know chemical technicalities, but the historian of science cannot entertain the same expectations, for the majority of his readers are not chemists but physicians or physicists, naturalists, astronomers or mathematicians, philosophers or sociologists.

A general treatise on the history of science is thus less technical than one on medical or geological history, but what it loses on that side, it regains on another, because it is far broader. The historian of chemistry is more of a technician, the historian of science is more of a humanist; he is in the fullest sense the historian of mankind.

The history of science being a field of endless complexity and incredible size, it would be very foolish to say, "This is the way to study it or to teach it, and there is no other." There are many ways, many points of view, each of which is acceptable and useful, none of which is exclusive of the others. Some of the points of view have already been indicated. There is the point of view of the historian who wishes to understand as fully as possible the culture of a nation or of a period; the point of view of a professional man of science who would explore the origin and development of his own knowledge; the point of view of a man of letters who would include science in his survey, either because great men of science are, might, or should be distinguished authors, or because no writer can help having some kind of scientific background; the point of view of the philosopher whose main concern is to show the complex relationship between science and philosophy (how much either influenced the other). There are at least three other points of view also, the logical, psychological and sociological, which deserve to be examined more carefully.

11

Logicians may be tempted to unravel the logical concatenation of scientific facts and to give a logical interpretation of discoveries. They are bound to be surprised by the results of their inquiries, for the chronological order of discoveries is often very different from the logical one. In science as in art "the wind bloweth where it listeth." What some people call the logic of science is largely casual and retrospective; it is nevertheless useful to bring it out. Discoveries are not always made in logical order, but it is worthwhile and helpful to explain them in that order.

The methods of teaching, which are logical enough, are almost the reverse of the methods of discovery. The teachers of a vast subject, say inorganic chemistry or theoretical mechanics, must put the fundamental notions first in spite of the fact that these notions may have been the very last to be discovered. The teachers are not concerned with the historical order; their main purpose is to explain science as simply and clearly as possible.

Another set of historians is interested in the individual aspects of scientific work, and ask questions like the following: How did it happen that John Doe made such or such a discovery? Is it to be explained in rational or emotional terms? How does he compare with other scientists as a man, or with other men? How was his temper affected by work, rest, or play, by success or failure? How was he influenced by his social environment, and how did he influence it? How did he express and reveal himself, or fail to reveal himself? What was the quality of his spirit? His love of truth, his love of beauty, his love of justice, his religion, to what extent were they developed? Or was he indifferent to the world around him, blind to everything except the narrow field of his research? Not only the psychologist but the humanist tries to answer such questions, and innumerable others.

Instead of considering men of science individually and trying to find the individual roots of their activities, one may consider them as members of a social group and investigate the social pressures to which they may have been submitted. According to the official Soviet philosophy, "dialectical materialism" (or "diamat" as it is called in eastern Europe), science is explained primarily, if not exclusively, in social and economic terms. There is a core of truth in such explanations, for science does

12

not develop in a social vacuum and men of science are citizens, whom the state or their employers can use and abuse in many ways. Every man of science needs a modicum of food and other comforts in order to do his work; if called to arms and killed in battle, his activities come to an end; if he is a physicist or astronomer, his opportunities will depend upon the laboratory or observatory to which he has been admitted and his freedom will be limited by the good or bad will of administrators or fellow workers. Yet nobody can completely control his spirit; he may be helped or inhibited, but his scientific ideas are not determined by social factors. Honest men of science have often continued activities detrimental to their material interests. Historians of science should describe such conflicts as carefully as possible, thereby helping us to understand various forms of society and the psychology of exceptional men.

A vast literature devoted to the problems of the impact of society on science and of science on society may be classified under the general heading "Science and Society." A number of books *ad hoc* are listed in the present writer's *Horus* (pp. 94–97), but that list is incomplete and more books appear every day. Sociologists are tempted to restrict their interest in the history of science to these problems and their endless implications.

There are obviously many theoretical motives for studying the history of science. A man of science would study that history in order to throw light upon his own task and to increase his enjoyment of it; a philosopher, in order to relate science to philosophy and account for some variations of the latter; a psychologist, to explore the peculiarities and possibilities of the human mind; a sociologist, better to understand the many relationships between scientists and the social groups to which they belong.

The people who study a subject for theoretical reasons are probably exceptional; most students submit themselves to definite training for practical reasons. They wish to qualify themselves for a trade or profession. Looking at it from their angle, the study of the history of science will complete the training of scientific teachers (to teach well one needs a kind of perspective which can be obtained only by historical inquiries); it will improve the qualifications of students for many parascientific positions, such as those of librarians, editors, curators of museums, administrators, and other men having to deal directly or indirectly with scientific pursuits.

Bibliography. — There is no elaborate textbook covering the whole history of science from its prehistoric beginnings up to now. On the other hand, there are innumerable books dealing more or less completely with one branch of science, with one period, with one kind of people, or with one country. The best guide in that labyrinth is provided by Sarton, George, *Horus. A Guide to the History of Science* (Waltham, Mass., 1952).

A general account of the history of science as much as it can be put in one volume may be found in Singer, Charles, *Short History of Science to the Nineteenth Century*, to mid-19th century (Oxford, 1941); Dampier, Sir William C., *History of Science*, 4th ed. (Cambridge, Eng., 1949).

Much more elaborate accounts are Thorndike, Lynn, *History of Magic and Experimental Science*, from the 1st to the 16th century, 6 vols. (New York; 1923–1941); Sarton, George, *Introduction to the History of Science*, from Homer to end of the 14th century, 3 vols. in 5 (Baltimore, 1927–1948); Sarton, George, *History of Science*, from prehistoric times to the end of the 4th century B.C., vol. 1 (Cambridge, Mass., 1952); Wolf, Abraham, *History of Science, Technology and Philosophy in the Sixteenth and Seventeenth Centuries* (new ed., New York and London, 1951); id., *History of Science, Technology and Philosophy in the Eighteenth Century* (New York and London, 1952).

Science has developed in so many directions and with such incredible exuberance in the 19th and 20th centuries that it has become almost impossible to cover it. Yet, see Darmstaedter, Ludwig, *Handbuch zur Geschichte der Naturwissenschaft und der Technik* (Berlin, 1908), a list of discoveries in chronological order which requires 273 pages to cover the period 3500 B.C., to 1799, and 800 pages to cover the years 1800 to 1908; Lark-Horovitz, K., and Carmichael, Eleanor, *Chronology of Scientific Development, 1848–1948* (Washington, D.C., 1948), very short yet useful. The difficulties of writing the history of contemporary science are discussed by Sarton, George, "Remarks Concerning the History of Twentieth Century Science," *Isis 26*, 53–62 (1936) [see below, p. 355].

[1955]

Four Guiding Ideas

F OUR FUNDAMENTAL ideas run through the author's writings like Leitmotive in a Wagnerian drama. These four ideas may be briefly called (1) the idea of unity, (2) the humanity of science, (3) the great value of Eastern thought, (4) the supreme need of toleration and charity.

1. *The idea of unity.* The unity of nature must be postulated, for if it did not exist, if there were no inherent unity and consistency in nature, there would be no possibility of scientific knowledge. It must be possible to explain a cosmos, but chaos is essentially unexplainable. The existence of science and its astounding consistency (in spite of occasional, partial, temporary contradictions due to our ignorance) prove at one and the same time the unity of knowledge and the unity of nature. The fact that the building up of science has been done in the past and is done today by men of various races and many nationalities, inspired by different faiths, speaking different languages, proves that these men have the same needs and aspirations, reason in the same way, and, as far as they collaborate in the essential task of mankind, are united. Their collaboration has often been unorganized and un-premeditated, various efforts have been made here and there, then or later, without plan or design; yet inasmuch as every scientific effort aims at the same general purpose, all those efforts did converge and harmonize. The unity of mankind is an underlying reality which no civil war can obliterate.

The unity of nature, the unity of knowledge, and the unity of mankind are but three aspects of a single reality. Each aspect helps to justify the others. That trinity is but the dispersion of a fundamental unity, which is beyond our material grasp, but within our loving hearts.

15

2. *The humanity of science.* Science might be defined as the reflection of nature (of everything that is) by the human mind. Perfect science could be reflected only by a perfect, godlike mind. Human science is of course very imperfect, not only in the past, in the "darkest" ages, but even now and later; it will always be imperfect, but it is indefinitely perfectible. The imperfection of science is explained and to some extent mitigated by its humanity.

Scientific results are always abstractions, and they tend to become more and more abstract, hence they seem to lose their humanity. Such appearances cannot deceive anybody except hard-boiled scientists who care only for results or logical sequences. A scientific theory may be as beautiful as the Parthenon; both are equally abstract if you choose to look at them as they are and do not wonder how they came to be, but as soon as you investigate their genesis and development, the theory as well as the Parthenon becomes human, intensely so. Indeed, both were built up by men, both are primarily and almost exclusively human achievements; because of their humanity they touch us in a way no natural object could.

Science is as human as art or religion, neither more nor less. Its humanity is implicit; it takes a scientifically educated humanist to draw it out, just as it takes a musically educated humanist to draw out the humanity of music. The well-tempered historian admires the achievements of science in themselves, but much more so in their becoming, that is, their humanity.

Science is not distinct from religion or art in being more or less human than they are, but simply because it is the fruit of different needs or tendencies. Religions exist because men are hungry for goodness, for justice, for mercy; the arts exist because men are hungry for beauty; the sciences exist because men are hungry for truth. The division is not as clear-cut as that, but it is sufficient to mark out main oppositions. Think of a triangular pyramid; the people standing on different faces near the base may be very distant from one another, but they come nearer as they climb higher. Bigots, little scientists, mediocre artists may feel very distant from one another, but those whose religion is deeper feel very close to the great artists and the great scientists. The pyramid symbolizes a new kind of trinity culminating in unity.

3. *The great value of Eastern thought.* The majority of historians

have restricted their attention to Western achievements, and thus they have gradually evoked a conception of Western unity (at least spiritual unity) from which Eastern people were excluded. They seemed to assume a cleavage between East and West.

It is true they could not ignore the Eastern, Jewish, origin of our religion, but that was in their eyes a kind of miraculous exception. All else in our culture was considered Western; the synagogue itself had been superseded by the church, the Western Latin church, out of which all the churches of the West have developed.

We now know that the origins of Western science (not only of religion and art) are Oriental — Egyptian, Mesopotamian, Iranian — and it has been fully proved . . . that the Arabic and other Oriental achievements were extremely important during the Middle Ages. Greek science (itself partly Oriental) could not have reached us as soon as it did without the help of Eastern dragomans. Those dragomans — Jews, Eastern Christians, Muslims — did not simply transmit to us the ancient treasure, they enriched it, they gave it a new vitality. I have proved that at least from the ninth to the eleventh century (three full centuries) Arabic science was supreme. In order to understand mediaeval science and mediaeval thought one must explore the writings of many people, Western and Oriental. For the purely Asiatic traditions the main languages are Sanskrit, Tibetan, Chinese, and Japanese; for the Western tradition the main languages are Hebrew, Greek, Latin, Arabic. Note that even in the case of traditions which are more specially our own, one has to take into account two Oriental languages, Hebrew and Arabic. To judge mediaeval thought on the basis of, say, Latin writings only would be just as unfair as if our times were judged exclusively on the basis of the English or the Russian language; indeed, the unfairness would be greater, because the communications between one linguistic area and another were not as frequent, rapid, and complex as they are now.

During the Middle Ages the linguistic areas were naturally separated from one another as they will always be, but it is misleading to divide those areas into two main groups, Western and Eastern. Some areas to be sure were unmistakably in one of these groups, Latin or Icelandic in the Western group, Chinese in the Eastern one. Others were intermediary. The Greek territory was partly Oriental, the Arabic and

17

Hebrew ones partly Western. Therefore, Arabic and Hebrew studies are not Oriental in the same sense as Sanskrit and Chinese are.

Greek books were translated into Arabic, Arabic ones into Latin, not for the sake of scholarly curiosity, but for practical use. Sometimes the original publications have disappeared, and we must then read Arabic texts to investigate Greek sources, or Latin texts to investigate Arabic ones. We may say that the mediaeval philosophy and science which concern us (Western people) most were written down and are preserved in four languages, Greek, Latin, Hebrew, Arabic; if we wish to go down to bedrock we must be prepared to read these four languages. The artificial classification, Eastern vs. Western, runs across the languages. A Latin text may represent an Oriental tradition, and an Arabic one may represent a Western tradition.

. . . Down to the fourteenth century the separation between East and West was artificial. It is true the separation between Central and Eastern Asia on the one hand and Europe, Africa, and the Near East on the other was much wider than that obtaining between Christendom and the Dār al-Islām, yet it was far from complete. There were Islamic bridges between the Near East and India, and Buddhist ones between India and China. There was no solution of continuity except for relatively short intervals. Some communities might be isolated (e.g., on islands or in the mountains), but none was completely isolated. The unity of mankind can be broken in some places and some times, but not everywhere and always.

Down to the end of the fourteenth century, Eastern and Western people were working together, trying to solve the same kind of problems; from the sixteenth century on, their paths have diverged, the fundamental if not the only cause of divergence being that the Western scientists understood the experimental method and exploited it, whereas the Eastern ones failed to understand it. Toward the end of the nineteenth century the divergence was extreme. We saw on one side engineers and mechanics together with physicians and missionaries, and on the other side "benighted natives"; that, I repeat, was the extreme division. Even in this connection the classification East vs. West, convenient as it might be to tough Westerners, was not quite correct. Happily a number of Easterners among us, wise men who upheld mediaeval traditions, helped us to solve the many outstanding problems which are not patient of scientific analysis, and taught us to live well and beautifully. On the other hand, some native Easterners learned our mechanical tricks and were able to compete successfully with our best experimentalists and our most ruthless industrialists.

The Western choice made possible the fantastic development of science and technology; it might have been a pure blessing if it had not been so often divorced from wisdom and generosity. The triumph of science was overwhelming; as it often gave immense power to barbarians over good men, it ended by undermining the very basis of any culture. Everybody except the blind can see that very clearly today, but it is a thousand pities they could not see it more promptly . . . We cannot live the good life with science alone, not even if our science were a hundred times better than it is. This introduces the fourth idea.

4. *The supreme need of toleration and charity.* No one can study the history of mediaeval science (or the history of science in general) without realizing the supreme need of toleration. Experimental proofs of this have been given repeatedly throughout the ages. Indeed, rulers, lay and ecclesiastical, have often tried to enforce creeds and opinions, and have not hesitated to punish offenders, sometimes with the utmost cruelty. They have often succeeded in killing or torturing thousands of people, but they have always failed in their main purpose. Intolerance is always destructive, not only of its natural and immediate victims, but of the oppressors themselves.

The root of intolerance is self-complacency, the belief that one is right, absolutely right, and that everybody else can be right only if he agrees with you without restriction. Anyone having such a belief will easily slip to the conclusion that it is his duty to oblige his neighbors, if necessary against their own will, to share his belief and its concomitant salvation. Mediaeval intolerance was essentially of religious origin, but it was sometimes extended to other fields, such as philosophy, politics, economics, even science itself.

The church was ever ready to persecute dissenters, not only among laymen, but even more among its own clerics. A long series of books were burned and men imprisoned or murdered during the fourteenth century . . . Even if one accepts the abominable doctrine that the end justifies the means, those crimes were not justified, for they did not attain their very purpose. They did not save the offenders, but they doomed to eternal punishment the persecutors. They did not save the church, but increased its peril and paved the way for the Reformation. In a long view nothing is more certain than the uselessness of persecution.

Should you want another experiment on a large scale, consider the history of Spain. As the reconquest proceeded, the kings and lords of Spain and their supporters became more and more impatient of dissent of any kind. Heresy hunters, calificadores, improved their methods and became gradually more violent, more desperate, and more implacable; they finally ended in persecuting not only heretics and infidels (Jews and Moors), but even their descendants. According to the rulers, lay or clerical, who arrogated to themselves the right to incarnate the conscience of Spain, no one could be a good man without limpieza (purity of blood). The total result of their efforts was the material and spiritual ruin of their country. In spite of that colossal failure, their methods have been imitated in our own times in other countries of Europe; it is not necessary to be a prophet to foretell with almost complete certainty that the final result will be the same as in Spain, to wit, self-destruction.

For another gigantic example which began its sinister development before the end of the fourteenth century, we may now turn to China. The self-complacency and the stupid autarchy of the Ming emperors, and later of their Ch'ing imitators, brought their immense dominions to the verge of irretrievable ruin.

Nothing is clearer to me than that self-complacency and self-righteousness are necessarily self-defeating. Instead of which we should always — either as individuals or as members of a definite group, religious, national, or professional — be very humble and very gentle. Not only is intolerance an evil, but so is contempt of others. In particular, Christians who hate or despise other Christians or even infidels cannot be good Christians according to their own doctrine (Matthew 5:22). Such men are bigots and hypocrites, they are dooming themselves.

Science is unable to teach us toleration and charity, but the history of science (e.g., in the fourteenth century) gives us inductive proofs of their need. If we fail to love our brother and to be patient with him,

20

if we cannot make the effort of understanding him but hasten to condemn him, our knowledge is of little account.

Without tolerance and mercy our civilization, whatever there is of it, is very precarious. Science is necessary but utterly insufficient.

The question has often been asked, "Does history teach anything?" We have just answered it. It teaches at least one thing, a very important one: that intolerance is not only criminal but stupid. Intolerance does not even serve its own purpose, which is to protect the group exercising it, for it seldom fails to jeopardize that very group, if not to destroy it.

The history of science proves the value of science for every individual and for society; it also proves the insufficiency of science.

To be sure, historians do not start out to prove such things, but the proof is implied in their recitals. Historical research can have no value unless it be carried out without prejudices, without any desire other than to find the truth (the most probable truth) and to tell it. Nevertheless, when a candid account is completed, it is the historian's privilege to draw conclusions, and such conclusions are true lessons, the lessons derived from the experience of our predecessors . . .

The history of science describes man's exploration of the universe, his discovery of existing relations in time and space, his defense of whatever truth has been attained, his fight against errors and superstitions. Hence, it is full of lessons which one could not expect from political history, wherein human passions have introduced too much arbitrariness. Moreover, it is an account of definite progress, the only progress clearly and unmistakably discernible in human evolution. Of course, this does not mean that scientific progress is never interrupted; there are moments of stagnation and even regression here or there; but the general sweep across the times and across the countries is progressive and measurable. The history of science includes the most glorious, the purest, and the most encouraging deeds in the whole past. The development of knowledge is more tangible in certain fields (say, geography) than in others (say, sociology), but it is always relatively tangible, and the stretches of obscurity or fogginess, such as are met occasionally in the Middle Ages, are likely to be periods of incubation or pregnancy.

The history of science is above all a history of good will, even at times when there was no good will except in scientific research, and of peaceful efforts, even at times when war dominated everything else. A day will come when this will be realized by more people than now — not only by scientists, but by lawyers, statesmen, publicists, even by educators — and when such history will be recognized as the experimental and rational basis of international life, of peace and justice. The history of man's approach to truth is also the history of his approach to peace. There can be no peace anywhere without justice or without truth.

In the better kind of world, which we all hope will be the fruit of this war, the children will be expected to learn the evolution of mankind, and the development of science will be shown to be the very core of that evolution.

"Does history teach anything?" The history of science will teach men to be truthful, it will teach them to be brothers and to help one another. Is not that enough? . . .

[1943]

Acta atque Agenda

IT IS my privilege as a veteran of our studies to invite you to look backward and also to look forward. When one surveys the books and memoirs which have been devoted to the history of science (as I have been obliged to do for the last forty years),[1] one is amazed by the amount of work which has already been done or is being done almost under our own eyes. As soon as one begins original investigations, however, one is brought to a standstill at almost every step because of the lack of precise information on this or that point and one realizes — more and more acutely as one becomes more learned and more prudent — the immensity of the work which remains to be done. My lecture will deal successively with the two aspects of that paradox: first the large amount of work already done, and second, the need of doing considerably more.

It must be admitted that our ancestors worked with greater intensity than even the best of us seem capable of doing. Let me tell you three anecdotes to illustrate their energy. Charles Du Cange (1610–1688), to whom we owe our best dictionaries for mediaeval Latin and mediaeval Greek, was said to work fourteen hours a day. On his wedding day, however, he worked only six or seven hours. We should not judge him too severely, we have no right to do so.[2] The masters of that age expected their pupils to work as much as they did. Professor Pictet of Geneva wrote to his colleague Bernoulli of Basel, whose son was working under his direction: "Sir, your son is a mediocre student; I

---

[1] See the Critical Bibliographies published in *Isis*, the first in the spring of 1913, the seventy-fifth in the spring of 1950. These seventy-five bibliographies register and often describe and discuss some 75,000 items. The seventy-sixth bibliography including 1650 items (to May 1950) appeared in *Isis 41*, 328–424 (1950).

[2] Henry Charles Lea, Minor historical writings (p. 373, Philadelphia, 1942; *Isis 34*, 235–236).

have never been able to make him work more than thirteen hours a day; unfortunately, his example is followed; young men refuse to understand that, in order to become useful scholars, their lamp must be lighted before that of the craftsman." I doubt whether professors of our own time would dare to expect that much from their students.[3] My third example refers to a time two centuries closer to us, though we are separated from it by the dreadful abyss of the two world wars. The late English archaeologist, Sir James George Frazer (1854–1941), wrote in 1876 to his tutor, apologizing for having read only 57 Greek and Latin works during the latest term! Do we ever receive such apologies from our students?

It must be added in fairness to our contemporaries that we are spared many efforts because of the progressive and cumulative nature of science and learning. Indeed, we are privileged to use the wonderful instruments which our ancestors have bequeathed to us. I am thinking chiefly of all the encyclopaedias, atlases, gazetteers, dictionaries which are standing on our shelves, ready to answer our questions at any time of the day or night. Even the scholars who are the most conscientious in mentioning their sources, do not (and cannot) mention the richest ones, all these works of reference which they need as much and use as often as their daily bread. There are some Greek, Latin, Chinese, and Arabic dictionaries of which I have turned over the pages so many times that I have literally torn them to pieces. What would our life be without them? Whenever I consult Pauly-Wissowa, Liddell and Scott, Du Cange, Giles, Brockelmann, the O. E. D., Dozy, Kazimirski, and tutti quanti, I cannot help expressing silently a message of gratitude to the authors and blessing their memories.[4]

The situation is the same of course when I consult the available treatises on the history of mathematics, astronomy, physics, botany, etc. In spite of the fact that these books contain many lacunae and

---

[3] The anecdote is told by Eugène de Budé, *Vie de François Turrettini, théologien genevois, 1623–1687* (p. 250, Lausanne, 1871). Pictet and Bernoulli are the names of two illustrious families respectively of French and German Switzerland. I assume that Budé refers to Jacob Bernoulli (1654–1705), professor of mathematics in Basel, and to Bénédict Pictet (1655–1724), pastor in Geneva and professor at the Académie.

[4] Each of those dictionaries and other reference books is based on all the preceding ones covering the same field, and thus each represents a long tradition of scholarship. Our gratitude is extended to all the authors.

errors, what would we do without them? I am thinking only of the honest books which were the fruits of lifelong scholarship, not of the futile compositions which have been hastily put together with a "sauce piquante." There are two ways of looking at those monumental treatises; the one is the ungrateful way of young pedants who discover a fault and think of their own superiority (it is easy to find fault, but to condense the scholarship of a lifetime in a single book is a rare achievement), the other is the grateful way of experienced scholars who appreciate fully the deeds (however incomplete) of their predecessors. Many people think of me as a hard worker, yet when I compare myself with those giants, I consider that I am nothing but a lazy dwarf and I feel very humble.

It is not possible to speak of all the pioneers of our studies, but I would like to evoke, for the sake of emulation, six of them: Cantor, Tannery, Sudhoff, Heiberg, Duhem, Heath.[5] These six have prepared the foundations for the work which we are doing today. To the younger men in this audience they may seem distant, yet such is the newness of our studies, that a veteran like myself was in touch with all of them, except Tannery (who died in 1904). Out of the five whom I was privileged to know, four were generous enough to help me (when I was young and unknown) in the launching of *Isis*; the fifth declined to help me for religious reasons.

MORITZ CANTOR

A family of Portuguese Jews emigrated to Denmark. In the course of time a branch of that family moved to Germany and Russia, giving birth to the illustrious mathematician Georg Cantor.[6] This Cantor was born in St. Petersburg but most of his life was spent in Germany, and he was professor at the University of Halle; he helped to develop

[5] They are listed in the chronological order of their birth years ranging from 1829 to 1861. If they were listed in the order of their death years, ranging from 1904 to 1940, the list would read Tannery, Duhem, Cantor, Heiberg, Sudhoff, Heath.

[6] Georg Cantor (1845–1918), *Gesammelte Abhandlungen mathematischen und philosophischen Inhalts*. Mit erläuternden Anmerkungen sowie mit Ergänzungen aus dem Briefwechsel Cantor-Dedekind. Herausgegeben von Ernst Zermelo. Nebst einem Lebenslauf Cantors von Adolf Fraenkel (494 p., portrait, Berlin, 1932). E. Noether und J. Cavaillès, *Briefwechsel Cantor-Dedekind* (60 p., Paris, 1937).

many arithmetical theories and may be called the founder of the theory of aggregates (*Mengenlehre*). Another branch of the same family had found refuge in Amsterdam, and out of that branch issued Moritz Cantor, who became professor in Heidelberg, and was the greatest historian of mathematics of our time. He reformed those studies and built a monumental work of such size and magnificence that all the other historians of mathematics were put on their mettle. That work, entitled *Vorlesungen über Geschichte der Mathematik*, was published in three large volumes (first editions, 1880 to 1898) carrying the story down to 1758; a fourth volume (1908), edited by him but written by other scholars, continued the story to 1799. Of course, the better a book is, the more criticisms, errata, and addenda it will elicit. Cantor's *Vorlesungen* were the subject of periodic criticism in *Bibliotheca Mathematica* (30 vol., 1884–1914) by Gustav Eneström (1852–1923; *Isis* 8, 313–320) and his collaborators. His example raised the standard of historical research and stimulated so many new investigations that his own history would require a deep revision; some parts of it would have to be completely rewritten. His treatise on the history of mathematics remains nevertheless the most elaborate ever produced, without any equal in any other branch of science.

Moritz Cantor was born in Mannheim on 23 August 1829; he was appointed a privat docent in Heidelberg in 1853 and the rest of his active life was spent in the service of that University and of the history of mathematics. He died in Heidelberg in 1920. At the time of his death he was 91 years of age, the Nestor of all historians of science.

When I was preparing the foundation of *Isis*, he was naturally one of the first scholars to whom I ventured to explain my ambitious project. He was then a man of 82, but he answered my letter very kindly and encouraged me, though he expressed his doubts concerning the possibility of writing the history of science. . .

Two very rich *Festschriften* were dedicated to him, the first on 23 August 1899, when his 70th anniversary was celebrated (*Abhandlungen zur Geschichte der Mathematik*. Heft 9, 666 p., portrait, published as supplement to the *Zeitschrift für Mathematik und Physik*, vol. 44, Leipzig, 1899). This enormous *Festschrift* was edited

26

by Maximilian Curtze and Siegmund Günther, and included a bibliography of Cantor's writings. The second, much smaller, was published at the time of his eightieth birthday by Günther and Karl Sudhoff (212 p., Leipzig, 1909). Both *Festschriften* are well indexed. The biographical facts used by me are derived from a letter written by himself to Tannery in 1888 (Tannery, *Mémoires*, vol. 13, 331–334).

PAUL TANNERY

While Cantor was the greatest historian of mathematics and Sudhoff the greatest historian of medicine at the turning of last century, Tannery might be called the greatest, and indeed the first, historian of science. Cantor was obsessed by his treatise on the history of mathematics, and the task he had undertaken had gradually become so enormous under his care that he could not pay much attention to the history of science and was even sceptical as to the possibility of studying it. Sudhoff was simply a learned physician without scientific knowledge outside of the medical field, and therefore his view of the history of science was necessarily lopsided and misleading. Tannery was one of the first men to study the history of science in full earnest and to claim the possibility, as well as the necessity, of teaching it.

Paul Tannery was born on 20 December 1843 at Mantes-la-Jolie, and died in 1904 at Pantin (both localities near Paris). He entered the Ecole Polytechnique in 1860, and after having graduated among the ranking members of his class, he spent a short time at the Ecole d'application des Manufactures de l'Etat, then began his career in the state monopoly of tobacco. For the remainder of his life, some forty years, he was in the service of that administration; but his evenings and holidays were devoted to the study of the history of science. His favorite fields were Greek science, Byzantine science, and the 17th century, and he was more deeply interested in the mathematical sciences than in the others, but from the very beginning and throughout his life he thought of the history of science as a whole. That is much easier, of course, for a mathematically trained man who has no difficulty in understanding the other scientific ideas, than, say, for a physician who is unable to grasp mathematical ideas, and is thus cut off from the very roots of science.

The first to understand clearly the need of studying and of teaching the history of science (the history of it as of an integrated whole) was the philosopher Auguste Comte (1798–1857), and it was under his influence, though long after his death, that a chair was created at the Collège de France in 1892. The first incumbent was Pierre Laffitte (1823–1903), who was then the head of the Positivist school. At the time of Laffitte's death, Tannery already enjoyed an international reputation as historian of science and he should have been elected to that chair, but thanks to administrative stupidity, another man was chosen who had no special qualifications for the office.

How can one explain such a blunder? It was due simply to the fact that the authorities had no clear understanding of what the history of science is. They would not have taken such a stupid decision in fields more familiar to them. For example, if they had had to elect a professor of Greek, they would have insisted on the candidate's deep knowledge of Greek (a knowledge, however good, of Icelandic or Lithuanian would not have been accepted as a substitute), or if they had had to elect a professor of crystallography they would have focussed their attention on the candidate's proficiency as a crystallographer, and not on his familiarity with comparative anatomy or with Islamic philosophy.

This denial of justice to Tannery was a severe blow to him, and he died soon afterwards, but it was also a blow to our studies at the Collège de France and in the whole world. We must not judge too severely the administrators of 1903, because there are many administrators who would make similar mistakes today, and for the same reason: they do not know what the history of science is, or, what is worse, they have a false knowledge of it.

To return to Tannery, no administrator, however powerful, could destroy his work, which insures his immortality. Whether he was professor or not is now immaterial. No one bothers to find out whether he received this or that honor or not; in the light of eternity, these academic honors, all of them, whichever they be, are futilities. The published works are the only things which matter for posterity. Tannery wrote only three books, *Pour l'histoire de la science hellène* (1887; 1930; *Isis 15*, 179–180); *La géométrie grecque* (1887); *Recherches sur l'histoire de l'astronomie ancienne* (1893); much of his endless activity was dedicated to the painstaking task of editing ancient writings. He helped to edit the works of Diophantos, Fermat, and Descartes, and prepared editions of Mersenne's correspondence and of Pachymeres' *Quadrivium*. He wrote a large number of short scientific papers and longer monographs, all of which are now very easily available to us thanks to the piety and magnanimity of his widow Marie Tannery (1856–1945), who survived him forty-one years and was busy all those years, spending the whole of her energy and of her fortune to publish his writings under the title *Mémoires scientifiques* in 16 quarto volumes (1912–1943).[7] The actual editing was done by J. L. Heiberg, H. G. Zeuthen, Gino Loria, and other scholars, but the motive energy was hers as well as the money needed to pay the printers.

For more information on Paul Tannery see the *Mémoires scientifiques*, passim, vol. 4 of *Osiris* dedicated to Paul and Marie Tannery (Bruges, 1938), and my article on Paul, Jules, and Marie Tannery (*Isis* 38, 33–51, 1947).

KARL SUDHOFF

One might be tempted to compare Sudhoff with Cantor because they were two splendid representatives of the golden age of German scholarship and because each of them covered with remarkable completeness the pre-19th century [history] of a whole science. Sudhoff represents the history of medicine as fully as Cantor represents the history of mathematics. There is an essential difference, however, in that Cantor's main purpose was to write a treatise covering the whole history of mathematics and his other writings were but intermezzi, while Sudhoff was essentially a writer of monographs, some of them very bulky and comprehensive, others on the contrary devoted to very small topics. In other words, his mind was analytical rather than synthetic; he was a genial stonecutter and sculptor rather than an architect building great edifices. It is true that Sudhoff wrote two histories of medicine, or rather he revised the history written by Julius Pagel and he collaborated on another composed by Theodor Meyer-Steineg, but his heart was not in that. His main interests were

[7] A final volume containing indices, compiled by Pierre Louis, has been ready for years, but is not yet published [this volume — "Biographie, bibliographie, compléments et tables" — was published in 1950]. For the contents of the 16 vol., see the reviews in *Isis*, as listed in *Isis* 38, 49 or in my *Introd.* (3, 1906).

monographic rather than didactic, but his monographs were scattered throughout the whole field of medical history. The fields which he liked best and to which he devoted most of his energy were: 1. Ancient, chiefly Greek, medicine; 2. Syphilis and other epidemics such as leprosy and plague; 3. Mediaeval medicine and surgery; 4. Paracelsus. He was one of the first historians of science to make systematic investigations of the collections of manuscripts and incunabula which are preserved not only in the larger libraries but also in monastic or cathedral archives, and to collect large numbers of photographs, far ahead of his immediate needs. He thus accumulated a treasure of unpublished documents which could be exploited in the course of time by himself and his students.

But I must not run ahead of my story. Karl Sudhoff was born in Frankfurt-am-Main, the son a Lutheran minister, on 26 November 1853. When the father retired the whole family moved to Zweibrüchen and later to Kreuznach, and thus Karl completed his gymnasium studies in that city. He continued his studies at the University of Erlangen, matriculated in the medical faculty, and graduated in 1875. In 1878, he began practising as a general practitioner, first in Bergen near Frankfurt, later, from 1883 on, in Hochdahl near Düsseldorf. His interest in the history of medicine had been developed during his student years, largely under the influence of Heinrich Haeser (1811–1884), whose famous treatise had begun to appear in Jena in 1845. When the third edition of that treatise appeared (1875–1882), Sudhoff was fully prepared to study critically each volume as it came out. The third and last volume of Haeser's work was devoted exclusively to epidemic diseases, and its influence on Sudhoff helps to explain the latter's lifelong interest in that special field.

In spite of his work as a practical physician, Sudhoff's career as a historian of medicine was already beginning to shape itself by 1898. A German society for the history of medicine and science was organized in Hamburg in 1901; Sudhoff was its first president, and one of the editors of its journal, *Mitteilungen zur Geschichte der Medizin und der Naturwissenschaften*, which began to appear in 1902.[8] His

[8] The two other editors were the historian of chemistry, Georg W. A. Kahlbaum (1853–1905) of Basel, and the historian of medicine, Max Neuburger of Vienna, who is still active today. A strange peculiarity of the society and of its *Mitteilungen* is that medicine was their first concern, and the other sciences a

30

great opportunity came a few years later, in 1905, when the widow of another historian of medicine, Theodor Puschmann (1847–1899), bequeathed her entire fortune to the University of Leipzig "to promote research in medical history." It is significant that the chair was offered not to any established professor but to Sudhoff, who was then unconnected with any university and thus began his academic career at the age of 53. We need not tell the rest of the story, for it is told by Sudhoff's publications, of which we can mention only a few: *Deutsche medizinische Inkunabeln* (1908), *Beitrag zur Geschichte der Anatomie im Mittelalter* (1908), *Beiträge zur Geschichte der Chirurgie im Mittelalter* (3 vol., 1914–1918).

Many of his publications were devoted to Paracelsus and he took part in the preparation of a new critical edition of Paracelsus' works (1922 ff.; *Isis 6*, 56–57).

In 1907, he founded the *Archiv für die Geschichte der Medizin*, to which he contributed a large number of monographs. In the same year he began the edition of the *Studien zur Geschichte der Medizin*, of which he was also the main author. In 1909, he founded the series *Klassiker der Medizin*, and in the same year he helped to found the *Archiv für die Geschichte der Naturwissenschaften und der Technik*, etc.

Sudhoff was not only the main student of his time in the medico-historical field, but he was also the outstanding animator of all efforts concerning the history of science in Germany. He retired in 1925 but continued his studies almost to the year of his death, which occurred on 8 October 1938.

A great many honors had ben heaped on his head by his native country and by many foreign societies, but unfortunately toward the end of his life he became a member of the Nazi party, and tarnished his own well-deserved glory with their infamy.[9] It would be unfair, however, to misjudge his lifework because of a foolish deed of his senility. His work preserves its full value, and we must recognize him as the main reformer of medico-historical studies; yet, we cannot help regretting that he did not die a few years earlier.

---

subsidiary one, as if medicine were a fundamental science and the pure sciences appendices to it! That tendency has been continued by other medical historians.

[9] For documentary proof see facsimile of the "lettre de faire part" announcing his death (*Isis 30*, 515).

Two *Festschriften* were dedicated to him, the first edited by R. J. Schaefer at the time of his 60th birthday (466 p., forming vol. 6 of the *Archiv für die Geschichte der Naturwissenschaften,* Leipzig, 1913), the second edited by Charles Singer and Henry E. Sigerist on the occasion of his 70th birthday (418 p., Zürich, London, 1924). At the time of his 80th birthday, many articles were published in various journals, chiefly in the *Bulletin of the Institute of the History of Medicine* (vol. 3, pp. 1–25, Baltimore, 1934), edited by his main disciple, Sigerist.

Elaborate bibliography of his writings in chronological order by Fielding H. Garrison and Tasker in the *Bull. of the Society of Medical History* of Chicago (3, 33–50, 1923). Same bibliography in methodic order by Sigerist at the end of the second *Festschrift* (pp. 398–418, 1924).

JOHAN LUDVIG HEIBERG

Heiberg was primarily a Hellenist but, under the influence of Hermann Diels (1848–1922) and other German scholars who were exploring the early Greek philosophic and scientific literature, he devoted a great part of his energy to the editing of Greek mathematical, astronomical, and physical writings.

He was born in Aalborg, Denmark, on 27 November 1854 and belonged to a Danish-Norwegian family, many members of which are known to fame.[10] He was one of the last and certainly the most illustrious of Madvig's [11] disciples at the University of Copenhagen. He dedicated himself early to studies of Greek palaeography in Italy. From 1884 to 1895, he was director of a private school of Copenhagen called the School of Civic Virtue; in 1896, he was appointed professor of classical philology and archaeology at the University and continued his teaching there until his retirement in 1925. He also continued to teach Greek in the private school until the end of his life. The opening of young hearts to the beauty of ancient Greece thrilled him as much as his own research.

His first investigations concerned Archimedes, and later he had the good fortune to discover in Constantinople a palimpsest containing the unknown Method as well as another Archimedian treatise which

[10] Literary people will think first of all of his illustrious namesake, Johan Ludvig Heiberg (1791–1860), philologist, philosopher, playwright and director for many years of the Royal Theater in Copenhagen. I do not know the exact relationship of the two namesakes; they are related but not in straight line.

[11] Johan Nicolai Madvig (1804–1886), primarily a Latinist, a master of verbal criticism, who reformed classical studies in Denmark, and attained an European reputation. John Edwin Sandys, *History of classical scholarship* (3, 310, 319–324, 1908).

was known only in a mediaeval Latin translation. His critical editions of Archimedes, Euclid, Apollonios, Heron of Alexandria, Ptolemy, Paulos Aegineta, etc. are fundamental tools for the historian of Greek science.

Heiberg was a great traveller, exploring not only the cities and their archives and libraries but the little towns of many countries, chiefly Greece, Italy, and France, the three countries which he loved best next to Denmark. He was interested in mediaeval Italy especially in its relationship with Byzantium. Like many learned Scandinavians he was a true polyglot, who was equally at ease in German, French, and Italian. He was also a lover of the fine arts and music. As if all that was not yet sufficient to occupy him, he undertook in 1900 with Anders Bjorn Drachmann and Hans Ostenfeldt Lange a critical edition of the works of the Danish philosopher and theologian Soren Kierkegaard (1813–1855). That edition was published in 73 parts and 14 vols. (Copenhagen, 1901–1906; new edition, 1920–1931). He was one of Tannery's oldest friends and it was he who suggested to Mme. Tannery the publication of the *Mémoires*, which were edited by him and by his colleague the great Danish historian of mathematics Hieronymus Georg Zeuthen (1839–1920).

Heiberg died on the fourth of January 1928.

A bibliography of his writings was appended to the reminiscences of his journeys in Greece and Italy, *Fra Hellas og Italien* (2 vol. in Danish, Copenhagen, 1929), 30 p. in vol. 2. These two volumes are not available to me; I know them only through a review by U. v. Wilamowitz-Moellendorff (*Deutsche Literaturzeitung*, 51 15–17, 1930).

For his biography and portrait, see Hans Raeder in *Isis* (11, 367–74, 1928) and Joseph Bidez in *Mémoires scientifiques de P. Tannery* (9 p. IX–XXVIII, 1929). See also *Mémoires* (15, 11–86, 1939).

PIERRE DUHEM

Born in Paris on 10 June 1861, Duhem was educated at the Collège Stanislas and at the Ecole Normale. He was trained as a mathematician and as a physicist and taught theoretical physics in Lille, then in Rennes, and finally (1894) in Bordeaux. His teaching is represented by a series of textbooks dealing with almost every branch of physics.

Out of the six men of whom I am speaking today, he is the only one who was an original and creative scientist. Under the influence of Massieu [12] and Willard Gibbs he had turned his attention early to thermodynamical and chemical problems. He was trying to develop a new theory which would combine Lagrangian mechanics with thermodynamics.[13] The necessities of his teaching obliged him to study other parts of physics (hydrodynamics, elasticity, electricity and magnetism) and in many cases he was able to introduce original views. His investigations were of such a nature that he passed naturally from pure science to the philosophy of science and to philosophy in general, a philosophy informed by his religious beliefs and by pragmatic tendencies. As Picard put it, "His physics, at first purely descriptive and symbolic, became asymptotic to a metaphysics." [14] The philosophy of science led him unavoidably to the history of science, because one cannot understand a scientific idea (in the philosophical sense) if one considers only its final stage; one must witness its origins and development.

The genesis of Duhem's thought is natural enough when one remembers that he was not dealing with simple medical facts as Sudhoff did, nor with old mathematical concepts, as Cantor, Tannery,[15] and Heath did (ideas the philosophical implications of which have been discussed so often that one is familiar with them), but with revolutionary ideas in the immensely complex field of physics. Hence

[12] François Massieu, Mémoire sur les fonctions caractéristiques des divers fluides (92 p. quarto, *Mémoires de l'Académie des Sciences*, Paris, 1873).

[13] His first book dealt with that subject, *Le potentiel thermodynamique et ses applications à la mécanique chimique et à la théorie des phénomènes électriques* (260 p., 1886). See also his later works, *Traité élémentaire de mécanique chimique, fondée sur la thermodynamique* (4 vol., 1897–99), *Thermodynamique et chimie* (496 p., 1902; 2nd ed., 1910; 3rd ed., 1930; English translation, 1903); *Traité d'énergétique on de thermodynamique générale* (2 vol., 1911).

[14] In his beautiful lecture on Duhem read at the Académie des Sciences on 12 December 1921. Picard's statement was amply justified by Duhem's own saying: "En un mot, le physicien est forcé de reconnaître qu'il serait déraisonnable de travailler au progrès de la théorie physique si cette théorie n'était le reflet, de plus en plus net et de plus en plus précis d'une Métaphysique; la croyance en un ordre transcendant à la Physique est la seule raison d'être de la théorie physique.

"L'attitude, tour à tour hostile ou favorable, que tout physicien prend à l'égard de cette affirmation se résume en ce mot de Pascal: 'Nous avons une impuissance de prouver invincible à tout le Dogmatisme; nous avons une idée de la vérité invincible à tout le Pyrrhonisme'" (P. Duhem, Notice sur ses titres et travaux scientifiques, 1913, p. 156 in *Société des Sciences physiques et naturelles de Bordeaux, Mémoires*, 1, 1917–1927).

[15] Tannery was also somewhat of a philosopher and his investigations of the pre-Socratic "physiologists" obliged him to consider metaphysical ideas. He did it with much penetration and clarity.

his long evolution from science and philosophy to the history of science.

Duhem was a devout Catholic and he was inclined to think that he had been discriminated against and prevented from obtaining a post in the Faculty of sciences of Paris for political reasons; he felt a grievance which was accentuated by two of his biographers. It is probable that his ambition was frustrated because of other reasons. In an exceedingly specialized world, he was handicapped by the complexity of his scientific curiosity and by its very depth and abstractness. He was too much of a physicist for the mathematicians, and too much of a mathematician for the physicists (not to mention the chemists). Moreover, he was a very proud man, independent, touchy, and caustic, and he did not make as many friends in Paris as would have been useful to him. If he failed to obtain a chair in Paris, he was to some extent compensated for that neglect by his election in 1900 as a corresponding member of the mechanical section of the Académie des Sciences, and when a new section of non-resident members was created in 1913, he was one of the first to be appointed, almost unanimously.

It is sad to reflect that France produced two very great historians of science, Tannery and Duhem, and that both failed to obtain their heart's desire, and what they considered their just reward, a professorship in Paris.

Duhem was unfortunate in another respect in that he was never in good health and his life was cut short too early, when he was only fifty-five.[16] He spent almost every summer in the old family estate at Cabrespine (Aube), and it was in those happy surroundings that his end came after a short illness on 14 September 1916. In spite of the relative brevity of his life and of the fact that many of his books were devoted to purely scientific subjects, his productivity as a historian of science was enormous.

His main historical works are: *Les théories électriques de J. Clerk Maxwell* (1902). *L'évolution de la mécanique* (1903; German translation, 1912). *Les origines de la statique* (2 vol., 1905–1906), *La théorie physique, son objet et sa structure* (1906; 2nd ed., 1914; German

---

[16] Of the six men dealt with by me he was the one who died at the earliest age. Tannery died at 61, Heiberg at 74, Heath at 78, Sudhoff at 85, and Cantor at 91.

translation, 1908); this is a book on the philosophy of physics, not on its history. *Etudes sur Léonard de Vinci* (3 vol., 1906, 1909, 1912). *Essai sur la notion de théorie physique de Platon à Galilée* (1908). *Le système du monde* (to be published in 12 volumes, but only 7 or 9 were written and only 5 published 1913–1917; *Isis 2*, 203–204; *3*, 125).

He was primarily a student of mediaeval scientific thought, and he explained the pregnancy of the work done by astronomers and physicists during the Middle Ages. He also proved that the men of the Renaissance like Leonardo da Vinci and even as original a man as Galileo were more deeply indebted to mediaeval predecessors than was previously understood and than they themselves realized.

The main studies on Duhem were published in the *Mémoires de la Société des Sciences de Bordeaux* (vol. 1 of the seventh series, in two parts, 726 p., portrait, Bordeaux, 1917–1927). The first part (1917) contains his biography by Edouard Jordan, elaborate bibliography and analysis of his work prepared by Duhem himself when he was a candidate for the Académie des Sciences in May 1913. The second part (1927) contains studies by O. Manville on Duhem's physics, by Jacques Hadamard on his mathematics, and by André Darbon (1874–1943; *Isis 41*, 55) on his work as a historian of science.

Emile Picard, *La vie et l'œuvre de Duhem* (44 p. quarto, portrait, Académie des Sciences, Paris, 1921). Henri Bosmans, *P. Duhem* (*Revue des questions scientifiques*, 58 p., Louvain, 1921).

Pierre Humbert, *P. Duhem* (150 p., Paris, Bloud et Gay, 1932; *Isis 21*, 399). Hélène Pierre-Duhem (his daughter), *P. Duhem*, préface de Maurice D'Ocagne (256 p., Paris, Plon, 1936; *Isis 27*, 161).

Benjamin Ginzburg, *Duhem and Jordanus Nemorarius* (*Isis 25*, 341–62, 1936). G. Sarton and Marie Tannery, *Appel pour l'achèvement du Système du monde* (*Isis 26*, 302–303, 1937). Armand Lowinger, *The methodology of P. Duhem* (184 p., New York, 1941; *Isis 34*, 33).

SIR THOMAS LITTLE HEATH

Thomas L. Heath was born in Lincolnshire on 5 October 1861. He was educated at the Caistor Grammar School, then at Clifton College, and finally at Trinity in Cambridge. He distinguished himself early as a classical scholar and a mathematician, but entered the Civil Service as a Clerk in the Treasury in 1884, and spent all his life in the service of the Treasury, reaching almost the top of the administrative ladder, and retiring in 1926.

His interest in the history of Greek mathematics was natural in a student who was a well trained Hellenist as well as a mathematician, and who had been stimulated by the examples given in his own language and during his own youth by Gow and Allman.[17] His earliest book, his first *Diophantos*, was written at 24, as a thesis leading to a Fellowship in Trinity; it was published by the University Press on the recommendation of Arthur Cayley. This first step determined the rest of his life, or at least the vocational part of it, for he worked hard at the Treasury, seven hours a day, but devoted his evenings and much of his free time to Greek mathematics. He was a great lover of music, especially Bach, Beethoven, and Brahms and an uncommon Alpinist. He spent many vacations in Switzerland or in the Dolomites: his first climb occurred in his student days, his last, fifty years later when he was seventy. He married late in life at the age of 53, and remembering his love of music, one is not surprised that he chose for his wife a lady, Ada Mary Thomas, who was a distinguished musician. Soon after his marriage he wrote (on 9 July 1914) to his colleague, David Eugene Smith, "My book on Greek mathematics has been stationary for a month or two owing to my having got engaged and then married! However, I hope I shall be resuming work upon it shortly." This reminds us of the story about Du Cange which was told above, except that Du Cange belonged to a sterner generation, and interrupted his work only for a few hours, not for a few weeks.

Considering the extent of his professional duties, which were exacting and could never be stopped for very long, and his love of music and mountain climbing, the amount of his scientific work is almost incredible.[18] It must suffice to indicate the main items: *Diophantos* (1885; second edition much improved, 1910); *Apollonios* (1896); *Archimedes* (1897); *Euclid* (3 vol., 1908; 2nd ed., 3 vol., 1926;

[17] George Johnston Allman (1824–1904), alumnus of Trinity, Dublin; professor in Galway, wrote the *History of Greek geometry from Thales to Euclid* (Dublin, 1889), was a friend of Comte. See Tannery's *Mémoires* (vol. 13, 3–124, portrait).

James Gow (1854–1923), of Trinity College, Cambridge, wrote a *Short history of Greek mathematics* (Cambridge, 1884). Both little books were very good for their time and size.

[18] A comparison obtrudes itself immediately with his Belgian colleague and equivalent Paul Ver Eecke, who translated the Greek mathematical classics into French, even as Heath translated them into English. Ver Eecke was a civil servant like Heath; he was born in 1867 and was thus six years younger. He is still alive and active. See *Osiris*, vol. 8 (1948) dedicated to him.

Isis 10, 60–62); *The Method of Archimedes* (1912); *Aristarchos with the history of Greek astronomy to him* (1913); *History of Greek mathematics* (2 vol., 1921; *Isis 4*, 532–535); *Manual of Greek mathematics* (1931; *Isis 16*, 450–451; *Greek astronomy* (1932; *Isis 22*, 585); *Mathematics in Aristotle* (1949; *Isis 41*, 329).

To these volumes, which complete one another and constitute in their totality a splendid monument to Greek mathematics and astronomy, must still be added a little one of a different kind, *The Treasury* (1927) wherein Heath wrote the history and described the functioning of the administration in the service of which he had spent the longest (if not the best) part of forty-two years.

When Sir H. Stuart Jones undertook a revision of Liddell and Scott in 1911, he applied to Heath for the mathematical terms. Heath checked the whole dictionary from the mathematical angle and filled many gaps. It seems hard to believe, e. g., that in previous editions the word asymptotos, which is so important from the mathematical point of view, was only defined as a medical term.

Sir Thomas Heath was a strong and healthy man who was hardly ever incapacitated by illness until 1939 when he caught influenza and pneumonia. He left London, retired to a country house at Ashtead in Surrey, resumed his work on his last book, but died of a stroke in the following year on 16 March 1940 at the age of seventy-eight.

For more information see *Osiris*, vol. 2 (Bruges, 1936) with a biography by David Eugene Smith, bibliography, and portrait. See also the notices by D'Arcy W. Thompson in the *Obituary notices of the Royal Society* 1940, and by R. C. Archibald in the *Mathematical Gazette 24*, 234–237 (1940).

The immense amount of work accomplished by those six men is even more astounding when we realize that none of them was a professional historian of science, except perhaps Sudhoff. The latter became a full professional (perhaps the first in history, and this proves again the novelty of our studies) in 1906 when he was appointed a professor of the history of medicine in the University of Leipzig. From then on, for a stretch of time which his vitality extended over thirty years, he did no work except in his chosen field. Remember, however, that he was 53 when this opportunity was opened to him, and that by that time he had been a practising physician for 28 years!

ACTA ATQUE AGENDA

As to the other men, their professional work remained different from their avocation. Cantor was primarily a professor of mathematics, and it was only during his final academic years that he could devote himself exclusively to the history of mathematics. Tannery was employed by the French state monopoly of the tobacco business; his main duties were those of a civil engineer and an administrator. Heiberg was a professor of classical philology and archaeology in the University of Copenhagen, and moreover he taught Greek in a private school of that city almost until the end of his life. Duhem was a professor of theoretical physics at the University of Bordeaux. Sir Thomas Heath was a civil servant, whose life was spent in the service of the British Treasury.

Many other historians of science might have been dealt with, even if we restricted ourselves to those of our contemporaries whose life and work are ended. Any attempt to enumerate them here would be invidious, because I would be bound to omit the one or the other. Every reader will name a few of them to himself. The six men I have chosen for special remembrance are sufficient to answer the questions: What is a historian of science? What do you expect him to do? These men gave us immortal examples.

As I am writing these lines, I am hearing that my old friend, Aldo Mieli, died on 16 February 1950. His own studies were not fundamental, but his fame is secure because of his lifelong efforts, in the face of great difficulties, to popularize the history of science and to organize its teaching not only in one country but all over the world. He was born in Livorno, Italy, in 1879, worked for a time in Siena, then in Rome, emigrated to Paris, and finally from Paris to Santa Fé (in the Argentine Republic), where the Universidad Nacional del Litoral had invited him to come. After having lost that position, he found a refuge in Buenos Aires and spent his final years in Florida (near that city), suffering grievously from physical and mental pains, enduring disease and poverty, yet continuing his work with heroic fortitude until the end. I am confident that our Argentinian colleagues will take care of the books and archives which Mieli left behind, and that they will not forget the generous exile who came to work with them and for them.

SARTON ON THE HISTORY OF SCIENCE

Mieli's main works are *I Prearistotelici* (Firenze, 1916; *Isis 4*, 347–349); *Gli scienziati italiani* (vol. I, part 1, Rome, 1921; *Isis 4*, 112–114); *Pagine di storia della chemica* (Rome, 1922; *Isis 5*, 173–174); *Histoire des sciences. Antiquité*, with Pierre Brunet (Paris, 1935; *Isis 24*, 444–447); *La science arabe* (Leiden, 1933; *Isis 30*, 291–295). Toward the end of his life he wrote in Spanish an elementary history of science under the title *Panorama general de historia de la ciencia*, of which two volumes were published, I. *El mundo antiguo*, II. *La época medieval* (Espasa-Calpe, Buenos-Aires, 1945–46). He wrote various smaller books and a great many articles and reviews.

Aldo Mieli had been one of the very first friends of *Isis*. His collaboration to it began with the first number, and continued until the time when the German invasion of Belgium interrupted its publication for five years. During this intermezzo Mieli founded a new journal, the *Archivio di storia della scienza* (Roma, 1919), the title of which was changed to *Archeion* in 1927 and to *Archives internationales d'Histoire des Sciences* in 1947. His vocation as a historian of science (for it was a vocation, and he remained throughout his life a real missionary *in partibus infidelium*) had given him a cosmopolitan point of view, and that point of view was fortified by the vicissitudes which obliged him to live successively in Italy, France, and the Argentine, and to speak and write in Italian, French, and Spanish.

His greatest achievement was the foundation in 1928 of the International Academy of the History of Sciences; he became its first Perpetual Secretary on 21 May 1929 and continued in that office until his death. He is the founder of our Academy and that is enough for his glory and for our gratitude.

That foundation seemed presumptuous, when it was made in 1928, and one might claim that it was premature but the logical order is not always the most natural nor the best. Indeed, in 1928, the history of science was just beginning to be recognized, and the study and teaching of it were organized in only a very few universities; indeed, its present organization is still very imperfect.[19]

One might think that it would have been better to organize our

---

[19] We are well informed regarding present conditions, because of the survey made in 1949 for the Academy by E. J. Dijksterhuis, La place de l'histoire des sciences dans l'instruction supérieure (*Archives 29*, 39–76, 1950). The list of courses offered in many universities is pretty long, but if one took off all the courses given by men who are definitely not historians of science and have no important publications ad hoc to their credit, the list would be much shorter.

40

studies more completely on various national bases before trying to organize them on the international scale, but I do not think so myself. In some cases national organizations might create deviations from the main purpose, as when the history of science became an essential part of the national propaganda.[20] The point to bear in mind (and Mieli was always very conscious of it) is that the history of science is of its nature an international subject and hence should be organized on the international scale first. The history of science is an essential part of the history not of this or that section of mankind, but of the whole of it.

The fact remains that the creation of an academy in a field which is not well defined (or is not understood by everybody in the same way) is a very hazardous undertaking. Every academy, be it noted, has its own weaknesses; all of them, even the oldest and most illustrious, are imperfect in that they have failed to include some men who should have been included,[21] and, what is even worse, they have included many fellows whom it would have been better to leave out. The difficulties of organizing an international academy are of course much greater than can be the case for national or provincial academies. In the case of the latter, it is relatively easy to collect information concerning each candidate; on the contrary, men nominated for fellowship in an international academy are scattered all over the earth, and we may be unable to obtain reliable knowledge with regard to the candidates who live far away, we may have to depend on hearsay or on written but uncontrollable testimonies. The embarrassment is extreme when the candidates have published all their books and memoirs in languages which are little known outside their own countries.

A truly international academy should be one of which all the members have an international reputation. This would imply among other things that the main works of each member would be available

---

[20] E. g., in Fascist Italy. See the seven volumes published by the Società italiana per il progresso delle scienze, *Un secolo di progresso scientifico italiano* 1839–1939 (Milano, 1939–1940; *Isis 35*, 190; *36*, 223).

[21] That kind of weakness was gallantly recognized by the Académie française in 1778, when it inaugurated in its meeting hall the beautiful bust of Molière, by Houdon, bearing the inscription, "Rien ne manque à sa gloire, il manquait à la nôtre." D'Alembert called that "une adoption posthume."

(either in their original form or in translation) in one or more languages of international currency.[22]

It is certain that our Academy is very heterogenous and there is no task more urgent for its own welfare and for the progress of our studies than to publish a biographical dictionary of all the members (dead and alive), indicating for each of them his formation, the range of his scientific and historical interests, and his main books or memoirs.

When one of its members dies, the Academy takes pains to publish his obituary in the *Archives* and that is very praiseworthy, but we would prefer to know our fellow members and their works as well as possible while they are still alive. Such a biographical dictionary[23] would help each member to define more concretely our field of studies, of which it might happen that he himself knew only a small part, and it would provide standards of comparison and thus improve the selection of new members.

By the way, of the six scholars of whom I gave a brief account above, only two were members of our Academy, Sudhoff and Heath, because they were the only survivors at the time when the Academy was founded (Heiberg died in 1928 just before its foundation). . . .

Many of the ideas concerning our studies, which are entertained not only by the average man but by men of considerable eminence in their own realm, are misleading. This is due to the fact that very few historians of science are nothing but that; in other words, very few are professionals; most of them must have another profession in

[22] The difficulties due to language have been discussed in my paper, The tower of Babel (*Isis* 39, 3–15, 1948) [see below, p. 287]. Let me repeat that the international currency of a language is determined not so much by the number of people who speak it naturally, but rather by the number of people using it as a second language.

[23] The term biographical dictionary may seem a bit ambitious. We use it faute de mieux. What we have in mind is a collection of short notices like those included in *Who's Who, Who's Who in America, American Men of Science, Directory of American Scholars*. Each notice would be brief and objective and should not imply any judgment. The notices relative to dead members would be derived from the published obituaries; those of living members, from their own answers to a questionnaire. The lists of publications should be restricted to the most important books and memoirs. The average length of a notice should not exceed 500 words, and the whole dictionary could be included in a small book, e. g., in the fourth edition of the Academy's Register.

order to earn a living. *Primum vivere* . . . Remember that out of the six men exhibited above as paragons, only one could be called a professional. Hence, one does not visualize a historian of science as one visualizes a mathematician or a geologist; these latter are tangible enough, the former hardly.

The confusion has been frequently aggravated by well-meaning administrators. Having suddenly discovered that the history of science is important, they would organize a series of lectures or a symposium and appeal to various members of their staff. Lacking knowledge of the difficulties involved and of the need of special training, they would find it perfectly natural to ask an illustrious astronomer to speak of the history of astronomy, or a professor of chemistry to deal with the history of chemistry (did he not receive the Nobel prize? And is not that a sufficient qualification?) Or else they would enlist the professor of Arabic for a lecture on Arabic science, and the professor of Chinese for one on Chinese science. A beautiful program would be printed and the public of that university (professors, students and hangers-on) would be astonished to find so many historians of science among them. Thank goodness! almost every member of the faculty is one! Of course, such a list of lectures is a kind of bluff, and the more illustrious the lecturers (if they are not in fact historians of science) the greater the bluff.

One could not repeat too often and too loud that a man interested in the history of science (yea, very interested) is not a historian of science, any more than a man interested in geology is *ipso facto* a geologist. Forsooth, I would go even further and say that the fact of teaching a subject is not in itself a guarantee that the teacher is a master of it. A professor of philosophy is not necessarily a philosopher, and among the men who give occasionally lectures or even whole courses on the history of science, only very few deserve the proud title of "historian of science."

Any discipline is gradually defined by the books of masters, the "masterpieces"; it is also defined by the teaching of great teachers. Research and teaching are two activities which are correlated, yet different and to some extent independent. Some of the best teachers do little research work, and the best investigators are not always good teachers; sometimes they dislike teaching, their heart is not in it.

Research is (or at least should be) pure and fundamental; teaching is applied; one always teaches with a definite purpose, in view of definite applications. One of these purposes is the diffusion of pure truth, but there are many other purposes about which educators often disagree. One may teach the history of science for the love of it (that is always the best reason), or to explain science, or to explain philosophy, or to explain history.[24] The purposes of students are even more varied, for they may "take" a course in the history of science for the love of it (that is of course the best reason), or to improve their scientific knowledge, to understand better the philosophy of science and of life, to obtain a new view of the past, or to provide a new string to their bow; some of them may "take" the course simply to get credit for it, fill a vacant hour, or balance their pabulum. We must not judge them too severely; it is wiser to remember the days of our own youth; our best efforts were not always rewarded but we gathered many fruits which we did not expect nor deserve. I like to think that even the students who took my courses for poor reasons, as it were by mistake, got something out of them, something worthwhile of which they will perhaps appreciate the value twenty-five years later.

One of the best opportunities for explaining a new discipline is opened to the masters who having been invited to teach it set forth their opinions of the task accomplished by their predecessors and the program of their own efforts in an inaugural lecture. Whenever such a tradition has been observed by the successive incumbents of a definite chair, the collection of their inaugural lectures is one of the best instruments for the understanding of the growth of their studies in that particular university. It is much to be hoped that whenever chairs are created in our universities for the history of science (as they will certainly be one after another in the near future) their incumbents will take pains to explain the ideas guiding their research and teaching in inaugural lectures suitably published. We have thus far only one such lecture, the one which was carefully prepared by Paul Tannery but which he did not deliver because the appointment which he so fully deserved, and which in spite of his modesty he had every reason to

[24] In Russia, the history of science, or at least the history of medicine, is taught on the basis of dialectic materialism, the course serving as a series of illustrations of that doctrine. Henry E. Sigerist, *Medicine and health in the Soviet Union* (1947, *Isis* 39, 202–203).

anticipate, was offered *in extremis* to someone else. The most important inaugural lecture on the history of science is one which was never given.[25]

There are thus far few jobs for new historians of science, few professions opened to them, but the number of opportunities will gradually increase and in the meanwhile the progress of our studies will depend upon a few scholars who have a definite "vocation." What do I say? It will *always* depend upon the scholars who are truly inspired. In the course of time, there will be many chairs, at least one in every respectable University, but it does not follow that there will be as many creative scholars as there will be "jobs" ready for them. Mediocre men think of "jobs" and consider themselves fortunate when they have landed a good one. It is more fortunate to have a mission, preferably with a job, but if necessary without one. As Carlyle put it, "Blessed is he who has found his work: let him ask no other blessing." [26] It is a blessing for a man to hold a good position, it is a far greater blessing for him to be raised aloft by an ambitious purpose, as when a noble conception seizes him and takes hold of him, body and soul. It is then no longer a man who has found a job, but a great job which has found a worthy man.

Timid and lukewarm scholars complain that they cannot do much in our line, because their other duties leave them no time and energy. This is seldom completely true. Where there is a will there is a way, and where there is a strong will, the will of a great personality, a path opens itself before him like a carpet which is unrolled before the king. Moreover, a large amount of good work can be done (and has often been done) by any competent scholar who directs his efforts towards a modest objective commensurate with his possibilities, and pursues his course year after year, in spite of interruptions, with patience and faithfulness. When a good man decides to proceed in a certain direction and continues steadily, it is astounding how much he can do in a lifetime, even if the daily portion is very small.

[25] P. Tannery, De l'histoire générale des sciences (16 p., extrait de la *Revue de Synthèse historique*, 1904). My copy of that admirable lecture was given to me, not by Tannery (I was still in high school at that time) but many years later, by Gustav Eneström.

[26] I do not know when and where Carlyle said that. The saying is printed on the title page of *The Life and Letters of Friedrich Max Müller* (1823–1900), edited by his widow (London, 1902).

There is a tremendous amount of work remaining to be done and it will be done gradually by devoted scholars, whether these receive adequate positions and rewards, or not. As better work is done the standard of our studies will be gradually raised, and these will be more generously appreciated by intelligent outsiders. Historians of science must win the respect of other scholars, and they will win it. The same evolution has taken place in other fields in the measure that those fields were cultivated with greater care and assiduity. For example, there was a time when the anthropologists were laughed at because the early ones were too dilettantish and immature; at present, thanks to the work of great masters, the anthropologists are highly respected; they are considered bona fide men of science and treated as such by universities, academies, and scientific societies. A time will come (perhaps more promptly than we think) when a "historian of science" will be treated honorably (if he personally deserves it) and be given as much recognition and as many opportunities as any other man of science.

The organization of new studies is made more difficult today (rather than facilitated) by the immoderate expansion of administrative methods. We suffer from too much administration.[27] Yet administrators do not do the work to be done; their task is simply to "administer" it, to direct it, to hire and discharge the workers, etc. However important their function (and we all recognize that a minimum of stewardship is indispensable) it cannot replace the work itself. What is even more ominous is the spread of what I would call an administrative way of considering projects, rather than a purely scientific or scholarly way. This is partly due to the fact that scientific projects are becoming larger and more expensive, and that the need of obtaining sufficient money is more and more difficult to satisfy. Though scholarly

[27] I can speak with confidence only of American conditions, but believe that the "disease" (overadministration) is not restricted to America. In my own university, the number of administrators has increased prodigiously within my own time; the complexity, cost, and relative importance of administration have increased in proportion. It is funny to hear people complain of overadministration in government who do not seem to realize that the disease is epidemic. The body politic being by far the largest body is its main victim, but it affects every group in proportion to its size; there are many bureaucracies other than state bureaucracy. The disease thrives in universities and other schools, hospitals, banks, industries, and business. There seems to be a general belief in administrative circles that the work done by three clerks could be done better by six or nine, and thus the cancer grows.

projects are far less expensive than purely scientific ones (e. g., the building and equipment of laboratories or observatories), their presentation is too often colored by administrative points of view rather than by scholarly ones.

It is true, the main tool of historians and especially of historians of science — an adequate library — is the most expensive of all tools and the hardest to build up (even when the needed capital is ready). Such libraries exist, however, in a great many places; they have been built to serve not only the men of science and scholars of their district but all the people, hence they should not be charged against any group of learned men but against the whole population. The historians of science should make the fullest use of the best libraries which are already available. Indeed, they would be very welcome in any good library: a good library needs scholars to justify its existence as much as a scholar needs the library to do his duty. As the building up of very large libraries has become almost prohibitive, if not impossible, there is no other solution than this one. The library cannot go to every scholar, hence the scholar must go to the library. Let the historians of science establish their offices in the greater libraries, or close enough to them.

On the other hand, those historians should not depend too much on administrative projects. The organization of series of lectures, symposia, committees is useful up to a certain point but should not be taken too seriously. Whenever I am enticed to take part in such things, I do not feel that I am working but rather that I am running away from my main duty; I cannot blot out a sense of truancy and guilt. Earnest scholars dislike conferences and palabras, for they see in them chiefly methods of wasting time for the benefit of ambitious busy-bodies. Too much administration and discussion stifles work rather than helps it. The main achievements have been brought into being, not by committees, but by heroic scholars, who had conceived a great design and vowed, "I will do it or burst." Some undertakings are so vast that they require the cooperation of many scholars, but even then they can hardly be carried out, unless there be at least one man who assumes spiritual responsibility for the whole; without his inspired guidance the individual efforts risk to be abandoned, or they cancel each other and remain futile.

There are many species of administrators of course. Some are great

47

men, who are fair and modest and truly helpful. Others are petty, ponderous, pompous, and pedantic, full of vanities. It is because of the latter that administrative efforts are often sterile. We do not need formulas and idle talk, but personal and devoted service.

In order to measure the amount of work which remains to be done in our field, it suffices to compare it with older fields, say English history or the history of English literature. In those fields so much research has already been carried through by many generations of scholars, each of whom could take full advantage of the accumulated experience of his predecessors, that there is hardly a topic of any importance which has not been explored from top to bottom. As Trevelyan remarked in order to discredit historical scepticism: "In this country at least I am certain that the sum of sifted and ascertained historical fact has greatly increased and is rapidly increasing, and that, partly as a consequence, truthful historical judgments on many important subjects are more frequently made and more generally accepted than ever before. What we may fairly call real historical knowledge is growing fast." [28]

The situation which historians of science must face is very different. Not only are there no textbooks like those available in the older fields, pedigreed textbooks descending from a long line of textbooks each of which has been revised and improved, but in many cases the fundamental monographs (without which scientific textbooks cannot be written) have not yet been prepared. Neophytes can hardly realize that, and when they begin to read a textbook, say on the history of physics, they are left with the impression that that subject is pretty well known. That impression is produced because the author of the textbook makes brief, peremptory statements, expresses no doubts, avoids moot questions. I assume that the author is honest, but if he is not and is a good and easy writer, the matter is even worse, for he does not even realize the existence of difficulties, talks through his hat, and is satisfied if he has succeeded in stretching out one after another a sufficient series of smooth sentences. Sss . . . how horrid! Many books on the history of science have been concocted in that way, and this could not happen in a better-known field, such as ordinary history, where the chances of

[28] George Macaulay Trevelyan in his Presidential Address to the Historical Association, January 1947; reprinted in his *Autobiography and other essays* (p. 72, London, 1949; *Isis 41*, 371).

detection would be uncomfortably numerous. A man writing about Biringuccio or Paracelsus, or even about Copernicus or Harvey can get away with a good amount of ignorance and nonsense. If he treated Oldenbarnevelt, Cromwell, or Washington with the same levity he could not escape with his whole skin.

When an expert historian opens a textbook on the history of science, or on the history of this or that science, at almost any page, he finds statements which are either wrong or misleading, he detects "holes" which need filling, or theories which cannot be accepted without further investigation and qualification.

Administrators should understand that while any intelligent teacher could give a course on American history which would be tolerably complete and accurate, it would be foolish to expect the same teacher to give a decent course on the history of physics (even if he were a good physicist and had some historical training).

Though I have delivered hundreds of lectures on almost every part of the history of science, I have seldom given one which satisfied me completely, because I seldom had enough time to investigate the subject down to the roots; the necessary monographs were lacking and it was impossible to produce them in a jiffy.

The lack of monographs is annoying for the fast writers of textbooks or for ordinary teachers, but it puts real scholars on their mettle. It is not so much the work done which stimulates the latter, as the terrae incognitae, the investigations which are crying for fulfilment. Historians of science are very fortunate indeed in that there is still so much pioneering to go through. A virgin field is more exciting than one which has been overcultivated for centuries.

The history of science should not be a refugium peccatorum; it is on the contrary a discipline which should attract the attention and the devotion of bold and adventurous spirits, hard workers and courageous pioneers.

I have spoken of some of the great scholars of the past. I know that many are working today, and I trust that many more will continue our work in the future for the whole Republic of Letters and do it much better than we can.

[1950]

49

The Scientific Basis of the History of Science

Among the many initiatives taken by the Carnegie Institution for the advancement of research along untrodden paths, one of the least known is the organization of systematic inquiries concerning the past of science. That initiative was taken by the second president, the late Dr. Robert S. Woodward, and continued and expanded by President John C. Merriam. It does credit to both and the more so because it was less appreciated. Indeed even today the number of people, not only in America but abroad, who understand the need of scientific work in that field is amazingly small. Administrators and educators are always ready enough to praise the history of science and emphasize the need of teaching it; they do not seem to understand that in order to write good books on the subject or to teach it well, it is necessary first of all to study it carefully, painstakingly, down to bed rock. If that study is not continued and constantly refreshed by the consideration of new documents or the reconsideration of the available evidence from new points of view, the subject is bound to degenerate into claptrap and falseness.

The matter can be put bluntly as follows: if the history of science is worth knowing (and educators seem to agree on that) then it should be known as well as possible, and any knowledge below the attainable standard should be treated with the same contempt as we would treat half-baked knowledge or quasi-knowledge in any other field, say geology or American history. If educators think that the critical study of the history of science is too expensive in time and money, very well, let them abandon the subject, for what can be the use of diffusing errors? They cannot have it both ways: if the history of science is as

50

important as they claim it to be, then it should be taken up seriously and not dealt with casually; it should be studied carefully, and no one should be allowed to teach it who had no firsthand knowledge of it and had not proved his ability to investigate it, or at least to appreciate critically the fruits of other people's investigations.

Let us suppose you are an astronomer and have been engaged for years in difficult investigations. Maybe you have taken yourself or collected a large number of spectra, and you are making an analytic study of them. When your analysis is carried far enough, you will publish the results in an elaborate memoir, which may (or may not) enrich our general knowledge of astral physics, stellar evolution, and cosmology. Such labor as yours is very difficult, the more so because you have become so fastidious about it, and it would be unbearably dull if you were not sustained by the hope of reaching a new parcel of truth, and thus increasing our knowledge of the subject, however little. What sustains you, above all, is that your inquiries and speculations are not idle, and that they would not be idle even if they proved sterile. You are working with your fellow astronomers in the right direction; you may be out of luck and fail to discover anything of great value; in any case you do not let down your associates, you do not cheapen their knowledge; you hold fast to your scientific ideals.

Almost any scientific investigations which are really worth while imply an infinite amount of drudgery which nothing could compensate and justify, except the thoughts which I have just expressed. In that sense it may be claimed that honest scientific work is one of the highest forms of altruism. The true scientist at the end of fruitless experiments is reconciled to his failure by the fact of his having succeeded in proving their fruitlessness. The path he followed led nowhere, but thanks to his exploration of it other scientists will be saved the trouble of entering it.

To be sure, when a laborious technique has to be repeated endlessly, the scientist, however devoted he may be to his task, cannot but experience moments of languor and discouragement. The work is so tedious, the goal so distant, and the reward uncertain. Is it worth while going on? Let us imagine that during one of these inevitable periods of disillusionment you are approached by a friend, "a man of the world," who says to you, "Why do you take such absurd pains to reach an un-obtainable aim? Even if you succeed in adding a new chapter, or a new footnote, to astrophysics, what of it? The crown of your labor will be an elaborate and unreadable memoir, which, even if you be lucky enough to have it printed, will hardly be published. For who will read it? Maybe a few other fools like yourself — that is all. Instead of wast-ing your time in that way, why don't you write a book explaining the marvelous facts which we already know about the stars, the numberless universes lost in the incredible depths of space? To think that so many of them have been counted, their prodigious distances measured, their chemical constitution analyzed, their history and fate determined! What a thrilling book one could write about that, a book that might be a best seller, would bring you wealth and fame. Every educated man would know of you; while if you persist in your stupid efforts, the best that you can hope for is the esteem and jealousy of a few col-leagues scattered all over the world; a mediocre fame and a mediocre fortune."

This example is imaginary but very plausible; so plausible indeed, and so probable that it requires hardly any imagination to produce it. We may be sure that almost every astronomer has met with that very temptation in one form or another. Some have succumbed to it (and we should not blame them hastily), others have resisted it and continued their task with more or less serenity.

Of course, every scientist will appreciate this kind of temptation and be able to see both sides of it. For it is equally obvious that no scientific progress can be made except by patient and austere in-vestigations, and that the discoveries which are made must be ex-plained from time to time to the public. It is certain that science is not advanced by the composition of readable and salable books, yet such books are much needed for the education of the public, including the scientists themselves, and for the awakening of new scientific voca-tions.

Far from blaming the *competent* authors of popular scientific books, we should praise them. To be sure, if they be truly successful, their financial reward is likely to be much greater than that of pure research and hence they need less encouragement; they received their reward and it should suffice them. I have often thought that elderly scientists should try to popularize their knowledge, and consider that duty as their last one, and not the least. However, only a few scientists will ever be able to do that well, as the performance of that final duty calls for literary qualities which are as rare as the qualities needed for scientific research and somewhat incompatible with them. Even if a scientist had enough literary talent to begin with, the chances are that years of inhibition have atrophied it, and by the time he would like to make use of it in order to fulfill his final duty, it may have died out altogether.

Now the temptation which I have described is far more common in the field of the history of science than in any other field, and far more insidious. Indeed in the other fields the distinction between creative research and popularization is well made and the respective functions and values of each are generally understood. Furthermore incompetent popularization is easily detected and promptly denounced. The historians of science alas! are so few in number, and their field so vast, that they cannot yet enjoy the same protection. While there is perhaps one popularizing physicist for a hundred doing spade work, the proportion is reversed with regard to the history of science. Indeed in spite of all the hullabaloo in favor of those new studies, the number of professional full-time scientists engaged in them is incredibly small. The historians of science who have the privilege of devoting their whole time to their studies and earning thereby a modest living, can be counted on my hands; I mean the historians of the whole world, not of a single country!

On the other hand the number of amateur historians of science, recruited from among scientists, historians, philosophers, and sociologists, is increasing steadily; and the number of popular books, some of them good sellers, if not best sellers, is larger every year. Some of these books are good enough as a first approximation, but most are poor. Nowhere is the backwardness of our studies more obvious. A book entitled "Men of Mathematics" can be successful in spite of its shortcomings, while a book on "Men of Art" or "Men of Religion" or "American Men" on the same level of scholarship would be promptly discarded by a host of competent critics.

This seems to be a vicious circle, for if the competent scholars in a given field are rare, the competent critics are rarer still, and yet criticism is at no time more needed, one would think, than when a discipline is beginning to shape itself. However, the situation is not as desperate as it looks, and the vicious circle will turn out to be a convenient helix, such as symbolizes the method of successive approximations in any field. The helix is still a bit flat, but it will rise gradually higher and higher.

The beginnings are always imperfect, not so much because intrinsic difficulties are not yet overcome, but rather because the difficulties are not yet recognized. As it is very easy for a scientifically trained man with a modicum of literary ability to write on the history of science, the number of imperfect publications on the subject is exceptionally large. It is no exaggeration to say that the majority of so-called historians of science today are blessedly unaware of the difficulties involved, and therefore their writing is very easy indeed, but untrustworthy and to that extent worthless.

To be sure, every subject was developed at first by amateurs, but not in the same pernicious manner as the history of science is developed today. The word "amateur" it should be noted has some excellent connotations. An amateur astronomer or naturalist, as there were many in past centuries, is a man who studies natural history or astronomy as a hobby. He does it, not to earn a living, but to spend his life according to his heart's desire. Such an amateur can hardly be distinguished from a professional of today, except that his zeal is if anything more genuine, and that he is ready to take more pains for his pleasure, not less.

The amateur historian of science is more often of an entirely different kidney. He is, for example, a distinguished scientist who has become sufficiently interested in the genesis of his knowledge to wish to investigate it, but has no idea whatsoever of how such investigations should be conducted and is not even aware of his shortcomings. His very success in another domain, the fact that he has long passed the years of apprenticeship, make it difficult, if not almost impossible, for him to master a new technique. He generally lacks the humility of a beginner, and publishes his historical results with blind and fatuous assurance. That is amateurism at its worst.

The good amateurs who were the pioneers of science (including a very few who were pioneers in our own field) were not content to steal the fruits of other people's orchards and let them rot; they were hard workers themselves, working for the joy of discovering the truth. Such as those will still appear from time to time and help us mightily in our advance, but we can never count on them. They may come or not; for the routine work of a developing branch of science, professionals are needed, men having undergone as good a training as possible, honest, and more interested in their studies than in fame or money.

We need not worry so much about the diffusion of knowledge, for that is largely a matter of business. The financial prizes which the successful writers of popular books may hope to obtain are so high that there will never be a shortage of such books. As to their quality, it will depend largely on the general level of knowledge available to specialists and to potential critics.

The specialist's duty is then simply to raise that level. He must continue to produce memoirs which only other specialists will study, but which will make progress in a definite direction possible. The situation is not different for the history of science than for any other scientific investigations.

It is true learned memoirs should not be quite as monotonous or as badly written as they often are. Some aridity is unavoidable, for example, when abundant results are presented in the form of tables or diagrams. One could not conceive anything more arid than a table or a map, which contains no phrases beyond the necessary technical words, numbers, and symbols; yet we are thus offered a synoptic view of complex data, and a better chance of understanding their varied relationships. For the imaginative scientist, a chart is not dull but full of meaning. However, in the writing of the memoirs there is far too much dullness which could be avoided with a little trouble, and should be avoided. The historian of science who is unable to explain the results of his investigations in a pleasant manner is more guilty indeed than other scientists, because we naturally expect from him, on account of literary training, more urbanity.

At this point it is necessary to make a distinction, often overlooked in America, between written and oral teaching. Every writer is a teacher of course, a teacher who never stops teaching as long as his books are read. And just as ordinary teachers may be divided into many grades according to their audiences, from the ones who help the awakening of childish minds in kindergartens, to those who guide a few mature students in university seminars; just so the writers of books teach many audiences, from the lowest "brows" to the highest. By the way, this has nothing to do with the "sale" of their books, for excellent books for the best students may sell very well, while books written as bait for the millions may fail altogether. The written teaching should be as accurate and precise as possible, for the student reading a book has every opportunity of appreciating every word of it. He may read it as slowly as he pleases, referring from time to time to other books, and reread the whole or parts of it as often as necessary.

Oral teaching is essentially different, for an audience, however carefully it may listen, cannot analyze the details, but only obtain a general impression of a subject. The "oral" teacher should have as deep a knowledge of the questions dealt with as possible and be able to give a fluent account of them. Accuracy in every detail can hardly be expected from him and could hardly be appreciated, but his general account should be as close to the truth as conditions permit. In fact it would be wrong for him to overload his account with details which would simply obscure his message without compensation.

The best proof that that distinction is generally overlooked is the common practice of "reading" papers at scientific meetings. It is clear that a paper carefully written for the sake of students who will examine it, each by himself at his own speed, cannot be meant to be read aloud to a group of other men, however attentive the latter may be. To read aloud in public a paper meant to be scrutinized quietly in one's own workshop is just as foolish as it would be to paint dainty miniatures on the surface of large walls. The walls call for broad frescoes; and so do listening audiences wait for general outlines, which they can understand and assimilate at once, not for microscopic analyses which they are unable to follow.

To return to the written papers, which are the true vehicles of expanding knowledge, much confusion is caused by the scientists who insist that historical knowledge need not be as detailed as historians would have it. To be sure, a vague knowledge of facts is generally sufficient for all but specialists, and our knowledge of most things is necessarily vague. However, that is not more true for the history of

56

science than for anything else. The situation is the same in every field. We can never be sure that we know a thing well until we know it with the utmost precision down to the smallest details, and it is the tendency of science to increase the precision obtainable, to carry on the search deeper and deeper, and to analyze the data more minutely. Indeed it is in that very way that many important discoveries have been made.

The historian of science has no hope of making great discoveries in little corners, as the scientist does, yet he is always urging himself to pursue the truth just as far as it will take him. After all, he is a kind of detective and judge, and, like the judge, he can never be sure of his facts unless those facts are as closely determined as possible. Vagueness covers a multitude of sins and errors, which can neither be detected nor got rid of, and tend to obscure and nullify whatever of the truth may be mixed with them. On the contrary, the more precise a statement is, the more tangible and correctible it also is. Historians who appear too fastidious or pedantic should not be hastily criticized. It is better after all to go beyond one's duty than to keep short of it. When all the details of a question have been duly analyzed and published, it is not necessary to burden one's self with them in other studies; it may thereafter suffice to outline the question and refer inquisitive readers to the earlier paper for more precise information.

Thus it happens that the basis of scientific history is bibliography, for we are always obliged to refer to various publications either for the original sources or for collateral evidence. Naïve and immature students often dream of avoiding these inconvenient references, by creating a collection of all the sources, or, worse still, anthologies of them. Many collections of texts and documents have indeed been compiled, but no collection has ever superseded completely the previous ones. At best, it has only been "one more collection," and one more perennial reference added to many others. As to anthologies, the idea that any scholar can select the essential, not only for other scholars but even for young students, is preposterous.

Similar fallacies are involved in the frequent requests relative to selections of the "hundred" or the "thousand" best books on the history of science. However well such a selection were made, it would very soon prove inadequate, except for elementary reference. The fundamental difficulty of historical research lies precisely in this, that no limited collection of books and documents is sufficient for every purpose, and that the intense study of any question may lead the investigator beyond the possibilities offered by the richest library or museum.

Amateurish interest in the history of science often takes the form of book collecting. One tries, for example, to gather all the fundamental books of science, the first editions [1] of the great classics, etc. No harm in that as long as the public libraries do not spend more than a small percentage of their income for "rarities." Collecting the latter should be left to rich men, because the cost is altogether out of proportion to the usefulness, and has become absolutely indefensible, now that it is possible to "film" any book at a relatively small expense. The microfilm of a book is equivalent to it for every purpose, except fetishism and snobbishness. The great classics are not always indispensable, and they are certainly very insufficient. The richness of a library for our studies depends not only on its possession of the "classics," but also and much more on the possession of thousands or millions of other books, each of which may be important or not in itself, and thousands or millions of scientific and historical papers. It is for that reason that an institute for the history of science owning a large library *ad hoc* would still be very inadequately equipped; it should be located in or near a general library, the richer and larger, the better.

The bibliographic approach to the history of science is fundamental, but it is just that, an approach, and nothing more. The investigation of any question must be preceded by the establishment of its bibliography; yet it is a matter of common experience that the best elements of any bibliography cannot be obtained before the question has been thoroughly investigated. In that sense one might say that the historical study of any question should begin with a good bibliography, and should end with a better one. It is for that reason that bibliographies compiled by mere bibliographers are seldom good; or to put it other-

---

[1] Collectors are always hunting for "firsts." Generally speaking it is not the first edition which a scholar needs most, but the best edition, which may be different from the first and is likely to include all that is included in the first, plus additions and corrections clearly differentiated from the original text. The determination of the best edition is sometimes difficult; different editions may be each the best for different purposes.

wise, the value of bibliographies tends to increase with the extra-bibliographical knowledge of their compilers. It is true that the mere fact of collecting is a source of knowledge, and no intelligent man can collect scientific books without learning much about the history of science, even if he reads only, in the way of collectors, a few pages of each book; yet there are better ways of learning. It is true also that any good collection is by itself a modest achievement in the right direction; it is like a gathering of the tools for the real workers to play with. The bibliographic and bibliophilic methods should always remain means subordinate to a higher end; should they predominate, scholarship would be debased. The bibliophilic approach is perhaps the most amusing of all; it is at one and the same time the most expensive and the poorest.

Scientists have a tendency to believe that historical work is too easy and they despise it accordingly, considering it as a kind of *refugium peccatorum* for their weaker brethren. On the other hand, they are often irritated by the "superior" attitude of some historians, not the best, who survey experimental efforts and the infinite drudgery of research, as it were, from an Olympian height. Historians, whose own scientific education is imperfect and too artificial, who never did genuine experimental work themselves, are apt to behave in the very objectionable way of those philosophers or theologians who were so confident in the superiority of their point of view that they did not hesitate to judge the efforts of scientists without taking the trouble of making a serious study of them. For example, remember the nonsense written by the Scotch metaphysician Sir William Hamilton (the "other" Hamilton) against mathematics, or the remarks on Darwin's theories made by the Bishop of Oxford at the Oxford meeting of the British Association in 1860.

Historians whose judgments would be as reckless as these would be equally contemptible, but it is well to bear in mind that, even when historians are as honest and painstaking as can be, they are still obliged to judge other people's efforts in a manner which must seem to the latter summary, abrupt, nay, offensive. It is in that sense that we often repeat the old saw, "criticism is easy but art is difficult." Criticism, good criticism at least, is not easy, but as compared with the criticized achievement it is an extremely short cut. Think of an explorer trying to reach the magnetic pole, or the top of the Himalayas, think of his courage and tenacity, of his sufferings, of his endless devotion; and then visualize the critic, who we shall assume is a competent and honest one, sitting in a comfortable armchair and reviewing, analyzing, and finally judging the other man's sacrifice within a week or less. Or think of a physicist repeating with equal faithfulness and ingenuity thousands of similar experiments, and then again visualize his critic, a competent and honest one, reviewing and judging that immense effort in a few pages or perhaps in a few paragraphs!

One can sympathize with the physicist's or the explorer's impatience, even when it is not justified. For the crux of the situation is this, that the creator is generally not the best judge of his achievement; he is too close to it, too keenly aware of the technical difficulties which he has overcome, and very often, almost unavoidably, too narrow in his own outlook. Now, to take a single instance, the value of an achievement is largely independent of the technical difficulties involved, and it is very hard for a technician to recognize that. The fact of overcoming great difficulties is praiseworthy but only to the extent that their overcoming was sufficiently worth while. Some clever technicians evoke in my mind the image of a man crossing the Niagara Falls walking on a tightrope. That is very difficult indeed and extremely dangerous, yet the achievement leaves me cold; I would hardly dare say so to the courageous artist who did it for I would be afraid of hurting his feelings. The scientific critic is not obliged to imitate my discretion; or rather his duty is to speak out and often to judge summarily scientific achievements which are as arduous and withal as futile as crossing the Niagara on a tightrope.

The paradox involved in the conflict between creation and criticism, or creator and critic, is at the bottom of all the misunderstandings between the scientist and the historian. I have discussed it before,[2] but must solve it again for the sake of rounding off my argument. Who would dare say that I have no right to criticize a dish because I am incapable of cooking anything myself? Creative efforts require a number of qualities which are very different from the purely critical ones,

[2] See my preface to vol. 29 of *Isis*: "Primum herbam, deinde spicam, deinde frumentum plenum in spica" (*Isis* 29, 9–14, 1938).

and sometimes antagonistic to them. It is not good for a creator, whether he be a scientist, or an artist, or what is commonly called "a man of action," to be too critical, for criticism would inhibit his efforts, and might even paralyze him altogether and dry up the source of his inspiration. This was neatly expressed by the French composer Rameau when he realized how his creative power waned in proportion as his critical power waxed: "From day to day my taste improves but I have lost all my genius." [3]

It is the historian's first duty to consider the facts of the case very carefully before formulating a judgment. He must make sure by all available means that the facts considered by him are pure and eventually disentangle them from the dross of errors and misunderstandings surrounding them. Thus far, he is doing what every scientist does, but there is a fundamental difference. The other scientists, except the anthropologists, have only material facts to take into account, and such facts, however complicated, are relatively simple as compared with human facts. Now the historian of science must be acquainted not only with a large number of material facts, but also with human facts. His every judgment implies some human facts. When he says, "Argon was discovered by Lord Rayleigh and Sir William Ramsay in 1895," he expresses the conclusion of an analysis involving not only the physical and chemical conditions leading to that discovery, but also the personal reactions of two remarkable individuals. Indeed the main difficulty lies there, and an equitable determination of the respective merits of both discoverers is a very subtle matter requiring not only technical knowledge, but wisdom. [4]

This example is not exceptional but typical. Every scientific achievement is primarily a human achievement. The historian of science is not a historian of nature (or "naturalist") but a historian of man. He is in the highest sense an anthropologist. It is rather intriguing, in that respect, that while the common anthropologist has long been accepted into the scientific fraternity, the historian of science is still held out of it. Thus the study of primitive thought is considered a legitimate scientific subject, while the study of the thought of the great pioneers and

[3] As quoted by Catherine Drinker Bowen and Barbara von Meck in their beautiful biography of Peter Ilyich Chaikovskii, *Beloved Friend* (p. 15, New York, 1937).

[4] For a discussion of that particular case, see *Isis* 8, 178–179.

intellectual leaders of mankind is pooh-poohed! This is not quite as absurd as it seems. The anthropologist has become a true scientist because he has undergone a true scientific training, and because he has finally succeeded in driving the dilettanti out of his domain. The historian of science is still necessarily an amateur, and, more often than not, a bad one. As historical dilettanti speak louder and to larger audiences than the austere investigators, they seem to dominate the field. In short, the historian of science has not yet won his claim to respectability. He is still an outsider and an outcast. Is it not high time to give him a chance of redemption? Educators who praise the history of science to the skies but can find no room on their staffs for historians of science have a share of responsibility in that pitiful situation.

The human elements, with which the historian of science is constantly dealing, increase the difficulties of his task immeasurably; indeed they increase it to the danger point, for the analysis involved is often so subtle as to be beyond the discipline of scientific method. On the other hand, they give to his studies their deep humanistic value. It is because of them that the historian of science is a kind of mediator between the scientists and the humanists, and is able (or would be able if given the opportunity and the means) to harmonize and unify whatever culture we may possess. This has been recognized, almost instinctively, by a number of distinguished scientists and scholars, but educators have not yet understood it, or at any rate have not yet translated their understanding into deeds.

The sayings of scientists on this subject are generally better known than those of scholars, and therefore I take pleasure in quoting here a statement made as early as 1880 not by a scientist proper but by a great scholar, the Sanskritist Max Müller: [5]

> You know that I am not a man of science in the usual, though far too narrow, sense of the word. But, although the science to which I have devoted the whole of my life, the science of man, is not yet formally represented in this College, depend upon it it will enter in; it is there already, it lurks in every corner, and I trust it will soon fill the whole College with its genial warmth

[5] He made it in the course of a speech at the opening of the Mason Science College, Birmingham, in October 1880. The quotation is taken from *The Life and Letters of the Right Honourable Friedrich Max Müller*, by his wife (vol. 2, p. 89, 1902).

and its quickening impulses. You mean to teach mathematics. Can you teach mathematics without teaching the laws of thought, without telling your pupils something about such men as Thales, Pythagoras, and Euclid, who were ancient Greeks, but who were men of science for all that? You mean to teach physiology and biology, the laws of life and nature. Are you likely to leave out the very crown of nature, man—to leave nature, like Hamlet without the Ghost, a nature without its spirit? A true College of Science could not live if it were to exclude the science of man. Man is the measurer of all things, and what is science but the reflection of the outer world on the mirror of the mind, growing more perfect, more orderly, more definite, more great with every generation? To attempt to study nature without studying man is as impossible as to study light without studying the eye.

Max Müller had given but little thought to the history of science conceived as an independent discipline (hardly anybody had in those days), but he understood deeply the necessary interpenetration of the sciences of nature and the science of man. Every historian, and more particularly every historian of science, is obliged to appreciate human achievements, which is difficult, and to judge the men themselves, which is far more difficult. Yet that duty is unavoidable. One of the functions of history is to explain men's motives and conduct, to criticize their deeds, to take warning from their errors, and to take advantage, as much as we can, from their virtues. The historian of science must explain the conditions of scientific discoveries and the evolution of theories; he must also introduce to the reader the men of science themselves, as men of flesh and blood, and tell the vicissitudes of their lives as truthfully as possible. Great scientific achievements are rare, great men of science are rarer still. It is important to describe their greatness when it occurs, and thus create noble emulations. The lives of such men as Faraday, Darwin, Pierre and Marie Curie deserve to be studied as the lives of saints, saints of a new kind, new models for the youth of today. It is the historian of science's duty to draw the portraits of those great leaders, and to hold them up for remembrance, gratitude, and devotion. In this way he continues and fulfills the old tradition of history as a mirror (*speculum*). It is his business to polish the mirror and to watch it as jealously as the astronomer watches his own mirrors. These reflect the stars, the historian's mirror reflects man. What is more important? I am not going to tell you, but please consider that the astronomer's mirror reflects the stars, and that the historian's mirror reflects the astronomer himself!

The history of science is a part of the humanities, an essential part of them. It is a science, because its purpose is to classify and organize a definite group of objective facts — but like every science, or more so, it is also an art. One can never consider all the facts, and even less classify and organize them. One must select one's data even as every artist selects his. The indetermination extends into two infinite directions, for in the first place, the facts are largely human facts and hence not as clear-cut as material facts but highly capricious and often evanescent; and in the second place, one must choose a few of the achievements among a great many, and a few men of science among thousands. To hold up to one's fellow men the mirror of history is a sacred function, the fulfillment of which is as difficult as anything can be. It is high time that efforts should be made to polish a good mirror for the history of science, for as long as that is not done, the mirror of history in general, the great mirror, will be very imperfect and very incomplete. What the historian of science is called on to do is to reflect carefully a group of facts which other historians have unaccountably neglected; these facts are not casual and irrelevant, but on the contrary highly relevant, yea, essential for the understanding of human progress and destiny.

It is not easy to find good men for that task, because there is not as yet an institute where they could be systematically trained and where everyday cooperation with their fellow workers would stimulate and enlighten them, and also because the needed qualifications are very complex. The minimum requirements are: experimental knowledge of science in general, and deeper knowledge of one or two branches of it; sufficient polyglottism; historical and philosophical training. In addition, there are other requirements which are less tangible but hardly less important. For example, there are ways of testing a man's acquaintance with historical facts and methods, but it is far more difficult to determine whether he has any historical sense. The same remark applies to philosophical knowledge, and indeed to every kind of knowledge. A man's actual knowledge is far less important than his ability to obtain further knowledge and to use it in the best manner at the proper time.

The historian's value increases with his experience and wisdom.

These two terms are frequently opposed as if the one represented something which can be gradually acquired while the other is an outright gift. That distinction is not as correct as it first appears to be. To begin with, one's wisdom may perhaps be improved, at least within a certain (small) proportion. Every human quality can be stretched out somewhat if sufficient pains are regularly taken to that effect. On the other hand, our experience will grow only if we have the gift of acquiring and retaining it, and of storing it properly in our brains.

What is clear is that the main qualifications of a historian are innate gifts, comparable to the gifts which make possible the development of a good scientist or a good artist. The historian of science, like any good specialist, must have a vocation; and if he have it, he must be prepared (but this is but another part of his vocation!) to take infinite pains in order to improve his qualities and make the best of them. The task to which he is addressing himself is so large that he cannot expect to succeed unless he devotes himself to it wholeheartedly, and not for a few years only, but for a lifetime.

The historian of science is often a scientist who is more interested in ideas than in technicalities, and who may have grown tired of laboratory work. It is a great mistake, however, to imagine, as is sometimes done, that failure to do well in the laboratory is a promise of success in the library. The would-be historian making that mistake is like the farmer's son who fancied he had a call to the ministry, because work in the fields was so hard and hot. These things have no causal relationship. Indeed if the failure were due to a lack of intelligence or application, it is clear that it would be repeated; if it were simply due to a lack of manual dexterity or instrumental ingenuity, it might be avoided in the new domain. Vocations, it is well to remember, should be characterized by positive qualifications, not by negative ones . . .

The teaching of the history of science should be as austere as the study of it, austere and humble. This does not mean that it should be unpleasant and ill-shaped; on the contrary it should be as elegant and urbane as possible, but without any use of "purple patches" and without any appeal to attractive but irrelevant notions.

The first need is to study the history of science as honestly and humbly as the biologist studies protoplasmic reactions or the physicist investigates the properties of matter. The second need, which can only be fulfilled in proportion as the first is, in the teaching of the truth thus discovered, in the same spirit, that is, the teaching of it in a simple, honest, and quiet way; as clearly and beautifully as possible but without extravagant claims or dramatic gestures.

There is an immense amount of work to be done with regard to the discovery of the truth as well as for its diffusion; it is a great and far-reaching undertaking for which the best men will hardly be good enough. Even from those men one should not expect too much, or at least anything sensational. We would expect them to do their best, to carry on honest investigations like other scientists and scholars worth their salt. Once in a while, there may be a genius among them, one seeing much farther than his fellows and making a new synthesis, but that is a gift of the gods which can neither be foreseen nor bargained for.

[1938]

Avicenna: Physician, Scientist and Philosopher

(9 8 0 - 1 0 3 7)

P ROFESSOR ARTHUR UPHAM POPE has done me the honor of inviting me to take part in this millenary festival. He wanted me to speak of Avicenna, the philosopher; it is impossible to speak of the philosopher only without missing the essence of his extraordinary personality and, therefore, I beg leave to broaden a little the scope of my survey. We know his early development pretty well, because he explained it in an autobiography extending to his twentieth year; the story of his life was then continued by his disciple, al-Juzjani.

His life. Before having reached the ripe age of twenty, Ibn Sina (let me call him so), in addition to his religious education, had already studied Aristotle, Euclid, Ptolemy, and Galen. His scientific curiosity was probably excited during his youth in Bukhara by the fact that his father was an Isma'ili. At the age of eighteen, Ibn Sina cured the sultan of Bukhara and thereafter devoted more and more time to medicine. He became not only the sultan's physician but also his general adviser. All this sounds like a fairy tale. He lived also in Jurjan, Rayy, and Hamadhan. He cured another sultan and thereby aroused the jealousies of rivals and suffered their persecutions. He was for a time imprisoned in Ferdajan, but happily, was permitted to continue his writing. He took refuge in Isfahan, and there spent the rest of his life. He died in 1037 at the age of fifty-seven. It is probable that he continued scientific, as well as philosophic, research throughout his life. His main works reveal his dual personality.

He evokes comparison with Galen, who was also philosopher and physician, and whose fame was partly due to that very duality. Until the eleventh century, Galen's glory was unique, then Ibn Sina's was associated to his, and until the Renaissance and even beyond they ruled together. Intrinsically, Galen of Pergamon and Ibn Sina of Bukhara are of equal size, but the philosophical knowledge and power of the latter was incomparably greater and his medical experience was greater too. How could it be otherwise, considering that Ibn Sina was standing upon the shoulders not only of Galen, but of all the Byzantine, Persian, and Arabic physicians who had appeared between them, that is, during a period of eight and a half centuries, as long a period as that which separated Ibn Sina from Pasteur! Galen and Ibn Sina were men of essentially the same kind, but living in very different ages and nations.

At the end of his life, Galen had compiled a bibliography of his own writings; Ibn Sina did the same at the end of his, and no doubt for the same reason. When men write as much as did these two, they find it difficult to find their way among their own writings, or even to remember them all without the help of bibliographies. Ibn Sina's lists 153 items and is incomplete.

It will suffice to speak of two among these items, each equally comprehensive in its own field: the *Qanun fi-l-tibb* (the Canon of medicine) and the *Shifa'* (Restoration to health). Judging from their titles, one might think that both of them are medical works, but that would be a mistake. The first is an enormous encyclopaedia of medicine, the second, an equally enormous encyclopaedia of philosophy. They are two of the greatest monuments in the world's literature. Both were written in Arabic as were the great majority of his books. He composed a few treatises and poems in Persian.

We shall center our discussion of Ibn Sina the philosopher on the *Shifa'* and of the physician on the *Qanun*.

His philosophy. Whence came his inspiration and his pabulum? I shall try to answer these questions as much as that can be done briefly. The oldest sources were Greek. It is told that he read the *Metaphysics* of Aristotle forty times and only understood it when it was made clear to him by al-Farabi's commentary. In addition, he studied the so-called *Theology of Aristotle* which all the Arabs took as genuine, but which

AVICENNA

is in reality a late Neoplatonic compilation, mainly derived from Plotinos' *Enneads*. The result is that when we read him, we can never be sure a priori whether his source is Aristotle or Plotinos.

Greek knowledge had reached him through two main channels, Byzantine-Syriac and Byzantine-Harranian. When it came through the first, the Greek writings had been translated into Syriac, then into Arabic, while the second transmission may have avoided the Syriac detour. By the ninth century, better translations were available and the texts explained by al-Kindi (IX–1).[1] A more elaborate commentary was prepared by al-Farabi (X–1), and it was this commentary which illuminated Ibn Sina's mind.

This introduces the Muslim sources, which were not simply the writings of al-Kindi and of al-Farabi but also the truly Muslim books. In the first place, the Qur'an majid, then the tafsir, its explanation, the hadith or tradition, the methods and contents of jurisprudence, fiqh. Every Muslim theologian was trained to discuss philosophical questions, such as predestination or free will. We may be sure that Ibn Sina had received such training, profited from it to the limit, and was as well prepared for the study of Aristotelian and Plotinian philosophy as any one could be.

His main philosophical work was the *Shifa'*, but he wrote many others, mainly the *Najat* or Salvation which is an abbreviated edition of it, the *Risalat al-hudud* (Definitions, proving his concern for exact thinking), the *Kitab al-isharat wal-tanbihat* (Signs and admonitions), and finally, *al-Hikma al-mashriqiyya* (the oriental philosophy) which he left unfinished.

To return to the *Shifa'* — it is an immense encyclopaedia dealing first with logic, second with physics, that is, all the natural sciences, psychology, cosmology, and finally with metaphysics. This last part forms the bulk of the treatise as well as its purpose and crown. Yet, note that a good part of the *Shifa'* is devoted to what we would call science. The philosopher in Ibn Sina, as in Aristotle, can never be separated from the man of science.

Ibn Sina's philosophy is focused upon the theory of being and the difference between essence and existence. The essence is the "quid-

---

[1] The numerals here and on following pages are chronological indications; e.g. (IX–1) means first half of the ninth century.

69

dity," the raison d'être, of an object. Existence is an accident which may be added to it or not. The essence is necessary, existence, accidental. In God alone are essence and existence united; God is necessary, all the rest is only possible or potential.

One of the main problems of Ibn Sina was to harmonize Aristotelian (or Plotinian) philosophy with Muslim theology; for example, how to reconcile the Aristotelian concept of the eternity of the world with the Muslim idea of creation *ex nihilo*. His solution was a strange compromise: the world is eternal but God is anterior to it. The Creator is Truth, Love, Life; He is pure intelligence. Creation issues from Him as an intellectual flux; it is at one and the same time a transmission of being and a radiation of intelligence.

In order to satisfy Muslim theology, it did not suffice to prove the immortality of the soul. It was equally necessary to prove the persistence of its individuality. Therefore, Ibn Sina introduced the principle of individuation. Matter is ugly and evil and tends to non-being. The soul is eternal and separate, even during life. After the body's destruction, the soul is capable of a new life of its own, like that of pure intelligence. Its eternal happiness is based mainly upon knowledge. Ibn Sina's task was extremely difficult, because he had to create or improve the available terminology even as he proceeded. Happily, he was helped in this by the exquisite morphology of the Arabic language. It was easier to create adequate terms in Arabic than it had been in Greek or than it would be in Latin or Hebrew. He had the advantage of using an almost perfect tool and he used it in a masterly way.

His terminology is very precise, as has been shown in great detail by Mlle. Goichon, but this cannot be explained in a short essay; moreover, the adequacy of it can be appreciated only by Arabic scholars.

It would seem that the Plotinian and mystical elements of Ibn Sina's thought became more prominent as he grew older. Was not that a special fruit of the universal tendency which he himself had described? Each being tends to its perfection, and this tendency becomes stronger as it rises higher on the ladder leading to God. Love comes down from the First Intelligence to the elements and then reaches up again. It is not proper to speak of a cosmical circulation of love (Ibn Sina does not do that) but of a descent and ascent.

AVICENNA

Ibn Sina was a great Persian poet. In spite of increasing poetry, his thought remained essentially scientific. That is why we can never leave out his purely scientific activities without the risk of misunderstanding him. He was always an intellectualist or a rationalist, but he was a rationalist who was aware of the limitations of positive knowledge, who understood and loved sainthood. I might remark apropos of this that there are two kinds of mystics. In the first place, there are those who are keenly aware of the mysteries of the world, all the mysteries which remain and indeed become deeper in spite of scientific analysis and synthesis. Many men of science, perhaps the greatest ones, are mystics of the first kind. In the second place, there are those who are not satisfied with the inherent mysteries (indeed, they are generally too ignorant to penetrate and appreciate them) and hence create artificial ones and indulge in wild fantasies. Many of the religious mystics are of the second kind, but Ibn Sina was unmistakably of the first.

The influence of his philosophy. Ibn Sina influenced al-Ghazali (XI–2) and Ibn Rushd (XII–2), but his direct influence upon Western philosophers is of greater concern to us at present. Strangely enough, his philosophy was known in the West half a century before Aristotle's. The great center of diffusion was Toledo, which had been reconquered from the Moors in 1085. From that time on, it was a Christian city, but one including many learned people who either were Arabs or who knew Arabic as a living language. The more intelligent Christians were well aware of the fact that the Arabic writings contained treasures of scientific and philosophic knowledge not yet available in Latin. The learned Archbishop, Raymond de Sauvetat (better known after his See, Raymond of Toledo), organized a kind of Academy wherein Christian scholars collaborated with Muslim and Jewish ones in the translation of Arabic writings into Latin.

It is natural that the Muslim members of the archbishop's circle should realize the importance of the *Shifa'* and of other Avicennian works and should want to translate them first. Those translations were begun circa 1130 while those of Aristotle's *Metaphysics* were begun only toward the end of the century, and two books of it, M and N, were translated only after 1270.

In the meanwhile, Western theologians were astonished and deeply

71

influenced by the *Shifa'* (or *Sufficientia* as they wrongly called it). At the beginning, they were as unable as the Arabic philosophers to distinguish between the Aristotelian and the Neoplatonic elements. As long as books M and N were not yet available to them, they were tempted to believe that some traces of them might be included in the *Shifa'* and that increased their curiosity.

The first proofs of Avicennian influences are given in the *De anima* of Domingo Gundisalvo (XII–1) and in various writings of the School of Chartres (XII–1). The Neoplatonism carried by Ibn Sina was reinforced by the one coming from other sources, or along other paths, in the Chartres and Augustinian writings. In 1210 and 1215, the study of Aristotle and of his commentators was forbidden in Paris, but those interdictions did not last very long and prove indirectly the interest taken in Aristotelian writings. Ibn Sina was more acceptable than undiluted Aristotelianism. For one thing, he had tried to harmonize faith with reason, a subject which was obviously out of Aristotle's scope.

William of Auvergne (XIII–1), teaching theology at the University of Paris c. 1228, was strongly critical of Aristotle, al-Farabi, Ibn Sina, al-Ghazali, but he made full use of their works as well as those of Ibn Sina's Hispano-Jewish contemporary, Ibn Gabirol. It was William who introduced into Latin scholasticism the distinction between essence and existence which became one of the pillars of Thomism. It was he also who went to Rome to plead the cause of Aristotle and obtained from Gregory IX, in 1231, the permission to teach his doctrine after revision. In the meanwhile, Christian schoolmen increased their knowledge of Ibn Sina and also of the Aristotelian text pure and simple, either directly or through the commentaries of Ibn Rushd (XII–2). The culmination of this was the work of St. Thomas (XIII–2). While Ibn Sina had tried to harmonize Aristotelianism with Muslim theology and Maimonides (XII–2) had tried to harmonize it with Jewish theology, St. Thomas reconciled it with Christian theology. All these men had one quality in common, they were intellectualists, helping readers to understand their faith and trying to persuade them not with sentimental homilies but with valid reasons and good logic.

Thanks to St. Thomas the application of ancient and mediaeval philosophy of Christian dogmatics was completed. Full use was made not only of Aristotle but also of St. Augustine (V–1), Boethius (VI–1),

St. John of Damascus (VIII–1) and above all, Ibn Sina. From the middle of the twelfth century on, every Christian schoolman was deeply indebted to the latter.

The early success of Ibn Sina had been due to the ambiguities arising from the Neoplatonism which was unconsciously an inherent part of his philosophy. This mixture of Aristotelianism with Platonism was reinforced by the teachings of the "Christian Plato," St. Augustine, and of the "Jewish Plato," Ibn Gabirol. All of these ideas were clarified and synthesized by St. Thomas' genius.

In his treatise on the soul, Ibn Sina told a remarkable parable. Imagine a man created blind but perfect in all other respects; his body is suspended in a vacuum, and he is unaware of his own members or of anything exterior to them. Despite all this, such a man would undoubtedly affirm his existence. This conceit comes very close to the Cartesian one "cogito ergo sum."

His medical and scientific activities. Let us now consider Ibn Sina's medical work and concentrate our attention upon the main book, *al-Qanun [fi-l-tibb]*, which was an encyclopaedia of medicine. The word qanun is simply the Greek word canon which we use to mean a standard. It was well chosen, for Ibn Sina's *Qanun* was the medical standard or the medical Bible for five to six centuries. It is divided into five main parts: I. Generalities (this includes much philosophy); II. Simple drugs in alphabetic order; III. Local diseases from head to foot; IV. General diseases, such as fevers, and much else; V. Compound medicines.

The *Qanun* was a synthesis of all the medical knowledge and wisdom available at the beginning of the eleventh century. That is, it was built upon Greek foundations, chiefly Hippocrates and Galen, and upon a Byzantine and Arabic superstructure. The whole of Galen had been translated into Arabic by Hunain ibn Ishaq (IX–2) and his school, and much had been added to Greek medicine in the Arabic treatises of Mesuë major (IX–1), of 'Ali ibn Sahl ibn Rabban al-Tabari (IX–1); the latter added information derived from Hindu sources, of al-Razi or Rhazes (IX–2), of Serapion senior (IX–2), Isaac Judaeus (X–1), Haly Abbas or 'Ali ibn 'Abbas (X–2), Abulcasis or Abu-l-Qasim al-Zahrawi (X–2), Ibn al-Jazzar (X–2), Abu Mansur Muwaffak (X–2), who wrote in Persian, etc. I enumerate these men, from among many more, to emphasize that Ibn Sina was standing upon the shoulders not only of Greek and Byzantine physicians, but also of many Arabic and Persian ones. This does not detract from his genius, which was great. Bear always in mind the comparison with Galen. Both men owe their glory to the same combination of philosophic and medical knowledge; both were giants standing upon the shoulders of giants.

To return to medicine, not only could Ibn Sina find a large mass of information in Arabic writings but he could use previous Arabic syntheses. The fruits of encyclopaedic efforts were available in the *Kitab al-hawi* (*Continens*) of al-Razi and the *Kitab al-maliki* (*Liber regius, Regalis dispositio*) of 'Ali ibn 'Abbas. Yet, his own synthesis was the best and the most popular. It was probably more to the *Qanun* than to the *Shifa'* that he owed the proud title of al-shaikh al-ra'is (the chief master) or similar ones which are still given to him in the Dar-al-Islam.

A man as admired and respected as Ibn Sina would naturally excite jealousies and enmities, and he would be calumniated. For example, as he failed to heal himself in his last illness (because it was the last and he had met his fate), his enemies declared that his medicine could not save his body any more than his metaphysics could save his soul. Such malicious sayings are simply the penalty of genius.

Ibn Sina was not only a physician but a man of science. Much of his scientific knowledge and grasp had already been illustrated in the greatest of his early works, the *Kitab al-shifa'* and in various monographs. He was a mathematician, a physicist, a naturalist, a geologist, a musical theorist, a chemist, and an astronomer. It is typical of his rationalism that he was opposed to alchemy and to judicial astrology.

His medical influence. The influence of his medical writings and especially of the *Qanun* in the Muslim East is proved by the abundance of Arabic manuscripts, Arabic commentaries, Persian and Turkish translations, commentaries, and adaptations. Its influence in the West was based upon the Latin translation made in Toledo by Gerard of Cremona, the same Gerard who translated the *Almagest* in 1175. This means that before the end of the twelfth century the two Bibles of Greek astronomy and Greco-Arabic medicine were opened to Latin students.

After that, almost every Latin medical treatise owed something to

AVICENNA

Ibn Sina. The *Continens* and the *Regalis dispositio* were published by the early printers but their success was much smaller than that of the *Canon*.

In spite of its immense size, no less than 14 incunabula editions of it were published in Padua, Milano, Strasbourg, Bologna, Pavia, Venice (5 different presses!), Lyon. There was also a Hebrew incunabulum (Naples, 1491). More Latin editions appeared during the sixteenth century, many adding other Avicennian texts or commentaries, glossaries, and other novelties. Indeed, the competition was extreme. Every printer of note wanted to produce his own Avicenna.

The first Arabic edition was printed before the end of the sixteenth century. This, however, was not an oriental edition (there was no Arabic printing in the East before the eighteenth century) but an Italian and Christian one (*Typographia Medicea*, Rome, 1593).

Some of the early editions of the *Canon* were based upon a new Latin translation prepared at the end of the fifteenth century and the beginning of the sixteenth by Andrea Alpago and his nephew, Paolo Alpago, who were physicians to the Venetian colony of Damascus. It is interesting to note that the Latin translations of the *Canon* were made in two steps: Toledo (XII–2) and Damascus (XVI–1). This is not the end. We still need a critical edition of the Arabic text and a critical translation in one of the Western languages of international currency. These are two enormous undertakings, however, each of which would require the lifelong devotion of a competent scholar.

When the learned men of the West acquired a direct knowledge of Greek medicine (as opposed to the indirect one via the Syriac-Arabic detour), many of them, to begin with Petrarca, developed anti-Arabic tendencies. Those tendencies reached a climax during the Renaissance. Yet, Avicenna's fame was hardly diminished. He had already been published so often in Latin garb that Latin scholars considered the *Canon* as they did the *Vulgate*, Latin publications, not Arabic, Hebrew, or Greek.

Among the almost innumerable Latin editions of the *Canon* (some complete, the majority partial) I shall mention only three. Peter Kirsten published an Arabic-Latin edition of book 2 (Breslau, 1609–10). As late as 1658, the learned professor Plempius began a complete Latin edition, but he could publish only books 1 and 2, and a part of 4 (Louvain, 1658). The French physician, Pierre Vattier, learned Arabic for the sake of reading Avicenna in the original and published a Latin edition of the parts of the *Canon* (in books 3–4) dealing with psychology (Paris, 1659).

75

These editions extending beyond the middle of the seventeenth century were not simply philological achievements, they were made in the same spirit as the Greek editions of medical classics had been made by Renaissance physicians. The purpose was to make the medical truth available in its purity to other physicians. In spite of growing hostility to the Arabs, Avicenna was treated by physicians in the seventeenth century with as much respect as Hippocrates and Galen. What better proof could one give of his enduring authoritativeness? No Muslim or Oriental scholar has attained as high a position and as strong and lasting an influence as Ibn Sina did.

CONCLUSION

Ibn Sina holds a place of supreme importance in the history of metaphysics. He is one of the links in the golden chain which unites such men as Aristotle, Plotinos, John of Damascus, al-Kindi, al-Farabi, and, after him, Ibn Rushd, Maimonides, and Thomas Aquinas.

He helps us to realize the greatness of the Arabic and Muslim contributions to mediaeval philosophy, a philosophy which was expressed in four major languages, Greek, Arabic, Latin, and Hebrew. To understand mediaeval thought one must not neglect any of the four strands whereof it was woven. In spite of dogmatic differences, Muslim, Jewish, and Christian theologies had in common a sufficient number of principles to help one another. Though Ibn Sina thought only of Islamic theology, he was able to facilitate the assimilation of Aristotelian metaphysics for Jewish and Christian purposes.

In spite of the metaphysical obsessions which could not be shaken off in mediaeval times, Ibn Sina was primarily, like Aristotle and Galen, a philosopher of science, a man who tried to understand the whole of positive knowledge. This was due, of course, to his being a practical man of science. As far as we can judge the evolution of his thought, we witness in it a double orientation — in the first place, towards scientific concreteness, in the second place, towards mysticism. That mysticism was caused by his growing awareness of the limitations of reason and by his humility.

Every scientific philosopher must needs follow the same pattern of investigation, but science has grown so fast and with such exuberance since the Middle Ages that it becomes increasingly more difficult, if not impossible, to repeat the encyclopaedic efforts of an Aristotle or an Ibn Sina.

We honor in him one of the heroes of science and philosophy.

BIBLIOGRAPHICAL NOTES

Anawati, G. C. *Essai de bibliographie avicenienne*, Cairo, 1950. (*Isis 42*, 314). 435 pages in Arabic, 20 in French.

d'Alverny, Marie Therèse. Notes sur les traductions médiévales des oeuvres philosophiques d'Avicenne, *Archives d'histoire doctrinale et littéraire du Moyen âge*, Paris, 1952, pp. 337–358. (To be continued.)

A critical edition of the *Shifa'* has been begun in Cairo. Vol. I dealing with the introduction to logic has recently appeared (1952). The whole work will extend to 30 vols. of some 300 pages each.

Livre des directives et remarques; French translation of the *Kitab al-isharat waltanbihat* by Amélie Marie Goichon. Paris, Vrin, 1951. 552 pp. (*Isis 43*, 132–133, 1952).

I am deeply indebted, as are all Avicennian scholars, to the many studies of Mlle. Goichon. See my article in *Isis 33*, 326–329, 1941, and the bibliography which is included. Add to it her book entitled *La philosophie d'Avicenne et son influence en Europe médiévale*, Paris, Maisonneuve, 1944; revised ed., 1951 (*Isis 39*, 245–246, 1948).

Medical works. There are as yet neither critical editions, nor critical translations of the *Qanun fi-l-tibb*. Apart from short articles and the chapters ad hoc in every history of medicine, there is no complete study of Avicennian medicine.

Gruner, O. C. *Avicenna. A treatise on the Canon, incorporating a translation of the first book*. London, Luzac, 1930 (*Isis 15*, 206; 402, 1931). Very insufficient. As this book deals with generalities, it will interest the historian of philosophy as well as the historian of medicine.

The bibliography included in my *Introduction to the History of Science* (Washington, D.C., Carnegie Institution, 1927, vol. 1, pp. 709–713) should be completed by the examination of sections XI and "Islam" in the Critical Bibliographies of *Isis*, beginning with the 19th in vol. 8, 728–739; 793–795, 1926.

[1955]

Maimonides: Philosopher and Physician

(1 1 3 5-1 2 0 4)

Lecture delivered December 13, 1954 to help celebrate the 750th anniversary of Maimonides' death in Cairo, in 1204.

IT WAS my privilege to take part in the celebration of the 800th anniversary of Maimonides' birth organized by the Department of Philosphy of Harvard University in 1935, and in 1953 I attended the VIIth International Congress of the History of Science meeting in Jerusalem under his auspices. Maimonides, or Rambam,[1] as he is affectionately called in Israel, died in Cairo seven hundred and fifty years ago and was buried in Tiberias, where pilgrims visit his tomb to this very day. The official seal of the Congress was derived from a coin of Tiberias, representing Hygieia, daughter of Asclēpios, goddess of health. The seal was a double allusion, first, to the mineral baths of Tiberias and, second, to Maimonides. The government of Israel honored the Congress by issuing a special stamp bearing a portrait of the revered master.[2] I am now welcoming the third opportunity of celebrating him.

Maimonides' memory has been highly honored throughout the centuries and not only by Jews but also Christians like myself. A great many books, poems, and studies have been dedicated to him and yet our essential duty has not yet been accomplished. There is not yet a complete edition of his Arabic and Hebrew works, indeed many of them have not yet been published at all. In 1932, the American Academy for Jewish Research outlined the plan of a critical edition

[1] Rambam stands for Rabbi Moses ben Maimon.
[2] Reproductions of the seal and stamp were published in *Isis* 45, 64 (1954).

of his *opera omnia*[3] but only three volumes have thus far appeared. We need a scholarly edition of all his works, and this should be done in the same style as the edition of Ibn Rushd's works sponsored by the Mediaeval Academy: that is, the works should be edited in Arabic, Hebrew, and Latin, for each mediaeval translation added something to the original text, or gave us means of understanding it better.

Though all of you are more or less familiar with him, it may be helpful to give a brief account of his life, to evoke him, the man, as he was eight centuries ago, to draw a portrait of him. But to see him well we must see him in his own background, a living man in a living environment. The city in which he was born was then one of the greatest cities of Europe, Córdoba, in Andalusia. Under the Umayyad dynasty which ruled Spain for almost three centuries (756–1031), Córdoba had become the greatest city of Western Islām, the rival of Baghdād in the East, and it was admired not only by Muslims and Jews but even by Christians. Hrosvitha (X–2), a Benedictine nun, had heard of Córdoba in her German cloister and called it the "jewel of the world." Córdoba had the singular honor of being the cradle of three outstanding philosophers, none of whom was a Spaniard: the Roman Seneca was born there in 4 B.C., the Muslim Ibn Rushd (Averroës) in 1126, and the Jew Maimonides in 1135. It is a remarkable coincidence that the two greatest philosophers respectively of Islām and of Israel were born in the same city within nine years. Their Christian emulator St. Thomas Aquinas, was born in 1225, that is, almost a century later than Ibn Rushd, not in southern Spain however, but in southern Italy. At the time of Maimonides' birth, Córdoba was ruled by the Almovarides (Murābiṭūn) but in 1147 they were displaced by the Almohades (Muwaḥḥidūn), who were puritans, intolerant, and drove the Jews out of the city.[4] His family was obliged to leave Córdoba in 1148, the boy was then thirteen; for the next ten

[3] A typewritten statement of seven pages submitted by the AAJR to the American Council of Learned Societies. I received a copy of it in December, 1932. Only three parts of the projected edition have appeared: (1) the treatise on logic (*Millot bahiggayon*) edited by Israel Efros (New York, 1938), (2) the treatise on resurrection (*Ma'amar teḥiyyot ha-metim*) by Joshua Finkel (New York, 1939), (3) the Epistle to Yemen (*Iggeret Teman*), by Abraham S. Halkin with an English translation by Boaz Cohen (New York, 1952; *Isis 44*, 112).

[4] These two dynasties, which ruled Spain from 1091 to 1147 and from 1147 to 1212, came from North Africa and were not Arabic but Berber; both were fanatically Muslim, the second even more so than the first.

years they drifted from place to place, Cordoban exiles in a Spain which was becoming more and more unfriendly to them; at some time they crossed to Morocco and by 1158 were settled in Fez (Fās). We do not know exactly what Maimonides was doing during that time, but we may be sure that he seized every opportunity of increasing his knowledge; he studied theology, philosophy, and medicine; whatever his earnings might be, they were most probably derived from the practice of medicine. Conditions were hardly better in Morocco than in Spain, however, and in April 1165 the family sailed to Acre (Saint Jean d'Acre), whence they travelled to Jerusalem and to Cairo. They established themselves at the end of 1165 in Fusṭāṭ, the oldest Arabic settlement in that district, just south of the new city.[5] In the following year, his father died and also his younger brother David, who was a jeweler and the main support of the family; from 1166 on, Maimonides had to provide for them with his medical practice. His activities were stupendous because he earned his living as a physician and yet was engaged in Biblical, Talmudic, philosophical studies and in writing books the mass and quality of which pass our understanding.

The life of a Jewish physician and rabbi was far more comfortable in Egypt than in the Maghrib, especially after the tolerant Fāṭimī dynasty (909–1171) had been replaced by the Ayyūbī (1171–1250).[6] Within another decade, Maimonides had become sufficiently well known as a physician to be patronized by the powerful wazīr al-Qāḍī al-Fāḍil 'Abd al-Raḥīm al-Baisānī, and thanks to him he was taken in the service of Salāḥ al-dīn al-Ayyūbī (sulṭān 1171–1193), a magnanimous king, well known in the West under the name of Saladin.[7] After Saladin's death, he was archiater to his eldest son, al-Afḍal Nūr

[5] Al-Fusṭāṭ was built about 641, destroyed in 750, then rebuilt; the new city al-Qāhira (hence Cairo) was then established north of it. In Maimonides' time (1168) Fusṭāṭ was again destroyed rather than be surrendered to the Crusaders, led by Amalrich, king of Jerusalem. It was probably a flimsy cluster of houses which could be easily rebuilt.

[6] There were Jewish court physicians already during the Fāṭimī regime, at least at the end of it; there were many under the Ayyūbī. In Morocco, on the contrary, it is probable that Maimonides had to hide his Jewishness; that was not difficult for in every aspect, save religion, he behaved and talked like and Arab. When his fame grew so much as to annoy some rivals, he was accused of having confessed Islām in Morocco; that is very improbable and unproven (G. Sarton, *Introduction to the History of Science.* 2, 375).

[7] Introduced to innumerable English readers in *The Talisman* of Sir Walter Scott (1825).

al-dīn 'Alī. He fell ill in 1200 and probably ended medical practice or reduced it considerably, being thus able to devote the remnant of his life to writing. He died in Cairo on 13 December 1204, at the age of 69; his remains were carried to Tiberias, presumably by the order and care of the Jewish community which was anxious that their revered master should lie in holy ground.

In short, Maimonides was born in Spain and completely educated in the Maghrib (Spain and Morocco); he spent there the first thirty years (1135–1165) of his life and that is more than is needed to shape a man; the larger half of his life, thirty-nine years (1165–1204), was spent in the Mashriq, almost exclusively in Cairo. It is thus impossible to decide whether he was a Westerner or an Easterner. There was another dualism in his life, for he was at one and the same time an Arabic physician who was not different from his Muslim or Samaritan [8] colleagues, and a Jewish theologian. This implied no contradiction, yet his life was a double life, and he was a giant in both of them. His activity was prodigious, for he was a physician and astronomer, a Talmudist, a rabbi, a philosopher, and he wrote many treatises some of which have remained classics to this day.

THE PHILOSOPHER

Among his philosophical books there is one on the art of logic (*sinā'at al-manṭiq*) — perhaps his earliest work — another on the unity of God (*fī tawḥīd*), etc., but it is better in this lecture to speak only of one, the *Dalālat al-ḥā'irīn*,[9] which is his own masterpiece and is one of the greatest monuments of mediaeval philosophy. Like all his other works except the *Mishneh Torah*, it was written in Arabic, which was his real language for every purpose except religious ones. The *Dalāla* being composed for the Jewish community was probably written in the Hebrew script and hence could not be used by the Arabs, though it was in their own language.[10] The first and only edition of the original

---

[8] The Samaritans driven out of Nāblus (Shichem) by the Crusaders had established themselves in Syria and Egypt, the intellectuals in Damascus and Cairo. One of Maimonides' successors as court physician was the Samaritan Sadaqa ben Munaja' (XIII-1).

[9] Meaning *Guide of the perplexed*, but Maimonides' enemies, changing only the first letter, affected to call it *Dalālat alḥā'irīn*. The change in writing or even in pronunciation was small, but great in sense, for *Ḍalāla* means error, perdition!

[10] The scientific language of most of the Jews, except the Qaraites, was Arabic,

text was printed in Hebrew type,[11] which means that Arabic scholars, unfamiliar with Hebrew, cannot read it except in a halting way.

The Hebrew translation has almost the standing of an original, for it was completed at Arles [12] in 1204, by a friend of his, Samuel ben Judah ibn Tibbon (XIII–1), who obtained his advice in the solution of difficulties. It was Samuel or perhaps the author himself who selected the title *Moreh nebukim* under which the work is almost universally known.[13] The book was so famous that a new Hebrew translation was made about ten years later by the Spaniard, Judah ben Solomon al-Ḥarizi (XIII–1). It is more fluent than Samuel's and Judah added a glossary and table of contents, yet the first translation is generally preferred. Both translations are equally important from the point of view of the tradition; for example, the second was the basis of the earliest Latin edition, *Doctor Perplexorum* (1520), of a Castilian version, and of many Hebrew editions.

In a sense the Hebrew translation was more important than the Arabic original, for soon after that time the Jewish communities of Western Europe became more interested in learning than the Eastern communities but gradually lost the use of Arabic.

The *Moreh nebukim* began with a long preface addressed to the master's favorite disciple, Joseph ben Judah ibn 'Aqnin (XII–2). The purpose can best be stated in his own words "to promote the true understanding of the real spirit of the Law, to guide those religious persons who adhering to the Torah, have studied philosophy [including

---

but the script was generally Hebrew. I have pointed out repeatedly that Eastern people attached more importance to script than to language (*Introd.* 1, 152, 333; 2, 102, 501; 3, 359); the language was immaterial except when religion was concerned. Thus it was the most orthodox people of Israel who opposed the selection of Hebrew as a national language; the use of the sacred language for profane needs was shocking to them (*Isis 45*, 76–77, 1954).

[11] We owe it to Salomon Munk, who added a French translation to it (3 vols., Paris, 1856–1866). The Hebrew text had been printed a long time earlier (Rome? bef. 1480), and the Latin translation soon afterward (Paris, 1520). There are innumerable Hebrew editions with or without commentaries; translations into Italian, German, English, French were printed repeatedly in the nineteenth century and after.

[12] Arles was then an important center of Jewish learning (*Isis 45*, 114, 1954).

[13] Critics of the book (and we shall see later that there were many of them and vociferous ones) could play the same trick with the Hebrew title as was done with the Arabic one. They affected to call it *Nebukat ha-morim*, perplexity of the guides (instead of guide of the perplexed).

what we call science] and are embarrassed by the contradictions between the teachings of philosophy and the literal sense of the Torah." That was a clear and noble purpose, indeed the noblest which a consecrated thinker could assume, for he did fully realize the value of science but never doubted the top priority of his faith. Hence it was absolutely necessary to reconcile Jewish theology with Arabic Aristotelianism, or faith with reason.

It is out of the question to give here a summary of the work, which is of considerable size, a real encyclopaedia of Jewish theology and Biblical criticism; a simple table of contents would already take far more space than is available, and that table would be of little use without long explanations. It discusses the existence of God, His attributes, His names, then the World which He created, its origin, changes, and destiny, man in the world and in the presence of God, the nature of free will, the origin and meaning of evil, the mystery of resurrection, the essence of Prophecy and the duties of Prophets, the significance of the Law, man's supreme duty, his knowledge and possession of God.

His sources were, in the first place, the Bible, Midrash, Talmud, and the writings of early Jewish doctors, and in the second place, Greek philosophy, especially Aristotle, whom he called the "prince of philosophers." As he did not know Greek, his knowledge of Greek philosophy and science was derived almost exclusively from the Arabic translations and commentaries, which were abundant. His familiarity with Plato was much smaller and with the Neoplatonists (such as Plotinus and Porphyry) almost null, except what he could not help getting indirectly and unconsciously.

The bulk of his non-Biblical, non-Talmudic knowledge came thus from the Arabic Muslim philosophers: al-Kindī (IX–1), al-Fārābī (X–1), the Rasā'il ikhwān al-ṣafā' (X–2), Ibn Sīnā (XI–1), al-Ghazālī (XI–2), Ibn Bājja (XII–1), Ibn Ṭufail (XII–2). His older contemporary, Ibn Rushd, influenced him less; I imagine that Averroës' writings fell too late in his hands to be assimilated. The same thing happens to all of us; we are ready to accept without objections the first good book which we read on any subject (e.g., a college textbook); should we read other books, however, we would become more and more critical, and we would tackle the last ones with impatience. When he finally got hold of Ibn Rushd's commentaries, his own mind was already made up and he quoted him only to state his disagreement. He was aware of Muslim controversies, for example, that concerning the uncreatedness and eternity of the Qur'ān, and also of Christian ones, for example, on the Trinity. He must have met many Copts in Egypt and there was an abundant Christian literature in Arabic. He referred to such men as Ioannes Philoponos (VI–1) and Ibn 'Adī.[14] There is no evidence that he had read the New Testament, though it was already available in more than one Arabic translation.[15]

To return to his knowledge of Aristotle which was fundamental for his purpose, his main source was al-Fārābī, while the best one, Ibn Rushd, was largely closed to him by his own incuriosity. This is another way of saying that his Aristotelianism was not quite pure, yet it was probably sufficient for his needs.

A few more words must be said about his Jewish sources. Philōn of Alexandria (I–1) writing in Greek was not directly available to him.[16] He was acquainted with some of the Geonim, especially Sa'adia ben Joseph (X–1), but not with Ibn Gabirol (XI–1).[17] Living in Cairo he had good opportunities of learning the Qaraite point of view; if he studied Benjamin Nahawendi (IX–1) he may have obtained some Philonic views from him. He had read some of the books of Abraham ben Ezra (XII–1) and of Joseph ibn Ẓaddiq (XII–1). All in all, his knowledge of mediaeval Jewish books was apparently less considerable than his knowledge of Muslim ones. It is possible, however, that he read more Jewish authors than he mentions.

Philōn, writing in the time of Christ, had tried to reconcile Jewish

[14] Yaḥyā ibn 'Adi (X–1), a Jacobite (Monophysite) of Baghdād. Georg Graf, *Geschichte der christlichen arabischen Literatur* (2, 233–249, Vatican, 1947). Philoponos was also a Monophysite, but he flourished in Alexandria, three centuries earlier.

[15] For example, the *Diatessaron* of Tatian (II–2) had been Arabicized by the Nestorian physician, Ibn al-Taiyib (XI–1), if not before. There were many Arabic translations of parts of the New Testament, the first being made from the Greek in the Mt. Sinai monastery (IXth cent.). Georg Graf, *Geschichte der christlichen arabischen Literatur* (vol. 1, 138–195, Vatican, 1944; *Isis 41*, 386; *43*, 173).

[16] Samuel Poznanski, Philon dans l'ancienne littérature judéo-arabe, *Revue des études juives 50*, 10–31 (Paris, 1905).

[17] Ibn Gabirol or Avicebron (XI–1) influenced the Christians far more than he did his own brethren. His main work, *Yanbū' al-ḥayāt, Fons vitae*, was translated into Latin as early as 1150, and was the first big source of Neoplatonism in the West.

theology with Greek philosophy, but that meant for him the Pythagoreans, Plato, the Stoics. Maimonides' task, almost twelve centuries later, was very different and far more interesting to the scientific minds of today, for he was trying to reconcile Jewish theology with Muslim Aristotelianism. A good part of his work had been done before him by Muslim theologians, for many theories were common to Muslim and to Jewish theology, yet much remained to be done and he did it splendidly. Muslim interest in the Old Testament was marginal, Jewish interest in it was central, absolutely fundamental. Maimonides gave an allegorical interpretation of Biblical anthropomorphism and concreteness, keeping clear at once of mysticism and of scepticism; for example, he explained prophetic visions as psychical experiences, and Jewish laws and customs from the point of view of comparative ethnology. He insisted that human perfection is inseparable from knowledge and that the acquisition of knowledge is one of the highest forms of religion. This was an old Pythagorean conceit but which he was stating with a new religious accent.

The dualism of his personality has already been referred to, but I failed to speak of the most fundamental aspect of it. He was at one and the same time an ardent Aristotelian, a lover of reason and science, and an orthodox and pious Jew. Reason, he thought, being a gift of God, cannot be irreconcilable with religion. It must be possible to give a rational account of the universe without traversing religious dogmas, for both the world and the faith are from God. The main stumbling block was the Aristotelian theory of the eternity of matter. How could this be reconciled with the idea of creation? His common sense revolted against the artificial doctrines of the Muslim atomists. He saw that one could not accept at once the eternity of matter and the account of Genesis; it was necessary to make a choice; he chose Genesis. This gives us a measure of his rationalism; he was ready to carry it to any extent compatible with his creed, but not further.

He was willing to agree with Aristotle concerning the sublunar world, but not above that. The things which Aristotle said concerning the superlunar world, the spheres and the Intelligences guiding them and his metaphysical opinions are conjectural or erroneous.[18] That is,

[18] There is an amusing contrast between his attitude and that of the mathematician David Hilbert (1862–1943), who at the end of his life during the Hitlerian

he bowed to Aristotle the scientist and even to the philosopher, but rejected the theologian; he could not do otherwise.

Being a physician, his philosophy was largely Galenic. What we would call natural law was for him design; all the regularities of nature are contingent upon the existence of a rational God. The world is one individual whole, rational through and through; for without rationality there could not be any knowledge or morality or religion. He denounced vigorously the absurdities of superstition and was ever ready to uphold the supremacy of reason. In common with every other philosopher who was more inclined to rationalism than to mysticism, he emphasized the ethical side of religion; man must be good before he can be wise.

Misunderstandings on the subject were largely due to the fact that, while Maimonides' rationalism was innocent enough, yet it was an opening wedge. The more conservative who considered the *Dalāla* with horror were instinctively right. He could not realize the revolutionary import of his views, but it is clear enough to us. All of which amounts to saying that Maimonides had a truly creative mind.

The *Guide of the Perplexed* was a tremendous stimulus to philosophical and theological studies, either directly or indirectly, because of the passionate controversies which it set in motion. His rationalism, moderate and prudent as it was, infuriated many rabbis, qaraite and orthodox, all those whom we would call fundamentalists, literalists, obscurantists. In 1234, some of those bigots in Languedoc were so blinded by their anger that they referred the dispute to a Christian authority, the papal legate at Montpellier, who was glad to oblige them by ordering the destruction of Maimonides' books.

A very different kind of enemies were the students of the Qabbalah, the readers of the *Sefer Yezirah* and of the *Sefer ha-bahir*,[19] who poisoned their intelligence with magical fantasies and immoderate dreams. Such books have always had an especially strong attraction for

---

nightmare refused to bother any more about sublunar matters! Sarton, Documents nouveaux concernant Lagrange, *Revue d'histoire des sciences 3*, 110–132 (Paris, 1950), p. 119.

[19] The *Sefer ha-zohar* is not mentioned because it was composed only toward the end of the thirteenth century. Hence, Maimonides could not criticize it; it was rather the opposite, its creation was a part of the revolt against the excessive intellectualism of Maimonides, Ibn Rushd, and their followers. *Introd.* (2, 366–368, 878–881).

unbalanced minds, whose destruction it helps to complete, and the more surely because of the genuine jewels which are embedded in them. The Qabbalah and Maimonidean rationalism were utterly incompatible.

Maimonides was thus caught between two fires, that of the extreme orthodox and bigots on the one side, and that of the occultists and magicians on the other.

In the course of time, the passions grew colder and Maimonides' wisdom emerged. An equal triumph was obtained by his contemporary, Ibn Rushd, with a singular difference. Ibn Rushd (or Averroës) was not only the greatest philosopher of Islām but also the last one. After his time, Islamic obscurantism and intolerance made rationalism almost impossible and the fame of Ibn Rushd was largely based not upon his original Arabic works but upon Hebrew and Latin translations of them; that is another story, however, which cannot be discussed now.[20]

Inasmuch as my lecture is devoted to Maimonides, let us now return to him and discuss what I believe to be the main point. Granted that the *Moreh nebukim* is one of the greatest books of the Middle Ages, what is its practical value today? It could still help us to solve some of our perplexities, but not as well as modern books which would render the same service in a language and in a form more adequate to present needs. Unfortunately, we are obsessed and thrown out of balance by many perplexities which Maimonides could not solve nor even imagine.

His task as compared with ours was relatively easy. It consisted in harmonizing an established religion with an established philosophy (and science); both religion and philosophy were accepted as true and hence were compatible by definition. A bridge was conceivable and possible and the only difficulty was to build it.

Our situation is vastly different. A good many of our people, even of the best of people, have neither established religion nor established

[20] It is for that reason that there are more Hebrew than Arabic MSS. of Ibn Rushd and that some of his works are lost in the Arabic original (*Isis 41*, 306–307; 45, 112). Some of Maimonides' books are also lost in the Arabic original, but that is less surprising because he was a Jew, and the Western Jews were soon unable to read Arabic.

philosophy, hence there is no question of building a bridge, for a bridge can only be laid upon two fixed piers, not upon unknown or moving ones. On the other hand, science has progressed so far in so many directions that it is raising cruel perplexities which were unthinkable in the twelfth century. The "atomic bomb" (and all that it implies) is the most obvious as well as the most painful of these perplexities, but there are numberless others. There is an abundance of scientific knowledge, but it is beyond the grasp of most people; these people cannot share its certainties and there is no certainty for them anywhere else. How could one harmonize hostile creeds and conflicting theologies with discordant and conjectural philosophies on one side and with silly gadgets or inhuman techniques on the other? [21] Is it possible to build a durable house upon quicksand?

Our need for a modern *Moreh nebukim* is urgent, but who will write it? And even if it were as adequate as it should be, how would it be possible to establish its authority?

THE PHYSICIAN

A good part of Maimonides' life was devoted to medicine. One might be tempted to say that the physician in him was the breadwinner and the theologian, a self-chosen missionary, but that would be an oversimplification. His medical masters were Hippocrates and even more so Galen and he fully shared the latter's ambiguousness and prejudices. Medicine was not a science in Galen's time nor even in Maimonides' time, a thousand years later; it was an art, but Galen had dreamed that it would be raised to a higher intellectual level by means of philosophy.[22] Maimonides shared that illusion. On the other hand, he had obtained a good amount of new medical knowledge from the Muslim physicians, chiefly al-Rāzī (IX-2) and Ibn Sīnā (XI-1).

The result of this is that in Maimonides' case as well as in the case of

---

[21] I did not refer to our political and economic perplexities which are not essentially different from mediaeval ones and are not as fundamental as theological and scientific perplexities are. The essential difficulties of our time are due to the exuberant and uncontrollable progress, not of science, but of technology. An excellent discussion of them is provided by Julian Huxley at the end of his recent book, *From an Antique Land. Ancient and Modern in the Middle East* (New York, Crown, 1954).

[22] I have descanted on that idea in a recent volume, *Galen of Pergamon* (Kansas University Press, Lawrence, Kansas, 1954).

Galen and Ibn Sīnā, the philosopher cannot be separated from the physician and one cannot discuss the latter without discussing the former.

The same moderate rationalism which inspired the *Moreb nebukim* informed as well his medical treatises. It is well expressed in the 25th chapter of the *Pirque Mosheh*:[23]

> It is my intention in this chapter to draw your attention to the ways of research (explanation) and belief. If anybody tells you in order to support his opinion (or theory) that he is in possession of proofs and evidence and that he saw the thing with his own eyes, you have to doubt him, even if he is an authority accepted by great men, even if he is himself honest and virtuous. Inquire well into what he wants to prove to you. Do not allow your senses to be confused by his research and innovations (his stories). Think well, search, examine, and try to understand (the ways of nature) which he claims to know. Do not allow yourself to be influenced by the sayings that something is obvious, whether a single man is saying so or whether it is a common opinion, for the desire of power leads men to shameful things, particularly in the case of divided opinions . . . I advise you to examine critically the opinions even of such an authority and prominent sage as Galen.

Such a statement was a reaction against the assertiveness of conceited doctors or deliberate quacks who enjoyed an open field in those days. We know what quacks would do even today if they were not restrained, and what they still manage to do in spite of restrictions; the lack of medical science and the rareness of medical certainty in the past (not only in ancient times or the Middle Ages but down to the nineteenth century) encouraged every imposture. Therefore, Maimonides was obliged to be a rationalist and a sceptic. In the *Moreh nebukim* he attacked the use of astrology, incantations, amulets, and other instruments of magic and folly.

While averse to superstitions of every kind, he was naturally and always a defender of genuine piety. This reminds us that a famous prayer, "the physician's prayer," has long been ascribed to him. That document might have been composed by him, for it is written in his own style and mood, but it is apocryphal.[24]

[23] The text which follows, not yet published, was kindly communicated to me by Dr. Süssman Muntner in August, 1954. It is quoted from his typescript with his kind permission.

[24] *Introd.* (2, 373). J. O. Leibovitz, The physician's prayer ascribed to Maimonides (*Dapim Refuiim*, vol. 13, 8 p., Tel Aviv, 1954). Its first publication occurred in the *Deutsches Museum* (Leipzig, 1783). Dr. Leibovitz's paper contains a facsimile of the original text of 1783 with Hebrew translation and discussion,

It is typical of the inveterate love of magic that in spite of his rationalism he became himself the object of a new superstition. Sick people are carried (even now) to the synagogue of Rab Mosheh (that is, his own synagogue) in the Ḥarat al-yahūd of Cairo, to sleep one or more nights in an underground chamber. This is a survival of the Egyptian and Greek rite of incubation.[25]

His medical education was begun in Morocco, and he practised medicine in that country. This is proved by many references in his writings (e.g., at the end of his treatise on asthma). That education was informal; he may have been an apprentice or assistant: to older physicians, that is not impossible, but there is nothing to prove it; we may be sure of one thing, he studied avidly all the medical books he could lay hands on in one way or another.

His sources were mainly Greek (in Arabic versions) and his first masters were Hippocrates and even more so Galen. He was well acquainted also with Dioscoridēs, and with the Arabic physicians, al-Rāzī (IX–2), al-Tamīmī (X–2), Ibn Juljul (X–2), Ibn Sīnā or Avicenna (XI–1), 'Alī ibn Riḍwān (XI–1), Ibn Wāfid (XI–1), Ibn Janāh (XI–1), Ibn Zuhr or Avenzoar (XII–1), al-Ghāfiqī (XII–2). The medical literature available in Arabic was abundant, and a man as inquisitive as Maimonides had time enough in his long life to explore most of it, but the nine authors just named were the most important in his experience. Five of them were Westerners, and four Easterners (al-Rāzī, al-Tamīmī, Ibn Riḍwān, Ibn Sīnā). To the Westerners might perhaps be added a fifth one, Ibn Rushd, but I do not know whether he got to know his medical writings. All of them were Muslims, except Ibn Janāḥ.

Those whom he used most were almost certainly al-Rāzī, Ibn Sīnā, and Ibn Zuhr.

His medical practice began in earnest after his arrival in Cairo in the spring of 1165, for that was the mainstay of himself and his family. His medical reputation was established when the powerful wazīr and

French and English summaries. Wall editions of the prayer, suitable for framing and hanging in doctors' offices, have been issued in various languages, e.g. *Morgengebet des Arztes* (Bern, 1914; *Isis* 2, 439).

[25] *Introd.* (2, 373). M. Meyerhof, *Essays on Maimonides* edited by Salo Wittmayer Barton (New York, Columbia University Press, 1941; *Isis* 33, 529), p. 265. For the old rite of incubation, see my *History of Science* (1, 123, 125, 331, 345, 388).

judge, al-Fāḍil ʿAbd al-Raḥīm al-Baisānī, took him into his service; later, he was appointed one of the physicians to Saladin's court, and still later, he became the archiater of Saladin's eldest son, al-Malik al-Afḍal Nūr al-dīn. Toward the end of the century his court service had become so onerous that a great part of his time was devoted to it.[26] In his famous letter of 1199, to his translator, Samuel ibn Tibbon of Arles, he complained of it and remarked that his intercourse was restricted to Muslims and that he had no chance of meeting Jews and speaking Hebrew except on the Sabbath. All his medical writings were written in Arabic, and as they were meant primarily for the use of his patrons, and other Arabs, they were certainly written in Arabic script. They were soon translated into Hebrew, however, and before that we may be sure that copies were made in Hebrew script for the Jewish community.

I shall now try to give you an idea of those medical writings, but before that it is our duty to pay homage to the three scholars to whom we owe the best of our knowledge. The first of these is Rabbi Hermann Kroner,[27] who collected and edited Arabic and Hebrew MSS. and edited some of them with German translations and commentaries. He managed to do all of that while he was in charge of a parish in a

[26] The waste of time was aggravated by the fact that he lived in the old city of Fusṭāṭ while the sultān's court was in the new city, al-Qāhira. The distance was less than two miles, but that was as much as twenty miles today. It is said that he gave medical lectures, but that is unproven; it is more probable that he had assistants who were his disciples or apprentices.

[27] As no obituary of Rabbi Kroner could be discovered by me, I wrote for information to his son, Jacques Kroner, M.D., who kindly answered in a letter dated New York, 11 Nov., 1954. The letter is too long to be quoted in extenso, but the following facts will certainly interest our readers. Hermann Kroner was a scion of a family of rabbis and scholars of Silesian origin. He was born in Münster, Westphalia, 21 March 1870. He graduated from the Gymnasium of Hannover, studied theology at the Jewish Theological Seminary of Breslau, and received his Ph.D. at Tübingen in 1895. His doctoral thesis, "Maimonides' Commentar zum Tractat Bezah," appeared in 1898; he was then already an Arabic as well as a Hebrew scholar. During the following years, he devoted a number of memoirs to Maimonides' theological and medical writings. All his scientific work was done in Oberdorf-Bopfingen, where he was rabbi of a district of Württemberg from 1900 to his death; he died on 30 July 1930, while he was vacationing in Badenweiler. His investigations were carried through on the basis of photostatic copies of MSS. which his friends obtained for him in many countries. They proved that work of fundamental importance can be done in a small town remote from the university centers and great libraries, provided there is enough intelligence, concentration, and tenacity.

very small town of Southern Germany, where he died in 1930. The second is my old friend, the Egyptian Max Meyerhof, who became the outstanding student of Arabic medicine, and died in Cairo in 1945.[28] The third is Dr. Süssmann Muntner of Jerusalem, who is preparing a complete edition of the medical works in their Hebrew form. Two of them have already been published and the others are ready in MS.; I had the privilege of examining them in his office when I was in Jerusalem in August 1953.

A few details about that important Hebrew edition follow. The treatise on asthma appeared in Jerusalem 1940 (*Isis 33*, 92), the one on poisons and their antidotes in 1942 (*Isis 34*, 243; *35*, 3–5). The publication was then interrupted because of the war. It will be resumed under the auspices of the Medical Association of Israel and will require some ten volumes in all; it is hoped that it will be completed within fifteen years. Dr. Muntner is engaged in other studies on Hebrew medicine [29] and much of his time is taken up by his own practice.

Maimonides is the author of ten medical treatises, all in Arabic but promptly translated into Hebrew; we may assume that they were written in Cairo during the last quarter of the twelfth century. A complete survey of his medical ideas would require the examination of other writings of his, such as the *Mishneh Torah* and the *Moreh Nebukim*, which contain medical digressions. I shall divide the medical treatises into three groups of three each and a final group of one. I. Those devoted to Galen and the Aphorisms; II. Monographs on special diseases; III. Hygiene; IV. Pharmacopoeia.[30]

I. Galenic and Aphorisms

He admired Galen very much; we might say that the Galen works constituted his medical basis (somewhat like the standard textbooks

[28] Meyerhof was born in Hildesheim in 1874. He spent twenty-five years of his life in Cairo, but remained a German citizen until 1935, when Hitlerism caused him to acquire Egyptian nationality. That is why we must call him Egyptian. Vol. 9 of *Osiris* dedicated to him in 1950 contains his portrait, biography, and bibliography.

[29] See *Isis 35*, 32, 180. His latest publication is the princeps of the *Sefer ha-roqhim* of Saladino di Ascoli, ca. 1430 (Tel Aviv, 1953) which I reviewed for the *Journal of the History of Medicine* (New Haven, 1955).

[30] The best general account of the ten treatises is the one given by Max Meyerhof in S. W. Baron's *Essays on Maimonides* (New York, Columbia University Press, 1941), pp. 274–285. I have used also my own account in *Introd.* (2, 371–373, 1931) where they were arranged in different order, and where the tenth of Meyerhof's list is missing, because it was discovered only in 1932, and published for the first time by Meyerhof in 1940.

which a doctor has conned in the medical school), and yet, as he obtained more knowledge from the Arabic literature and his own experience, he became more and more critical of him.

1. *Al-mukhtaṣarāt* (extracts). Anthology of passages taken from the medical books of Galen. This is lost in Arabic, but there are several Hebrew translations none of which is yet published.

2. *Sharḥ fuṣūl Abuqrāṭ* (Explanation of the *Aphorisms* of Hippocrates). Commentary on the Arabic translation of the *Aphorisms* by Ḥunain ibn Isḥāq (IX–2), including many criticisms. Incompletely preserved in Arabic; the Hebrew translation made by Moses ben Samuel ibn Tibbon (XIII–2) in 1257 or 1267 is not yet completely published.

3. *Fuṣūl Mūsā fi-l-ṭibb* (Maimonides' medical aphorisms). This, his largest medical work, is best known under its Hebrew title, *Pirqe Mosheh*. Though published under his own name, it is completely derived from the writings of Galen and other Greek doctors; the *Aphorisms* are stated in his own words, however. It is divided into twenty-five books each of which deals with a separate branch of medicine (anatomy, physiology, pathology, etc.). The last book contains an elaborate criticism of Galen, including a list of some forty examples of contradictions in the master's writings and a defense of Biblical conceptions against Galenic teleology.

The *Fuṣūl Mūsā* was translated into Hebrew by Zerahiah ben Isaac Hen (XIII–2) in Rome 1277, then again by Nathan ha-Me'ati (XIII–2) in Rome 1279–1283. This second Hebrew version was badly printed in Lemberg 1834–35. A Latin translation from the Arabic with Christian interpolations was published as early as 1489 in Bologna, then again in Venice 1500 (Klebs 644.1–2), and with the *Liber Almansoris* of al-Rāzī in Venice 1497, 1500 (Klebs 826.2–3). Maimonides' fame in Christian Europe was based on these *Aphorismi* some of which were frequently quoted after the words "Dixit Rabbi Moyses . . ."

II. Monographs

4. *Maqāla fi-l-bawāṣīr* (on haemorrhoids). Explaining that the ailment is often caused by bad digestion and constipation and that the best way of healing it is by means of a light diet, preferably vegetarian.

This was edited in Arabic language, Hebrew script, with German translation by Rabbi Kroner (*Janus* 1911).

5. *Maqāla fi-l-rabw* (on asthma). In this treatise, composed c.1190, Maimonides insisted on diet and climate for a cure and remarked that the dry climate of Egypt was particularly favorable. He warned against the abuse of drugs.

Translated into Latin by Armengaud son of Blaise (XIII–2). Twice translated into Hebrew, first from the Latin (?) c.1320, by Samuel ben Benveniste (XIV–1), second from the Arabic by Joshua Shatibi [31] about the end of the fourteenth century. Rabbi Kroner was preparing an edition based upon the Arabic and Hebrew MSS. but died before he could complete it. The Hebrew text was edited by Süssmann Muntner (Jerusalem 1940; *Isis* 33, 92).

6. *Kitāb al-sumūm wal-mutaḥarriz min al-adwiya al-qātila* (on poisons and antidotes against mortal drugs). Written in 1199 for his patron the wazīr al-Qāḍī al-Fāḍil. Twice translated into Hebrew, one translation being made by Moses ibn Tibbon (XIII–2). The Latin translation *De venenis* was made in 1307 by Armengaud son of Blaise (XIII–2) for Pope Clement V; it enjoyed some popularity.

The subject was of great medieval interest, because poisons were often used to get rid of enemies; every ruler was obliged to protect himself against such risks; moreover, people might be poisoned by snakes, mad dogs, scorpions, etc., and many poisoned themselves with aphrodisiacs.[32] He describes clinical cases of poisoning, e.g., by belladonna and by cantharides.

An edition of the Arabic text was being prepared by Rabbi Kroner at the time of his death. Hebrew text edited by Süssmann Muntner (Jerusalem 1942; *Isis* 34, 243). French translation from the Hebrew and the Arabic by Rabbi I. M. Rabbinowicz (70 p., Paris 1865; facsimile reprint Paris 1935).

III. Hygiene

The third group of three treatises may be classified under the title hygiene. Medieval physicians were as keenly aware as the ancients of how difficult it was to cure diseases; when the physiological equilibrium was broken, it was almost impossible to redress it; it was easier to preserve the equilibrium and not to allow it to deviate too much from the normal. In this as in other matters, Maimonides was following Hippocrates and Galen but also his own instinct. The principle of *vis medi-*

---

[31] Meaning Joshua of Jatiba (in Valencia province). Moritz Scheinschneider, *Die arabische Literatur der Juden* (Frankfort a.M., 1902), p. 215.

[32] For poisons, *Introd.* (3, 1241), for aphrodisiacs, *Introd.* (2, 79; 3, 296).

catrix naturae was as well understood by him as by them. The physician should be modest and expectant; he should try to help, not hinder, the natural reactions of the bodies. Only charlatans profess to know more and with greater certainty.

7. *Maqāla fī tadbīr al-ṣiḥḥa* (Regulation of health). This is his main treatise on health and the most popular medical book of his after the *Fuṣūl Mūsā*. It was addressed, c. 1198, to al-Malik al-Afḍal Nūr al-dīn 'Alī, Saladin's eldest son, who suffered from fits of melancholia. It is divided into four parts: (1) explanation of the case and general hygienic and dietetic rules with frequent references to Hippocrates and Galen, (2) easy remedies for use in traveling or when no physician is available, (3) hygiene of the soul, partly derived from Aristotle and al-Fārābī, (4) summary in the form of 17 aphorisms.

The psychotherapeutic rules of part 3 are especially important; their introduction into this *regimen sanitatis* was natural enough because the patron for whom it was written was a psychopathological case. Psychosomatic medicine was far from being a novelty; it was well represented in Greek medicine; [33] Maimonides' interest in it, however, was greater than usual.

The popularity of this work is witnessed by the occurrence of many Arabic MSS., a Hebrew translation made in 1244 by Moses ibn Tibbon, two Latin translations made, one from the Arabic in 1290 by Armengaud son of Blaise, and the other from the Hebrew by Giovanni da Capua (XIII-2), for the pope's physician.

The Arabic text was edited with a German translation by Rabbi Kroner (*Janus 27–29*, 1923–1925). There are at least two editions of the Hebrew text (Prague 1838, Jerusalem 1885). The Latin text *De regimine sanitatis* was printed by Ripoli in Florence as early as c. 1481 (Klebs 643) and many times afterwards, e.g., Pavia 1501.

8. *Maqāla fī bayān al-a'rād* (on the explanation of accidents or fits). Written for the same Malik al-Afḍal c.1200; it is an elaborate regimen, made necessary by the sultan's increasing melancholy.

It was translated into Hebrew and into Latin, probably from the Hebrew, by Giovanni da Capua, *De causis apparentium accidentium*. The first Latin edition (Pavia 1501) was in the form of an appendix (which it was) to the *De regimine sanitatis*. The Arabic text was edited by Rabbi Kroner with Hebrew and German versions (*Janus 32*, 12–116, 1928).

[33] E.g., Zalmoxis and Hippocrates (*History of Science*, 1, 344, 1952).

9. *Maqāla fī-l-jimā'* (on sexual intercourse). Dedicated to al-Malik al-Muẓaffar, a nephew of Saladin, who was sulṭān of Ḥamā from 1178 to his death in 1191. It is derived mainly from Ibn Sīnā and Ibn Zuhr. This is one of the most important chapters of hygiene, of greater urgency in the Islamic environment because of polygamy.[34]

Translated into Hebrew by Zeraḥiah ben Isaac Ḥen (XIII–2) in Rome c.1277, and also into Latin. The Arabic text was edited by Rabbi Kroner with Hebrew and German versions (144 p., Oberdorf-Bopfingen, 1916), who edited also a shorter Arabic version (*Janus 21*, 203–247, 1916). The Latin text is still unpublished.

IV. Pharmacopoeia

This final group includes but a single work, the Arabic MS. of which was discovered only in 1932 in the Aya Sofia library by Hellmut Ritter.

10. *Sharḥ asmā' al-'uqqār* (explanation of drug names). It is a glossary of materia medica in 405 chapters, each of which deals with a drug. It was beautifully edited and translated into French by Max Meyerhof, *Un glossaire de matière médicale de Maimonide* (Cairo 1940; *Isis 33*, 527–529).

It is not a treatise on materia medica but a glossary of about 2000 Arabic names,[35] to which are added their equivalents in Greek, Persian, Berber, Spanish. He probably began this collection for his own use in Morocco; it is typical that the forerunners mentioned by him are all Westerners.[36] The work was finally written or edited in Egypt, as is proved by many references to plants and drugs used in that country to this day. His patrons were Arabs and his medical practice was conducted in the Arabic language. This is illustrated very strikingly in this glossary, which does not include a single Hebrew name of plant or drug, although many such names occur in his rabbinical commentaries.[37]

[34] Georges Henri Bousquet, *La morale de l'Islam et son éthique sexuelle* (Paris, 1954).
[35] Many of those Arabic names are foreign names (Greek, Syriac, Persian) in Arabic transcription. No terminology is more international than that of drugs because the drugs themselves were imported from many countries and were often known under their original names.
[36] To wit, Ibn Samajūn (end of 10th cent.), Ibn Juljul (X–2), Ibn Wāfid (XI–1), Ibn Janāḥ (XI–1), al-Ghāfiqī (XII–2). Only one of these, Ibn Janāḥ, was a Jew.
[37] As shown by Immanuel Löw, *Flora der Juden* (4 vols. in 4, Wien, 1923–1934; *Isis 6*, 428; *23*, 573).

Brief as it is, this enumeration is sufficient to establish the size, variety, and importance of Maimonides' medical contributions. He was not a great physician; he was not an inventor as al-Rāzī was, but he was a wise physician, and in those days objective medical knowledge and scientific methods of diagnosis or treatment were so few and shaky that wisdom and what one might call medical intuition counted for very much. Modern physicians still need those psychological qualities, but their judgment is solidly based on physical, chemical, and biological tests which did not exist, and could hardly be conceived, until last century, almost seven centuries after his time of activity.

THE ASTRONOMER

Such a subtitle, "The astronomer," may seem a little ambitious and to claim more for Maimonides than he would have claimed for himself. Yet, in his philosophical synthesis and even in his rabbinical commentaries, he had been obliged to investigate the scientific knowledge available in his time in order to understand the universe. This meant primarily cosmology, and, as far as science was concerned, astronomy. Together with his favorite disciple, Joseph ben Judah ibn 'Aqnīn (XII–2), he studied astronomy, primarily in the *Istikmāl* of Yūsuf al-Mutamin, king of Zaragoza (XI–2),[38] then in the works of Jābir ibn Aflāḥ (XII–1) and Ibn Bājja (XII–1). They were acquainted with many other books in Arabic, but the authors just mentioned were their main sources. It is noteworthy that all these men were Westerners; Ibn Bājja, as well as King Yūsuf, was born in Zaragoza, Jābir was a Sevillan and Joseph ben Judah a Moroccan. This confirms our feeling that Maimonides' education was virtually completed in the Maghrib. Of course, as he was a genuine scholar he continued to increase and improve his knowledge until the end of his life, but the essential was built up before his emigration to Egypt. In the *Dalāla* he explained Ibn Bājja's criticism of Ptolemy; in the long mediaeval conflict between the pure Ptolemaists and the Aristotelians (or between those who used epicycles and eccentrics on one hand, and those who favored the theory of homocentric spheres on the other) he was on the side of the

---

[38] According to Joseph ben Judah, who was more of an astronomer than his master, the *Istikmāl* ought to be studied together with Euclid's *Elements,* the *Almagest,* and the *Mutawassiṭāt* (Middle Books, Introd. 2, 1001). This proves the importance he attached to it.

latter.[39] Like Jābir, he doubted that Mercury and Venus were nearer than the Sun. All this does not mean much because he was not a practical or creative astronomer, but he was doing all he could to be as well informed as possible and his defense of Aristotelian astronomy was significant.

The strength of his rationalism was proved in the letter which he addressed in 1194 to the rabbis of Marseille, condemning astrology in the strongest terms. The Hebrew text and Latin translation of that famous letter was edited by Johannes Isaac Levita (Cologne, 1555), and the Hebrew text alone was edited again by Alexander Marx (Cincinnati, 1926; *Isis 11*, 172).

He was deeply concerned with the Jewish calendar and his astronomical knowledge ad hoc was primarily derived from al-Battānī (IX–2). The matter, which is too technical to be discussed here, was investigated by many scholars, notably Solomon Gandz and Otto Neugebauer.[40]

RABBINICAL COMMENTARIES

This paper is already so long that I must abandon the idea of discussing the work he did as a Rabbinical scholar, except to mention the three main books:

First, the *Kitāb al-sirāj* (Book of the lamp) begun in Spain, c.1158, and completed in Cairo, in 1168, of which two parts are especially well known, the *Shemonah peraqim* (eight chapters) on ethics, and the Jewish creed in thirteen articles included in the prayer books.

Second, the *Kitāb al-farā'iḍ* (on the divine precepts), listing the 603 commandments contained in the Torah. Note that these first two books were written in Arabic, but were promptly translated into Hebrew.

The third and most important of these books was composed in Hebrew, but soon translated into Arabic, which proves that there were then a number of Jews who could not read Hebrew with sufficient ease. It is the *Mishneh Torah* (repetition of the Law, Deuteronomy), more

---

[39] *Introd.* (2, 16–19).

[40] *Introd.* (2, 379). Otto Neugebauer, *The Astronomy of Maimonides and its sources* (Cincinnati, 1949). Solomon Gandz devoted many papers to the Jewish calendar. He had completed before his death (1954) an English translation of Maimonides' treatise *Qiddush ha-ḥodesh* which will be published in the *Yale Judaica Series*.

often called *Sefer ha-yad* (Book of the hand) or *Yad ha-ḥazaqah* (the strong hand).[41] It is a book which soon obtained a semi-canonical status in Israel in spite of frequent opposition to it.

This enumeration was given to illustrate the immense and almost incredible labor which he accomplished. Each of his three fundamental activities (philosophy, medicine, and rabbinics) was sufficiently massive to insure the fame of a man, and he combined the three of them.

HIS INFLUENCE

Even before the time of his death, his authority was completely established in Jewish-Arabic circles. It was continued by his immediate disciples, such as Joseph ben Judah ibn 'Aqnīn, his main translator Samuel ibn Tibbon of Arles, and by members of his own family, his son, Abraham ben Moses, Abraham's two sons, David and Obadiah, David's two sons, Abraham II and Solomon, and the son of Abraham II named Joshua, finally his nephew, Yūsuf ibn 'Abdallāh Abū-l-Ma'ali. There were prominent members of his family in Cairo and Damascus until the end of the fourteenth century and some of them succeeded him as head (nagid) of the Jewish community. All of them wrote in Arabic.

As to the Jews of other communities, east and west, not all of them followed his teachings. The orthodox were offended by his liberalism and the qabbalists by his rationalism. Throughout the ages, rationalists have always been a minority; during the Middle Ages (whether Jewish, Christian, or Muslim) they formed a very small minority indeed.

In Islām the rationalist minority was so small that Maimonides' illustrious contemporary, Ibn Rushd (Averroës), was swept away and almost forgotten. Islamic fanaticism was carried to such an extent that the greatest philosopher of Islām was also the last one and that obscurantism dominated until last century (it is still very powerful today, but not predominant).

In Christendom the situation was far more complex, for philosophical and theological activities were always great in Maimonides' time,

[41] It was called *Sefer ha-yad*, because it is divided into fourteen parts, and the word *yad* (hand) reads numerically 10 plus 4.

and they grew up with increasing intensity. The mantle of Maimonides fell upon the shoulders of Thomas Aquinas (XIII–2), who did for Christendom what he had done for Israel.

The whole of Jewish philosophy after Maimonides stems from him and from Ibn Rushd, directly or indirectly, until Spinoza's time, when it begins to flow together with Cartesianism, and becomes an intrinsic part of modern philosophy.

Aristotle was the giant of Greek philosophy; he influenced in some way or another all the philosophers and many of the men of science of the last twenty-three centuries. Three great religions were established after his time and each of them had a supreme teacher who revived Aristotelianism and harmonized it with his own faith — Ibn Rushd for Islām, Maimonides for Israel, St. Thomas for Christendom. We should be thankful to all of them. Each of us is a little better and perhaps a little wiser because of them. They helped us to understand the things which are supremely important, and those — like money, titles, honors — which are important only for a few days and then vanish as if they had never been.

ADDENDUM

MAIMONIDES AND HARVARD UNIVERSITY

When John Harvard was dying "at Charlestown,[42] of a consumption" on September 14, 1638, he whispered his last will, "My books and half my estate to the College, the rest to my beloved wife." Under that nuncupative will the College received about £200 and over 400 volumes, and because of this munificent gift it was called henceforth Harvard College.

Before that time, some people of New England had left small legacies to churches, but John Harvard's was the first legacy to a school. A Commencement speaker who delivered a Latin oration, c.1670, remarked that John Harvard had followed Maimonides in considering the school superior to and more sacred than the synagogue. This was a reference to the *Mishneh Torah, Tefillah,* XI, 14: "It is allowed to convert a synagogue (beit knesseth) into a school (beit midrash), but it is not allowed to convert a school into a synagogue for the sanctity of a

[42] The village of Charlestown where the Harvards lived was facing old Boston across the harbor; it is now a part of the City of Boston.

school is greater than that of a synagogue, and we may promote a thing to a higher grade of sanctity but we must not degrade." [43]

It is noteworthy that in the early years of Harvard, three centuries ago, a gentile member of the college knew the *Mishneh Torah* well enough to make this very apt quotation from it.

[1954]

[43] Admiral Samuel Eliot Morison, *The Founding of Harvard College* (Cambridge, Mass., Harvard University Press, 1935; *Isis* 25, 513–520), p. 220. For Charlestown, see p. 216; for the books of John Harvard's bequest, pp. 263–270.

The Quest for Truth

A Brief Account of Scientific Progress
during the Renaissance [1]

MANY PEOPLE misunderstand science, and hence one can hardly expect them to have a fair idea of its history. The history of science might be defined as the history of the discovery of objective truth, of the gradual conquest of matter by the human mind; it describes the agelong and endless struggle for the freedom of thought — its freedom from violence, intolerance, error, and superstition.

The history of science is one of the essential parts of the spiritual history of mankind; the other main parts are the history of art and the history of religion. It differs from these other parts in that the development of knowledge is the only development which is truly cumulative and progressive. Hence, if we try to explain the progress of mankind, the history of science should be the very axis of our explanation.

Another preliminary remark is needed to define the frame of this study. It is not enough to say "the Renaissance," because that word is not understood by everybody in the same way. Let us define it as the period which elapsed between the Middle Ages and the modern age; but the Middle Ages did not end abruptly and the modern age did not begin suddenly, and their ends and beginnings were not by any means the same in different countries. Italy was ahead of the other countries and her awakening was already begun by the middle of the fourteenth century, in Petrarch's time. We might define the Renaissance *grosso*

[1] Many years ago, I took part in another symposium on the Renaissance, organized by Mount Holyoke College. My contribution, "Science in the Renaissance," was included in *The Civilization of the Renaissance*, by James Westfall Thompson and others (University of Chicago Press, 1929). I have never reread it; hence this lecture is independent of it.

modo as the period extending from about 1350 to the death of Giordano Bruno in 1600, or to the death of Cervantes and Shakespeare in 1616; one might even stretch it a little further, to 1632, when Galileo published his first great book, the *Dialogo dei due massimi sistemi del mondo*.[2] Remember that every great book of science closes a period and opens a new one. Remember also that no period is valid for all nations nor for the whole of any single nation, for the men and women living at any one time are never spiritual contemporaries. Some of our own contemporaries have not even reached the Renaissance — they are still living in the Middle Ages; others are not even as advanced as that; they are still living in the Stone Age. It is because of such disparities that the progress of technology is so frightening; our ancestors were uneasy when guns were used by children: our own fears are deeper, and we shudder to think that atomic bombs might fall into the hands of men who in every respect (except technology) are still barbarians.

To return to the Renaissance, it was, among other things, a revolt against medieval concepts and methods. Of course, every generation reacts against the preceding one; every period is a revolt against the preceding one, and so on. Yet, in this case, the revolt was a bit sharper than it usually is. It is not sufficiently realized that the Renaissance was not simply a revolt against scholasticism; it was also directed against Arabic influences (especially those represented by Avicenna and Averroës). The anti-Arabic drive was in full swing in Petrarch's time. Such a revolt and struggle for independence was a symptom of growing strength. In spite of its triumph it was not completed; there are still many Arabic elements in our language and in our culture.

One of the medieval traits was the fear of novelties.[3] The Renaissance was more tolerant of them and sometimes it welcomed them, or went out of its way in order to find more of them. Each novelty created trouble, but as they impinged on the minds with increasing frequency, one got used to them and distrusted them less; one ended by liking

[2] That *Dialogo* is, to a large extent, an epitome of Renaissance thought. It will be easier to appreciate this when the new English text, edited and elucidated by Giorgio de Santillana, is published by the University of Chicago. It is scheduled to appear in 1952.

[3] That fear was reflected in the language; for example, the Arabic word *bid'a* means novelty, but it also means heresy. The Spanish word *novedad* had similar undertones.

them. In most cases, however, the novelties were rather superficial. For example, the Renaissance artists discovered the beauty of the human body, but that had never been completely forgotten.[4] They discovered the beauties of ancient art, new accents in poetry, new rhythms in music; they discovered ancient books and were anxious to publish them. All that was very exhilarating.

In the field of science, the novelties were gigantic, revolutionary. This explains why timid people are afraid of science; their instinct is sound enough; nothing can be more revolutionary than the growth of knowledge; science is at the root of every social change. The Renaissance scientists introduced not a "new look" but a new being. The novelty was often so great that one could hardly speak of a Renaissance or rebirth; it was a real birth, a new beginning.

Put it this way: The Renaissance was a transmutation of values, a "new deal," a reshuffling of cards, but most of the cards were old; the scientific Renaissance was a "new deal," but many of the cards were new. This will be shown simply and briefly, too briefly. I cannot help that. My message must be delivered in a single lecture. It is as if I were invited to paint as quickly as possible an immense fresco. Here it is. The fresco will be divided into a dozen panels, which I shall invite you to contemplate, with indulgence, one after another.

1. THE DISCOVERY OF THE EARTH

Geographical discoveries were initiated by Henry the Navigator, and in this respect the Renaissance was heralded not by Italians but by Portuguese. Their initiative was followed gradually by other nations. It is hardly necessary to recite those heroic deeds, for everybody is familiar with them. A few names will suffice to awaken your memories: Bartholomeu Dias (1488), Columbus (1492), Vasco da Gama (1498), Amerigo Vespucci (1497–1504), Magellan (1519–1522), etc. The Renaissance was truly the golden age of geographical discovery; by the year 1600 the surface of the known earth was doubled. Was not that an achievement of incredible pregnancy? The earth was doubled! It was not only a matter of quantity, but one of quality as well. New climates, new aspects of nature were revealed.

Ancient and medieval navigations had been largely coastal; mari-

---

[4] For medieval examples, see my *Introd.* (3, 1256).

ners seldom spent many days without sight of land. They knew the seas, but now they had conquered the oceans; they learned to know the arctic regions, the deserts, and the tropics.

Each of us can measure those novelties, for if he searches his own mind, he may be able to recapture the deep emotions which he felt when he found himself for the first time in the middle of the ocean, or in the heart of a tropical jungle, or when he tried to cross a desert or glacier. These discoveries, which are fundamental for each of us individually, were made for the whole of mankind in the fifteenth and sixteenth centuries.

We are all aware of those geographical discoveries which added new continents and innumerable islands to our estates, but relatively few people realize that new aspects of nature were discovered in the very heart of Europe, that is, the high Alps, which earlier men had been afraid of exploring. This was a new world in the heart of the old one. The severity and danger of the Alpine climate had deluded medieval minds into believing that the high mountains were the abode of gnomes and devils. In this they were less advanced than the Buddhists of India, China, and Japan, who regarded the mountains as sacred, and built temples on their slopes and at the very tops. The earliest Alpine expeditions began very timidly in the fourteenth century, but did not assume any importance before the sixteenth century; by the end of that century some forty-seven summits had been reached.[5] Two main purposes could be served in Alpine expeditions; the first was aesthetic or religious, the second was scientific. One might risk one's life in difficult ascents in order to enjoy the beauty of nature and the sublimity of God, or in order to understand the mysterious climate obtaining at high altitudes, and to observe the shape of the mountains and the plants and animals that inhabited them. The first man to combine in himself both purposes was Leonardo da Vinci.

2. THE NEW EDUCATION

Any renaissance must express itself in the field of education, for when men begin to think and feel in a new way they are eager to modify teaching methods in proportion to their own spiritual change. Un-

[5] The first treatise *ad hoc* was that of Josias Simler, *De Alpibus* (Zürich, 1574). It is a very curious fact that Alpinism stopped at the end of the sixteenth century and did not begin again in earnest until the end of the eighteenth century.

fortunately, the great majority of schools were informal and the teacher of genius could hardly emerge from the local and temporal circumstances which limited his activities. For example, the *Casa giocosa* established by Vittorino da Feltre in Mantua in 1423 did not survive him. The same remark might be made about great educators like the Catalan Juan Luis Vives (1492–1540) and the Englishman Roger Ascham (1515–1568). New pedagogical ideas cannot be effective unless they be incorporated in an educational system of some permanence.

A development of greater stability had been begun in the meantime by the Brothers of the Common Life in the Netherlands, at the very end of the fourteenth century. By the way, this is another aspect of the early Renaissance which is not Italian. Its importance can hardly be exaggerated. The *Devotio moderna* was an attempt to reconcile the humanities with Christianity. This could be done only on a mystical plane, but the Dutch Brothers did it very well, and their influence spread rapidly in northwestern Europe. By the middle of the fifteenth century there were already some 150 of their schools in the Netherlands, France, and Germany, and those schools remained the best of their kind until the sixteenth century. Many great men were educated by the Brothers of the Common Life, the two most famous ones being Cardinal Nicholas of Cusa (1401–1464), who loved them, and Erasmus of Rotterdam (1466–1536), who was irritated by them. By Erasmus' time the schools had lost their spiritual power; in the second half of the sixteenth century they were replaced and eclipsed by the Jesuit colleges.

Much credit for the educational revival must be given also to the reformers. From the Protestant point of view, a modicum of education was a religious duty. Every Christian should be able to read the Scriptures by himself. Therefore, Martin Luther was very deeply concerned with public education. In 1524, Magdeburg organized new schools on the plan which he had recommended. Other schools were established in many German cities, and their availability to the children was gradually increased; it has been claimed that the public school system of the German Protestant states was the first model of our own. The inspirer and organizer of that system was Philip Melanchton (1497–1560), whose influence was so pervading and lasting that he fully deserved the title given to him, *Praeceptor Germaniae*.

THE QUEST FOR TRUTH

3. THE NEW MATHEMATICS

Historians of art never fail to discuss the new conception of perspective which was largely due to Florentine artists but which grew also in Flanders and Germany. This implied a certain amount of mathematical thinking, but that amount was very small, almost negligible. The new mathematics which we have in mind is something more profound and infinitely more complex. We cannot do more than refer to its main aspects, and the references are almost meaningless except for mathematical students, but this cannot be helped. The history of mathematical ideas is peculiarly difficult to explain (even to mathematicians), because the first achievements were made in Babylonia, matured in Greece, incubated in the Arabic world, and gradually reappeared in the West. The astonishing flowering of the fifteenth and sixteenth centuries concerned trigonometry and algebra. Trigonometry was revived by Germans like Regiomontanus (1436–1476), then by Georgius Rhaeticus and Bartholomaeus Pitiscus; algebra by Italians, like Scipione del Ferro, Nicola Tartaglia, Geronimo Cardona (1501–1576), and Lodovico Ferrari. The gradual introduction of a number of operational symbols prepared the writing of equations as we do, and the theory of equations began to take shape. The climax of Renaissance mathematics was reached by such men as the Italian Raffaele Bombelli (fl. 1572), the Frenchman François Viète (1540–1603), and the Fleming Simon Stevin (1548–1620). In 1585, the last named published his invention of decimal fractions and decimal weights and measures. He then explained with great lucidity an idea which the Anglo-Saxon world has not yet been able to grasp to this day.

These mathematical discoveries are not as tangible as the geographical ones; yet they were deeper. The Conquistadores were very materialistic, greedy and inhuman; the mathematicians were the opposite in every respect and their conquests were spiritual ones, conquests of pure reason, the scope of which was infinite.

4. THE NEW ASTRONOMY

Now let us travel to Frombork in Poland, where Copernicus was ending his days in 1543. His great treatise, the first copy of which was brought to him on his deathbed, explained the new astronomy. It was not radically new, for the fundamental idea of it had been outlined before by Aristarchos of Samos during another Renaissance (the Hellenistic Renaissance of Alexandria). Yet, Aristarchos' views had been rejected by the leading astronomers of antiquity and had been driven underground. To re-explain them, as Copernicus did, after more than eighteen centuries of discredit, was very much the same as a new creation. The sun was put back in the center of the world, and the earth reduced to a planetary status. The implications of this as set forth by Giordano Bruno and others were not simply of astronomical interest, but of philosophical importance. It is a strange paradox that at the very time when man was beginning to conquer nature he was obliged to drive himself away from the center of things; in proportion as he grew wiser he had to make himself smaller. That is all right, of course. The purpose of science is to discover the truth irrespective of consequences.

It is pleasant to recall that Copernicus was helped in his computations by a much younger man, Georg Joachim Rhaeticus, who visited him and lived with him for more than two years. In 1539, when Rhaeticus arrived, he was only 25, while Copernicus was 66. The main point is this: Copernicus was a canon of the Cathedral of Frombork, while Rhaeticus was a professor in the Protestant University of Wittenberg. At a time when the hatred dividing Catholics from Protestants was getting as hot as hell-fire, the old canon and the young Protestant mathematician were living and working together like brothers. Science is not simply international, it is almost always *au dessus de la mêlée*; it unites all men in a sublime task, the quest for truth. It may be added that in the sixteenth century Catholic and Protestant theologians were united in one common hatred, their hatred of the Copernican theory, which conflicted with the Scriptures.

Copernicus was a poor observer and it had been easier for him (as it had been for Aristarchos) to formulate his new theory, because he was not embarrassed by good observations. (Science proceeds by successive approximations; if the early astronomers had been given excellent telescopes, they would have been so bewildered that they would have been unable to understand anything.) The new vision which had been opened by Copernicus warmed the enthusiasm of a Danish boy, Tycho Brahe, who was to become one of the best as-

tronomical observers of all time. He was able to accumulate a large
mass of observations which were more accurate than his simple instruments seemed to warrant, but these observations increased his
perplexities, and he felt obliged to abandon the heliocentric hypothesis (even as Hipparchos had felt obliged to do seventeen centuries before him) and to adopt a kind of compromise. This was not
the first time (nor the last) that careful observations drove out a
theory which was good, but not good enough, and required some corrections in order to be admissible. The final establishment of the
Copernican theory by Johann Kepler (1609, 1619) is outside our frame,
yet the fact remains that Copernicus was the first to formulate it without equivocation. This he did in 1543.

Many medieval astronomers had realized the growing inadequacy
of the Julian calendar, but their claims for reform had remained un-
heeded. Pope Gregory XIII, helped by the Bavarian mathematician,
Christopher Clavius, and buoyed up by the spirit of novelty which informed his time, finally accomplished the much needed reform. The
"novelty" was less profound than that of the Copernican theory, but
it was more tangible to the mass of the people. The good Catholics
who went to sleep on October 4, 1582, woke up the next morning on
October 15. That was startling enough, was it not? But the surprise
was restricted to Catholics. The reform had come just too late; if it had
been decided upon before the Reformation, the whole of Latin Christendom would have accepted it without demur. At this time, however,
self-respecting Protestants could not receive a new calendar from the
hands of their chief adversary. Therefore, they continued to use the
Julian calendar (in English until as late as 1752), and one could already have taunted them with Voltaire's sarcasm: Those idiots "prefer
to disagree with the sun than to agree with the Pope."

5. THE NEW PHYSICS AND CHEMISTRY

Changes in physics were less radical than in other fields, and the
situation of chemistry was even more confused. The medieval incubation of mechanical ideas was not by any means completed. We owe
many little clarifications to Italians like Tartaglia, Cardano, Benedetti,
Guido Ubaldo; but the ablest clarifier before Galileo was the Fleming,
Simon Stevin. Stevin, the greatest mechanician in the nineteen cen-

turies between Archimedes and Galileo, introduced new ideas into statics and into hydrostatics.

In the meantime, the intense rivalries of colonizing nations encouraged the progress of navigation and of the physical sciences which would increase the accuracy of sailings and minimize their dangers. The main requirements were geodetic, astronomic (better methods of taking the ship's bearings), cartographic; one needed faster ships and better instruments to navigate them. Geodetic improvements were due to the Frenchman Jean Fernel and the Dutchman Gemma Frisius; better maps to the Portuguese Pedro Nuñez and the Flemings Gerhard Mercator and Abraham Ortelius. Who has not seen the splendid geographic atlases which were produced in the sixteenth century? Not only did they provide a large mass of information of vital importance to statesmen and merchants; some of their maps were so beautiful that it is a joy to look at them.

One of the first fruits of oceanic navigation was a better knowledge of magnetic declination, for the compass was one of the sailor's best instruments, but its readings could not be trusted without taking occasional deviations into account. The magnetic observations and other knowledge useful for navigation were put together by Englishmen like Robert Norman (1581) and William Barlow (1597) and by Simon Stevin (1599). At the very end of the Renaissance, William Gilbert published the first great treatise on magnetism (1600); it is significant that his knowledge of terrestrial magnetism, rudimentary as it still was, induced him to outline cosmological implications.

In optics the best work was done by Italians like Giovanni Battista della Porta (1538?–1615) and Maurolycus, but progress was not very tangible. In spite of the fact that so few physical (and chemical) phenomena could be accounted for in rational terms, the results were so alluring that the investigators were full of conceit. They were aware of the nearness of mysteries the penetration of which might expose them to suspicion. Della Porta's famous book was entitled *Magia naturalis* (1538). Various little academies were founded in Italy during the sixteenth century; they were somewhat in the nature of exclusive clubs and secret societies; the members were often known to each other by nicknames; their academies offered them means of discussing the elusive "secrets" which they hoped and feared to disclose. At any rate, they gave them privacy and protection against the misunderstandings of the ignorant and the bigots.

Physical "secrets" included chemical ones, but in the field of chemistry the fundamental ideas were even more difficult to separate and to define. Vision and understanding were obscured by alchemical fancies around which had gathered all kinds of superstitions. The defeat of alchemy was not really begun until the end of the seventeenth century, and its completion required still another century of patient work. In the Renaissance it was out of the question, and historians of chemistry look upon that period as the golden age of alchemy.

6. THE NEW TECHNOLOGY

The only branch of technology which has never become inactive is the art of warfare. In this age, as in all others, most technicians were concerned with that art, trying to find new weapons, to improve the old ones, or to defend themselves more effectively against the weapons of their enemies. The invention of new arms and new armor was always the main obsession of men, good or bad.[6] Even as great an artist and as serene a man as Leonardo da Vinci was obliged to devote much of his attention to such problems. Yet the greatest invention of the Renaissance was a peaceful one: the invention of typography. It is hardly necessary to indicate what the art of printing meant for the diffusion of culture, but one should not lay too much stress on diffusion and should speak more of standardization. Every manuscript was in many respects unique. Printing made it possible for the first time to publish hundreds of copies that were alike and yet might be scattered everywhere. It was now possible (as it had never been before) to refer to a definite statement made on page X of such or such a book; the reference made by a scholar in Oxford might be checked immediately by his colleagues in Salamanca, in Bruges, or in Vienna. Steady advance implies the exact determination of every previous step; this now became incomparably easier. That "divine art," as the early typographers did not hesitate to call it, was invented about the middle of the fifteenth century in Germany. Thus, we see once more that the early Renaissance was not

[6] A list of early treatises on war technology is given in my *Introd.* (3, 1550–1554). Those technicians were Germans or Italians.

exclusively Italian; the most pregnant initiatives were taken far away from Italy — in Portugal, in Holland, and in Germany.

The invention of typography was considerably enriched by the invention of engraving, which was accomplished and vulgarized at about the same time. Woodcuts and copperplates did for the graphic arts exactly what printing did for letters. Works of art could be diffused and standardized. The two inventions, printing and engraving, were of immense importance for the development of knowledge. Printing made possible the publication of mathematical and astronomical tables which could be depended upon; engraving, the publication of books with illustrations representing plants, animals, anatomical or surgical details, chemical apparatus, etc. One good figure is more revealing than many pages of text; the use of illustrations obliged the author to be more precise than he could have been, or wished to be, without them.

The new technology was symbolized by the publication of illustrated treatises by Vannoccio Biringuccio of Siena (1540), Georgius Agricola (1556), Lazarus Ercker (1574), all of which included a wealth of information on mining, metallurgy, chemistry, the founding of guns and bells, the making of weapons and gunpowder, the casting of alloys such as type metal, the coining of money, and many other arts and crafts. This suggests that, thanks to printing and engraving, the Renaissance was a vigorous age of stocktaking and encyclopaedism as well as of invention. Every bit of knowledge could now be garnered and preserved forever. Words and images were immortalized.

7. THE NEW BOTANY

One aspect of the Renaissance has often been described and emphasized: the publication of the Latin and Greek classics, many of which had been lost because they were represented by single manuscripts, which were buried and forgotten in the corners of neglected libraries. The discovery of such manuscripts was as thrilling as the discovery today of papyri or clay tablets. There were incunabula editions of the great botanical books of antiquity, those of Theophrastus and Dioscorides, but those early editions were not illustrated. The descriptions of plants, even when correct, were confusing, because they referred to another flora than that of western Europe. In this case, the classics had to be rejected and the work of botanical description had to be done over. The pioneers, "the fathers of botany," were Germans like Otto Brunfels (1530), Leonhard Fuchs (1542), Hieronymus Bock, and Valerius Cordus; and they were followed by Flemings like Dodonaeus, Clusius, Lobelius, Busbecq, by Englishmen, Italians, etc. Not only were new herbals illustrated, some of the illustrations were very beautiful.

Botany was then an essential part of medical teaching, and the use of illustrated herbals intensified the need of direct observations. The ancient botanists had been satisfied mostly with names, an abundance of synonyms, and the enumeration of qualities or virtues; the German "fathers" and their followers had added images; now there was a growing desire to see and handle the plants themselves. Botanical gardens were attached to the medical schools (the first university garden was in Padua, 1545); dried plants were collected in herbaria by Luca Ghini (who died in Bologna in 1556) and by many others. A new botanical knowledge was within reach, and brisk emulation caused it to grow rapidly in a great many places.

8. THE NEW ZOOLOGY (AND MINERALOGY)

Animals were studied in the same spirit as plants, and students of natural history were stimulated by the discovery of new countries beyond the seas, where plants and animals were either radically new, or sufficiently different from those already known to be startling, to cause perplexities, and to invite further investigations. There emerged a new kind of scientist, the traveling naturalist, the scientific explorer. The greedy adventurers of early days were now replaced by men in search of knowledge. The quest for truth inspired them with a missionary zeal, and they were prepared to suffer many hardships for the sake of science.

The discoveries made in foreign lands excited the naturalists who were obliged to stay at home, such as physicians, professors, and the keepers of botanical gardens and greenhouses, and necessitated their describing more accurately and more completely the faunas and floras of their own countries. Thus exploration abroad caused deeper investigations and led to better knowledge of all the forms of life which could be observed nearer home.

This reminds me that I almost forgot to speak of the mineralogical investigations. Some minerals were generally included in the early herbals, and the search for mineral drugs was increased in the sixteenth century. The main mineralogical work, however, was done and had always been done by prospectors in search of rich ores. This was part of the business of mining such as was described in *De re metallica* of Agricola (1556), mentioned above. The collectors of precious stones had never stopped their activities, and their business was roused when more gold and silver was mined in Europe and America.

By 1600 the knowledge of the three kingdoms of nature was radically different from what it had been in the Middle Ages; it was incomparably richer, and, what matters even more, it was more genuine; a larger proportion of it was based on direct observations. This does not mean, unfortunately, that all the early fantasies had been eliminated; the average Renaissance naturalist was able to make good observations, and he became abler to make better ones every year, but few of them were strong enough to reject deeply rooted superstitions. The amount of information, old and new, genuine or not, was so enormous by the second half of the sixteenth century that it made necessary the encyclopaedic efforts of Conrad Gesner of Zürich and of Ulisse Aldrovandi of Bologna.

9. THE NEW ANATOMY

The new anatomy was created by Leonardo da Vinci and by Andreas Vesalius of Brussels. Leonardo was not an amateur anatomist, as so many artists were, but an indefatigable investigator who spent more time in elaborate dissections than most professionals. He examined almost every organ of the human body, taking copious notes and making admirable drawings; yet all that work was kept in his archives and remained practically unknown until the last century. On the other hand, Vesalius published in 1543 his *Fabrica*, which became known at once and which marks the beginning of a new era in anatomical studies. Mark that the same year, 1543, was the era of the new anatomy as well as of the new astronomy; it was one of the golden years of the Renaissance.

114

THE QUEST FOR TRUTH

10. THE NEW MEDICINE

Among many great physicians it must suffice in this brief outline to mention three who were outstanding in their respective lines, true pioneers who represent three different countries: the Swiss Paracelsus, the Italian Girolamo Fracastoro, and the Frenchman Ambroise Paré.

Paracelsus of Einsiedeln, near Zürich, is the best exemplar of the new medicine which had not yet completely emerged from medieval confusion. At his best, he was a pioneer in many directions — in the study of mental diseases, as the founder of iatrochemistry (chemistry applied to medicine), and as the distant herald of homeopathy. He was an adventurous experimentalist, yet his sounder views were crudely mixed with metaphysical and magical ideas, and his rational cures could not always be separated from miraculous ones. His study of the diseases of miners was the first to be devoted to occupational or industrial medicine. He was original to the point of extravagance, indiscreet and bombastic, generous and foolish — a kind of medical gypsy, restless and dogmatic, a man of genius, a great doctor, and a charlatan.

The scientific fame of Fracastoro of Verona rests mainly on his treatise on contagion (1546), in which he suggested that infection is caused by the transmission, from a person who is diseased to one who is healthy, of minute bodies capable of self-multiplication. This was an adumbration of modern theories (it could not be more before the discovery of microscopes and much else). His popular fame was based on another book of his to which we shall refer presently.

Ambroise Paré (1510–90) was a military surgeon whose native genius had not been inhibited by the scholastic medical education of his time and by irrelevant Latin learning; he was able, therefore, to take full advantage of every one of his innumerable observations with an open mind. He introduced so many novelties that he may be called the founder of modern surgery. His modesty was equal to his experience; it is well illustrated by a familiar statement of his: *"Je le pansai, Dieu le guerit"* (I dressed his wound, God healed it).

These three great men reveal the complexity of the Renaissance, for they were as different as they could be: Paracelsus the rebel, Fracastoro the classicist, Paré the wise practitioner. Paracelsus' genius was still in many respects medieval, Fracastoro's ancient, Paré's modern; yet they were children of the same century.

11. NEW DISEASE

It was not enough for the Renaissance to have great physicians; the age indulged itself in new diseases. When we said above that one might consider the middle of the fourteenth century as its starting point, we were not thinking only of Petrarch and Boccaccio and of the new culture which they symbolized, but also of the Black Death, whose first outburst (in 1348–1352) was so terrible that one-fourth of the population was destroyed and another fourth at least completely demoralized. This was perhaps the most frightful calamity of its kind in history, and it was of such extent and rigor that one could hardly find a better dividing line between the old age (the Middle Ages) and the new one. The Black Death did not stop in 1352; it flared up repeatedly throughout the fourteenth century and later. It was not, however, even in 1348, a new disease, but simply the worst example of a very old one.

The Renaissance suffered two other diseases which were peculiarly its own. The first, physical, was syphilis; the second mental, was the fear of witchcraft.

Syphilis made so dramatic an appearance at the siege of Naples in 1495 that it is difficult to resist the conclusion that it was really a new disease imported from the new world. That hypothesis cannot be completely proved,[7] but it is strengthened by two sets of considerations. In the first place, syphilis has very definite symptoms, and it is hard to believe that all of the great physicians of the past would have overlooked them if they had been present. There is no mention of those symptoms and no description of any disease suggesting syphilis in the abundant medical writings anterior to 1495, in Greek, Arabic, or Latin. In the second place, the explosive development of syphilis at the end of the fifteenth century suggests that it was a new disease for which Europeans were utterly unprepared.[8] The lack of syphilis literature before 1495 was compensated by its abundance afterwards.

[7] The literature concerning the origin of syphilis is immense and never ceases to grow. As Editor of *Isis*, I receive every year a few more books or papers on the subject.
[8] In the same way, smallpox, introduced by Europeans into America, destroyed a very large number of Indians (*Isis* 37, 124). Many other examples could be adduced concerning not only human diseases, but also plant and animal pests.

THE QUEST FOR TRUTH

The most remarkable publication *ad hoc* was the Latin poem written by Fracastoro in 1531, if only because it was that poem which gave its name to that disease (after the romantic shepherd Syphilus, who contracted it).[9] Fracastoro's poem enjoyed considerable popularity. The author's main intention was to sing the praise of a new remedy, *guaiacan* (*guaiacum, lignum sanctum,* holy wood). The discovery of that wonderful drug (as it was thought to be at the beginning) confirms the American origin of the disease. According to a medieval conceit, God had placed remedies close to the diseases which they could cure, counterpoisons near the poisons, etc. Now, if syphilis came from the West Indies, it was natural to hunt for a drug in that part of the world. This was done and the herb duly found; it was the one which the Indians called in their language *guaiacan.*

The German humanist Ulrich von Hutten (1488–1523), who had cured himself with *guaiacan,* wrote a treatise on the subject (1519) which he dedicated to the Archibishop of Mainz. At the end of it he did not scruple to say something like this: "I hope that Your Eminence has escaped the pox, but should you catch it (Heaven forbid, but one can never tell) I would be glad to treat and cure you." This is another typical Renaissance trait. The good archbishop realized that no offense was meant and took none. Syphilis was then a terrible disease (more terrible than now), but it was not considered more disgraceful than other diseases, and it caused less hypocrisy than it does today.

The other disease, much more terrible than syphilis, was the fear of witchcraft which became virulent at about the same time. The virulence was caused by a bull of Innocent VIII (1484) and exacerbated by the *Malleus maleficarum* (1486). This was a treatise written for the guidance of inquisitors; it explained how to detect, convict, and punish the witches. Looking at it from our point of view it might be considered a textbook of sexual psychopathology. The fear of witches caused their persecution, and the persecutions increased the fears. There appeared and spread everywhere a mass psychosis the like of which was not experienced again until our own days. The procedure followed in many witch trials was scrupulously recorded, and therefore we are very well informed. Many witches confessed their crimes and described their association with the Devil; their descriptions of

[9] Syphilis is the only disease having a poetic name.

117

the latter tally so often that one might take them as an objective proof of his reality. These poor women who were burned to death were neurotics whom we would send to hospitals. The witchcraft delusion could not be cured by theologians, who could detect only sin and heresy; it was instead a matter for physicians who recognized pathological conditions. The first physician to see that was the Dutchman Johann Weyer, who cannot be praised too highly for doing what he did as early as 1563.[10]

These medical subjects have been discussed at greater length than the others, because they are easy to describe and because they illustrate some aspects of the Renaissance less glorious than the usual ones, yet essential for its understanding. The sixteenth century was a golden age of humanities and of art, but it was also an age of intolerance [11] and cruelty; it proved itself sometimes to be inhuman to a degree which was hardly surpassed at any time except our own.

12. THE NEW ARTS

To return to more pleasant aspects (we must recognize the gloomy parts, though it is unwise to dwell on them overmuch), the quest for truth was so continuous and fervent and it was carried on by so many great men of many nations that mankind approached much closer to its goal, and at greater speed, than had been possible in medieval times. The consequences of that quest can be observed in every kind of endeavor, whether material or spiritual.

. . . Take perspective. That was in a sense a mathematical subject, but its adaptation to drawing and painting was realized in the fifteenth century by a number of artists: Filippo Brunelleschi, Leon Battista Alberti, Paolo Uccello, Piero della Francesca, Leonardo da Vinci (all of them Tuscan or closely connected with Florence). The first two were architects, and it is hardly necessary to point out the many connections between architecture, on the one hand, and mathematics,

---

[10] For more information on this very great man see *Isis* 25, 147–152, 1936.

[11] I have not spoken of the wars between Catholics and Protestants which disgraced Europe and Christendom, because that would have taken me too far aside. The repressions of witchcraft and heresy were often confused by the inquisitors, and more so by the public. We should be indulgent, because similar delusions and confessions disgrace our own times. All considered, it is not quite as disgraceful, however, to kill one another in the name of Marx as to do so in the name of Christ.

physics, and engineering, on the other. The architectural renaissance implied a scientific renaissance. The painters needed not only the new geometrical (or linear) perspective; they needed also the subtler knowledge to which the Middle Ages had given the same ambiguous name, perspective — aerial perspective, we call it. This was a mixture of optics, meteorology, and theory of shades and colors. With regard to this, artists received some assistance from men of science, but the best work in the West was done by Leonardo de Vinci. In their fresh enthusiasm for the beauty of human forms the artists needed some knowledge of anatomy, and here again Leonardo was their outstanding guide. Other tasks required the help of geographers, geologists, mineralogists, naturalists, and in this case the best exemplar (aside from Leonardo) was the Frenchman Bernard Palissy.

The main problems of life cannot be solved by men of science alone, nor by artists and humanists. We need the coöperation of all of them. Science is always necessary, never sufficient; we are starving for beauty, and where charity is lacking, nothing else is of any avail.

To return to art and science, the need of both and the feeling for both, the most illustrious representatives of that ambivalence are the Florentine, Leonardo da Vinci (1452–1519), and Albrecht Dürer (1471–1528) of Nuremberg. They were contemporaries, the second a little younger than the first; but they did not meet, nor did they influence each other to any degree. Being children of the same eld, their scientific problems were the same, but Dürer devoted more time to art, and Leonardo to science. Leonardo was a better scientist and a deeper philosopher than Dürer. He was, above all, a great anatomist and a great technician; he invented many machines, but (this is almost incredible) he paid no attention to the greatest inventions of his age (indeed, of all ages), printing and engraving. On the other hand, Dürer, being a practical man, a man of business, was one of the first to exploit both inventions. He created hundreds of woodcuts and engravings, and three books were written, illustrated, engraved, printed, and published by him. Leonardo was a dreamer and, from the world's point of view, a failure; Dürer was a very successful man. I can admire them both, but I love Leonardo. He was the finest flower of the Renaissance, the best illustration of that radiant age in two respects: the first is the one indicated by the very name Renaissance — rebirth, novelty

119

(everybody appreciates that); the second is the realization, more complete in himself than in any other man, that art and science, the pursuit of beauty and the pursuit of truth, are two complementary undertakings.

Leonardo saw clearly five hundred years ago what very few people are able to see today, and the few who do see it can only do so because they are standing on his shoulders . . .

A final remark. Rapid and oversimplified as it has been, my account has brought to light, among other things, the fact that the quest for knowledge has always been international or supranational, even more fundamentally so than the quest for beauty. The Italians could have created all of their masterpieces just as well if the Germans, the Flemings, and the English had not existed. On the contrary, scientific discoveries always implied the collaboration of many nations. No scientific achievement can ever be explained within the limits of a single country. This was made clear in my summary, in spite of the fact that it was necessarily restricted to the western world. If I had been able to speak of India, China, and Japan, I would have shown many curious relationships, but my time has been too short to do justice to the West alone, and hence I had to abandon the East. Please remember that and forgive me.

The personality of Leonardo was so overwhelming that it embraced many Oriental elements as well as western ones. This is another title of his to our admiration and our gratitude.

[1952]

Leonardo da Vinci

(1 4 5 2 - 1 5 1 9)

Sᴇʀ ᴘɪᴇʀᴏ ᴅ'ᴀɴᴛᴏɴɪᴏ was a notary, scion of a long line of notaries, in the little village of Vinci, perched in the foothills of Monte Albano in the Val d'Arno. By a woman of that village, Caterina, he had a boy who was born in 1452 [1] and named Leonardo. The boy's parents married soon after his birth, but they did not marry each other. Caterina was given to a peasant of the village, while Ser Piero was united with a noble lady. The child was brought up in his father's house. His stepmother died early and was replaced in the course of time by three other stepmothers; Ser Piero had many legitimate children and Leonardo's position among them was ambiguous and painful. Yet he grew up from the obscurity and humiliation of his birth to become the very incarnation of the Italian Renaissance, and we might say its supreme flower. He was typical of the Renaissance in that his roots went deep into the Middle Ages, but it was typical only of his own genius that he became one of the outstanding heralds of the modern world. There was in him another mark of distinction which caused him to be unique in the history of mankind: he excelled not only as an artist but also as a man of science.

If he had been born in wedlock, it is highly probable that his father would have provided for him the full education that was available in those days. Leonardo would have been well trained in Latin and

[1] The exact date of Leonardo's birth has been known only since the discovery by Emil Möller of a set of memoranda written in his own hand by Leonardo's grandfather (see E. Möller, "Der Geburtstag des Lionardo da Vinci," *Jahrbuch d. preuss. Kunstsammlung 60*, 71–75, 1939). From the new document we learn that Leonardo was born in 1452 on "Saturday 15 April, at 3 o'clock of the night" (that is, at 3 o'clock in the morning of 16 April) and that he "was given the name Lionardo" (the Tuscan form of Leonardo).

possibly in Greek and might have been sent to the University [2] or to a school of law or medicine. His education would have been the conventional one of his day; he would have been crammed with all kinds of rhetoric, dialectics, and metaphysics — dead things learned by rote, not only without experiments but out of touch with reality. Happily, he was an illegitimate child whom it would suffice to breed to some art, craft, or trade. We may assume that the little bastard gave early proofs of his artistic tendencies, of sundry peculiarities, and of his general queerness. At any rate, he was still very young (say 13, perhaps younger) when Ser Piero placed him in the house of Andrea del Verrocchio (1435–1488). That was about the year 1465, and from that time on Leonardo lived away from his family. His father remained in Vinci until 1469, when he settled in Florence, having been appointed notary to the city. Ser Piero had always been a man of substance; he was now more substantial than ever and his family larger, but Leonardo was out of it. One must be grateful to him, however, for having banished the boy from an uncongenial home to Verrocchio's house in the Via del Agnolo. This was an extremely happy choice. Verrocchio had been trained as a goldsmith (and as late as 1471 that was still his main profession, for he called himself then an *orafo*), but he was also a painter and sculptor; he had studied geometry for the sake of architecture (none of his architectural projects have come down to us); he was a wood inlayer and a bronze founder; and sometimes he had to do the work of a mechanic. In his *bottega* (or studio), Leonardo could obtain the best education of his time, not only for art but for independent and scientific thinking. In those days, the artists had to do everything themselves without outside help; they got ready suitable panels or canvasses, ground and mixed pigments, prepared oils, varnishes and glues. Sculpture presented special difficulties, for internal armatures must be provided, and when the sculptor is working on a heroic scale (as Verrocchio had to for the statue of Bartolommeo Colleoni) he may require mechanical gadgets of various kinds. Verrocchio was one of the greatest artists of the Renaissance; he it was who transmitted the artistic ideals of Donatello to Leonardo; we all know that, but it is not sufficiently appreciated that it was he also who transmitted to Leo-

[2] A university had been founded in Florence in 1349; it was merged in 1472 with that of Pisa (*Introd.* 3, 472). Leonardo could easily have attended it, if that had been his father's wish.

nardo many technicalities of scientific research and the love of science.

Leonardo remained in Verrocchio's house and studio at least ten years, and it was there that he obtained almost the whole of his education. Not only that, but his companionship with the old master had been so long and intimate that they influenced each other, and therefore, it is as easy to find Leonardo traits in Verrocchio's work as Verrocchio ones in the early Leonardo paintings. In addition to those two mutual educators, there were many others, for Verrocchio's fame was so great that many artists visited his house, such men as Perugino, Botticelli, Lorenzo di Credi; the brothers Pollaiuoli had a studio close by, and we may imagine that all these men visited one another, fraternized or quarreled, exchanged impressions and experiences. In addition to the practical problems which Verrocchio and Leonardo were facing every day and which had to be solved, they were given opportunities for contemplating all the questions which agitated the minds of their contempararies, and those questions were offered to them not in academic pretense but in a free commerce of ideas such as life itself would set going.

Verrocchio's *bottega* was an excellent cradle for Leonardo's genius. We do not know the details of his education, and it would probably be almost impossible to describe it. It was not like the conventional education of a college boy who takes courses A, K, T, and so on; the dean's office can eventually furnish a chart of it. The information thus given by the dean is exceedingly superficial; yet it guides and limits our curiosity. For Leonardo we have no guidance whatsoever, except his extant works of art and an abundance of notes.

He took early the habit of jotting down the ideas which occurred to him, ideas expressed by means of words and drawings, and a large amount of them have come to us. There are many collections of them in various libraries and museums, and all have been reproduced in facsimile editions with transcription, translations, and explanations. There are also two elaborate anthologies.[3] These transcriptions and

[3] The best is by Jean Paul Richter (1847–1937), *The literary works of Leonardo da Vinci* (1883); new edition revised by himself and by his daughter, Irma A. Richter (2 vols., London, 1939). This book is, unfortunately, very expensive. Another anthology was prepared by Edward MacCurdy, *The notebooks of Leonardo da Vinci* (2 vols., New York, 1938). I have reviewed both works in *Isis* 35, 184–187 (1944). My quotations in this article include the numbers which they bear in the Richter edition, where the Italian text may be found and references

translations are needed, because the notes, being recorded for his own use, were often abbreviated and practically all were written in mirror writing.[4] Why did he do that? We can only guess. It is possible that he was left-handed and that he began writing that way unconsciously. (Experiment: try to write a few words, say LEONARDO DA VINCI, with both hands at the same time, guiding your right hand as usual but allowing the left hand to move freely; the left-hand words, ICNIV AD ODRANOEL, are the mirror image of the right-hand ones, a fact which you can easily verify with a mirror.) Keen minded as he was, he realized that there was an advantage in that, for his notes would be safer from indiscretion and could not be stolen from his as easily when the *quaderni* containing them were lying about in his room. The main trouble with those notes is that very few are dated; some *quaderni* are dated, but that is not very helpful, for it is clear that Leonardo often inserted a note in any blank space that was available (we should remember that paper was not as cheap then as it is now and that people did not like to waste it as we do). Thus, many pages were written not at any one time but filled in gradually on different occasions. The notes following each other in a *quaderno* are not in strict chronologic order like the items in a daybook. As a result, though we know Leonardo's thoughts on a great variety of subjects, we are seldom able to date them; when these thoughts evolved, we are generally unable to say in what direction. We shall come back to that presently.

Before going further, it will be useful to tell briefly the events of Leonardo's life. The first thirty years were spent mainly in Florence. Though he was accepted as a master in the Compania di San Luca, the Florentine guild of painters, in 1472, he continued to work with Verrocchio, and was still living under the latter's roof as late as 1476 (*aet.* 24). He remained, if not in Verrocchio's house, at least in Florence until 1482/83, when he entered the service of Lodovico Sforza, duke of Milan.

He had nourished his mind and exercised his skill in every possible way; it seems that his earliest efforts were in the field of drawing and

---

to the MSS. The Oxford University Press published in 1952 in the World's Classics an abridgment of the Richter edition.

[4] That is writing which is like the image of ordinary writing in a mirror. In order to read it one should place it before a mirror and examine its reflection.

sculpture; yet he had also begun to paint, and his first masterpiece, the Adoration of the Magi, was produced in that early period. He had also begun to think of engineering problems, for example, how to make the Arno navigable from Florence to Pisa,[5] how to design better mills driven by water power. Hydraulic problems fascinated him throughout his life, and no wonder, if we remember that the power of running water was then the only physical power which could be captured and tamed (wind power could be used, but less well, for it was too capricious). Moreover, he was already familiar with almost all the scientific and technical problems of his day; yet he had failed to establish his own prosperity. Ser Piero, no doubt, would have pronounced him a failure. Perhaps he was somewhat aware of that himself and became anxious to do greater things and to safeguard his future.

We have the draft of a letter which he sent about 1482 to Lodovico Sforza. That letter is pathetic to a degree, for it illustrates the infirmity of genius in the face of competition. At the age of thirty, every practical man endowed with a minimum of intelligence and common sense has found his way; he is already holding a good position which will become better and better as the years go by; by that age, a man of great talent is already illustrious. But Leonardo was not simply a talented man — he was, for better or worse, a man of genius. Having been too deeply immersed in his works, ideas, and ideals to think of his career, he finds himself now — at the time of his maturity — at a loose end, with little money, no commissions, no prospects. Therefore, he must beat his own drum and "sell" himself to the tyrant of Milan. That is one of the bitter ironies of fate: the practical man may never have to "sell" himself in that way, because he has been doing it all the time quietly and implicitly; he has "inserted" himself in an organization and proved his usefulness not by words but by his adaptation to the job and to the requests of his chiefs. The man of genius does not think of all that, cannot adapt himself to a given task, and tries rather to adapt a task to his spiritual needs; a day comes, however, when his material needs must be satisfied, and then he must advertise himself in a manner which the practical and "respectable" man would consider shocking. Let us read Leonardo's prospectus in that light: [6]

[5] He came back to that project when he returned to Florence c. 1500.

[6] There is no proof that the letter was actually sent to the duke but that is very

Most Illustrious Lord, Having now sufficiently considered the specimens of all those who proclaim themselves skilled contrivers of instruments of war, and that the invention and operation of the said instruments are nothing different from those in common use: I shall endeavour, without prejudice to any one else, to explain myself to your Excellency, showing your Lordship my secrets, and then offering them to your best pleasure and approbation to work with effect at opportune moments on all those things which, in part, shall be briefly noted below.

(1) I have a sort of extremely light and strong bridges, adapted to be most easily carried, and with them you may pursue, and at any time flee from the enemy; and others, secure and indestructible by fire and battle, easy and convenient to lift and place. Also methods of burning and destroying those of the enemy.

(2) I know how, when a place is besieged, to take the water out of the trenches, and make endless variety of bridges, and covered ways and ladders, and other machines pertaining to such expeditions.

(3) Item. If, by reason of the height of the banks, or the strength of the place and its position, it is impossible, when besieging a place, to avail oneself of the plan of bombardment, I have methods for destroying every rock or other fortress, even if it were founded on a rock, &c.

(4) Again, I have kinds of mortars; most convenient and easy to carry; and with these I can fling small stones almost resembling a storm; and with the smoke of these cause great terror to the enemy, to his great detriment and confusion.

(9) [8] And if the fight should be at sea I have kinds of many machines most efficient for offence and defence; and vessels which will resist the attack of the largest guns and powder and fumes.

(5) Item. I have means by secret and tortuous mines and ways, made without noise, to reach a designated [spot], even if it were needed to pass under a trench or a river.

(6) Item. I will make covered chariots, safe and unattackable, which, entering among the enemy with their artillery, there is no body of men so great but they would break them. And behind these, infantry could follow quite unhurt and without any hindrance.

(7) Item. In case of need I will make big guns, mortars, and light ordnance of fine and useful forms, out of the common type.

(8) Where the operations of bombardment might fail, I would contrive catapults, mangonels, *trabocchi*, and other machines of marvellous efficacy and not in common use. And in short, according to the variety of cases, I can contrive various and endless means of offence and defence.

(10) In time of peace I believe I can give perfect satisfaction and to the equal of any other in architecture and the composition of buildings public and private; and in guiding water from one place to another.

Item. I can carry out sculpture in marble, bronze, or clay, and also I can

---

plausible. We have only a draft in *Cod. Atl.*, folio 3912; its genuineness has been doubted, because it is not in mirror writing; apart from that fact (which can be easily explained), the writing looks very much like Leonardo's. We quote the English translation as in Richter, no. 1340.

do in painting whatever may be done, as well as any other, be he who he may.

[32] Again, the bronze horse may be taken in hand, which is to be to the immortal glory and eternal honour of the prince your father of happy memory, and of the illustrious house of Sforza.

And if any of the above-named things seem to any one to be impossible or not feasible, I am most ready to make the experiment in your park, or in whatever place may please your Excellency — to whom I commend myself with the utmost humility, &c.

Most pathetic of all in that appeal is that Leonardo, whose only achievements (as opposed to ideas and projects) were in the field of art, does not speak much of his artistic genius. He knew that the duke of Milan was a *practical* man, who might patronize artists or not, but who needed engineers and mechanics, especially for war purposes. Therefore, his "prospectus" gives first place to bridges (how to build them and how to destroy those of the enemy), to scaling ladders, cannons, and other war engines, to methods of besieging and sapping, and so forth. The first nine paragraphs are devoted to such things; it is only in the tenth (and last) that Leonardo refers to his creative ability as an architect, metal caster, sculptor, and painter. One often derides and condemns the chemists engaged in the making of atomic bombs or poisonous gases, but here we must witness one of the greatest artists of all time offering himself as a military engineer.

His offer was acepted, and Leonardo was in the pay of Lodovico il Moro from 1483 on. His main responsibility to the duke was that of an engineer, for peace and war, but happily he was given or took enough time for artistic and scientific purposes. He continued to experiment and cogitate on many artistic and scientific problems, and discussed them with the virtuosi who were attracted to the court of Milan. Before leaving Florence he had seen his master, Verrocchio, struggling with the immense project of the equestrian statue of Bartolommeo Colleoni,[7] and he probably wished to emulate him. What a glorious challenge! He first thought of making a statue of Francesco Sforza,[8] but he failed to realize that equestrian statue or any other.

[7] The project was submitted in July 1479 by the Signorie of Venice to Verrocchio and other sculptors. Up to that time, there existed but one modern equestrian statue, the Gattemelata of Donatello (*c.* 1444). Aside from the artistic problem, the task of casting such an enormous mass of bronze was exceedingly difficult. Leonardo must have heard Verrocchio discuss the matter many times.

[8] See the end of his letter to Lodovico. Francesco was Lodovico's father, duke of Milan from 1450 to 1466.

The Virgin of the Rocks and the Last Supper date from the Milanese period (1483–1499). This period came to an end when Lodovico, who had joined a league against the French, was defeated by Louis XII (1499) and imprisoned. Leonardo and his friend Luca Pacioli (1450–1520) took flight and sought refuge in Venice.

This opens what might be called the third and last period of Leonardo's life — the wandering years — the life of a refugee roaming from one Italian town to another. We find him in Mantua and Venice, in Piombino, Siena, Urbino, Cesena, Imola, Rome, Florence, Milan, Rome again, but always active as an artist, an engineer, even more so as a man of science and a sage.

The most fruitful of these years of wandering were spent in Milan, which was then under French domination. The digging of canals, which he had begun under Lodovico, was continued under the French, but much of his time was given to art, and especially to painting. He was then the recognized master of the Milanese school (the school which we now call Leonardo's school); Michelangelo was not there to annoy him (these two giants were not comfortable in the same city); the younger artists were paying homage to the aging master. His Leda and John the Baptist were composed during that time. Nor did he neglect his scientific investigations. It is probable that the majority of his anatomical dissections and drawings were made then. He was encouraged in this by the anatomist Marcantonio della Torre (1478–1511). On the other hand, he was discussing mathematical problems with Luca Pacioli, and it was probably he who provided the illustrations for the latter's book on divine proportion.[9]

This second Milanese period, the last oasis in his pilgrimage, was brutally stopped when the Holy League (the Pope, Spain, and Venice) succeeded in defeating the French. Maximiliano (Lodovico's son) was permitted to reenter Milan at the end of 1512. Three years later Francis I invaded Lombardy, won the battle of Marignano (September 13, 1515), and Milan was again in French hands. In the meanwhile, Leonardo, who had obtained the patronage of Giuliano de' Medici (whose brother Leo X was pope, 1513–1521), went to Rome with his favorite disciple, Francesco Melzi (c. 1492–c. 1570); they

[9] Pacioli's *Divina proportione* was written before 1498, but it was published only in 1509 (in Venice).

reached the Eternal City at the end of 1513. Leonardo was invited to stay at the Vatican, and he undertook various experiments. The atmosphere was not as friendly, however, as it had been in Milan. Not only was Michelangelo throwing his immense shadow over the place, but a German mechanician, Giovanni degli Specchi, was creating trouble because of his jealousy. In 1516 or early in 1517, Leonardo and young Francesco left Rome, to accept the hospitality of Francis I. The latter had offered to the old artist a pension and the castle of Cloux near Amboise which was then his own residence. It was there that Leonardo spent the last years of his life. He was still very active in many directions; he was projecting a canal which would connect the Rhone; he had brought with him his collection of anatomical drawings and three paintings, his John the Baptist, the Sant' Anna with the Virgin and Child, and the portrait of a lady. This last was probably the Mona Lisa del Giocondo, because it so happens that these three paintings are in the Louvre to this day.

On the 23rd of April 1519, Leonardo called a notary to draw his will; he bequeathed his main treasure, his MSS, to Francesco Melzi. He died shortly afterward, on the second day of May 1519.

We may now come back to Leonardo's work, and especially to his scientific work, which requires explanation. The paintings must be seen in reproductions, or better in their glorious reality; the scientific ideas are not tangible. Let me help you. There were in him two kinds of interests which were obvious from the beginning of his apprenticeship in Verrocchio's bottega; it is worth while to put them together, because they reveal the duality of his genius. The first concerns the art of painting and the other mechanics, the invention of gadgets.

The first is natural enough, for in a studio most of the discussions would center on the art of painting and the other arts and their respective requirements and qualities. One can easily imagine the altercations which would occur between rival masters, master and disciple, or any artists who were engaged in different undertakings. Is painting better than sculpture? Is it a science or not? Or is there any science in it? Being philosophically minded, Leonardo was always trying to integrate the various forms of his activity, and being a painter, he sometimes tried to subordinate everything to painting or to explain the excellence of that art over all others. Leonardo did not simply accumulate a large number of notes on all those questions, which exercised his mind every day, but he seems to have tried to organize them and to put them in good order. Fra Luca Pacioli wrote to the Duke Lodovico Sforza on February 9, 1498 that Leonardo had "completed a treatise on painting and the movements of the human figure," and Giorgio Vasari recorded (in 1550) that a Milanese painter had shown him a MS of Leonardo which he intended to have printed in Rome. Such a MS, if it existed, is lost. The chances are that Leonardo had spoken to his friend of his intention of writing a treatise on painting, and that Fra Luca had taken that intention for a reality. It was a reality in the sense that Leonardo had an abundance of notes, some of them exceedingly well worded, but the notes were not put in good order, and the treatise was not completed. After his death, the MSS which had been bequeathed to Francesco Melzi were probably analyzed by Melzi or somebody else; some 944 excerpts were taken from 18 MSS and put together in a MS of the sixteenth century now in the Vatican Library (Codex Urbinas 1270). That MS was the indirect source of the book *Trattato della Pittura di Leonardo da Vinci movamente dato in luce*, dedicated to Christina, the former Queen of Sweden (Paris, 1651). We do not know who "composed" that book, but there is no reason to doubt the genuineness of its contents. The items are Leonardesque in their expression, but many of them represented old traditions. Linear perspective had been discussed by Filippo Brunelleschi, Leon Battista Alberti, Paolo Uccello, Piero della Francesca,[10] and we might almost say by every artist of the Renaissance, except that the majority of these artists were not very articulate and thought of subjects less in words than in images, or, if they thought in words, these words have long vanished.

Leonardo did not worry only about the more scientific items — optics, perspective, light and shade, theory of colors — but he dealt with subtler questions of esthetics, and some of his reflections — a curious mixture of empiricism and metaphysics — remind us of Chinese meditations going back at least to the sixth century. Yet no man of the West anticipated Leonardo; his meditations followed certain paths which

[10] All of them Florentines except Piero, who was Umbrian; all were Leonardo's contemporaries, except Brunelleschi, who died in 1446. Leonardo must have known personally Alberti and Uccello.

130

were not followed again by Western artists, except perhaps by Ruskin.

Leonardo was a born mechanician. At a time when machines were relatively rare, and when almost every kind of work, whether domestic, agricultural, or industrial, was hand work, he was always thinking of gadgets. Refer again to his letter to the duke of Milan printed above. He is conscious of the need of machines and of the immense possibilities which they open. It is true that men, some men at least, had always been familiar with war engines, and these had been gradually improved throughout the centuries.[11] Leonardo, living in an age of violence, had given much thought to the tools of war, but he was thinking also of other machines, which could be used not to kill people and not to destroy their wealth but to increase it.

From boyhood on, Leonardo dreamt of canals and of water power. Riverways afforded the best means of transportation, the only easy means, but rivers could not be of service unless they were sufficiently controlled. How could heavy wares be safely carried down the Arno from Florence to Pisa and to the sea? Moreover, the running waters could be made to turn wheels and the wheels might be used to move various engines. Leonardo's head was full of ideas on the subject.

Air power could be exploited as well, not only by means of windmills but in the way birds used it. Flying is one of the old dreams of mankind, witnessed by early myths like that of Daidalos and Icaros, but Leonardo dreamt more deeply than any of his predecessors or rather, instead of dreaming vaguely and ineffectively like a poet, he began to think of the subject as does an experimentalist and an engineer. The birds do fly, don't they? How do they manage to support themselves in the air, to fly, and direct their flight? He carefully observed the adjustment of wings and their flexing, the various kinds of feathers and the adjustable tails used for gliding, soaring, balancing, and alighting before and against the wind. Such complex and accurate observations were not repeated until the nineteenth century. Leonardo may justly be called one of the pioneers of aviation.

His head was teeming with mechanical ideas, and these ideas were

[11] For a list of fourteen treatises on war technology written in the fourteenth and fifteenth centuries, see my *Introduction to the History of Science* (3, 1550–1555). It cannot be proved that Leonardo knew and used any of them, but he lived in the same atmosphere and could tap the same oral and manual sources.

expressed in notes and drafts, working drawings (the equivalent of our blueprints). Some of those drawings are so clear and precise that it has been possible on the basis of them to construct models of Leonardo's machines and gadgets.[12] It cannot be denied that he invented them, but it does not follow that he was the first inventor. The investigation of technical priorities is sometimes difficult in the case of modern inventions; in the case of more ancient ones it is impossible. There were many inventors and almost all of them were illiterate or unable to describe their inventions in writing. Their minds did not work that way; they were mechanically, not literary, minded. And even if they had been able to describe their inventions, why should they have done so? There were no patent offices and secrecy was the only method of protection. Leonardo's case is not an exception to that rule, for he did not publish his drawings and apparently never had the wish of publishing them; he was satisfied when he had made them as carefully as possible and then closed his album.

The case of Leonardo is unique in another way. He was just the opposite of the average inventor whose motives are worldly, and who, if he invents anything, is not satisfied until the machine works and pays. Leonardo was so deeply immersed in his ideas that he did not try to make them work and pay. His interest was philosophical, and therefore he did not think only of particular machines but also of mechanics, mechanical theory in general. In this he had many medieval predecessors in various countries, for there was an old tradition going back to Archimedes (III-2 B.C.) which reappeared at intervals throughout the centuries.[13] All these men were obsessed with mechanical ideas. It is not necessary to assume that Leonardo da Vinci was acquainted with their writings; he probably was not, or his acquaintance with them was but vague and casual. Questions of theoretical "pure" mechanics had been in the air for centuries. He was repeatedly asking himself, as these others had done, such questions as

[12] These models were brought together by the International Business Machines Co. and have been exhibited in the Metropolitan Museum and many other places. See the Catalogue *ad hoc*.

[13] Leonardo seldom quoted "authorities"; he did not bother about them. Yet there are in his notes half a dozen references to Archimedes. In his mechanical notes, he referred also to Biagio Pelacani of Parma (XIV-2) and to Albert of Saxony (XIV-2), one reference to each. This does not prove either that he was very familiar with their writings or that he was not familiar with those of other mechanicians.

what is the difference between heavy and light bodies, what is gravitation, what is the weight of a body and what is its center of gravity, what are force and motion, impetus and impact? Then what are the mechanical elements? How does one drag or lift a body, cut, break, or rotate it? These remarks apply not only to his mechanical inventions but to his speculations concerning water power and its use, or air power and flying. He was not simply a mechanic but a mechanician; [14] one might even call him a pioneer in the fields of hydraulics [15] and aerodynamics (what is meant is that those technical terms are used correctly when we speak of him).

It is not enough to say that most of those questions were insoluble in Leonardo's time; it was not even possible to formulate them in a scientific way. They were gradually isolated, recognized, formulated, and finally solved by such men as Galileo, Huygens, Wren, Newton. The originality of Leonardo da Vinci was that he combined within his own soul such theoretical aspirations together with the wish to solve practical, everyday, industrial problems, and his ambivalence is betrayed by the fact that when he had conceived a solution and drawn the blueprint he was satisfied. He stopped dead at the very point where a practical inventor would have begun to feel excited and to get busy in good earnest.

Leonardo's mechanical contrivances have excited the admiration of our mechanical age, and some of our present-day inventors may have felt justified by his extraordinary example. Methinks I hear one of them exclaim, "There was a man of the Italian Renaissance, one of the greatest artists, who had desires and ambitions like our own." No, he was not at all as they are; this has already been suggested above, and I shall prove it more fully later on.

[14] Let us illustrate his love of pure science with two maxims out of many: "Mechanics are the Paradise of mathematical science, because here we come to the fruits of mathematics" (no. 1155); "Those who fall in love with practice without science are like a sailor who enters a ship without a helm or a compass, and who never can be certain whither he is going" (no. 1161).

[15] Leonardo's views on hydraulics were collected in 1643 by the Dominican Luigi Maria Arconati, whose MS compilation is in the Vatican (Barberini 4332). It was edited by Francesco Cardinali, *Del moto e misura dell' acqua* (Bologna, 1828; reprinted 1923). A collection of Leonardo's mechanical notes was edited with great care by Arturo Uccelli, *Leonardo. I libri di meccanica* (quarto, Milan, 1940).

The historian of science is impressed by Leonardo's gadgets, but much more so by his long and patient work in the field of anatomy. In order to understand its originality, we must see it in proper perspective. It has often been repeated that anatomy was neglected in the Middle Ages because of religious prejudices. Anatomy was not completely neglected, and dissections, even human dissections, were made from time to time, but these dissections were few and they were not made with sufficient application nor with sufficient freedom of thought. The shackles of the medieval anatomists were less religious than scholastic. Medical men had not acquired the habit of seeing with their eyes open without prejudices. Indeed, they were so much dominated by older masters such as Galen and Avicenna that they were not only blind to reality but able to see things which were not there at all; Galen's words were more convincing to them than reality itself! It is a bit difficult for us to imagine such a state of mind, though it has not yet completely disappeared. The renovation of anatomy was finally accomplished by men who were good observers, had dexterous hands and sharp eyes, and were not inhibited by prejudices. Two such men followed each other within half a century; the first was our Leonardo, the second, born a few years before Leonardo's death, was the Fleming Andreas Vesalius. The main honors must go to the latter, because Leonardo did not publish anything, while Vesalius' great book (1543) was the basis of modern anatomy.

Leonardo carried out a good many dissections; toward the end of his life he could claim to have dissected the bodies of some thirty people, including young and old, male and female, and even a woman with an unborn child in her womb. It is almost certain that he dissected more bodies than the professors of anatomy before his time; for not only were university dissections few and far between, but the professors did not lower themselves to that kind of dirty work. The dissection was generally made by an underling under the eyes of the professor who was sitting in his cathedra holding the textbook before him and giving occasional directions to the prosector. It was very difficult for the professor to see much from his high chair, and he was paying more attention to his book than to the cadaver. Leonardo's attitude was absolutely different. He worked alone, did not try to teach anybody but himself; he was not an expositor of Galen using the

134

corpse as illustration; he was primarily a student of nature, anxious to unravel her secrets. The difficulties and the horror of such work done in those conditions, and the infinite patience which it required, can hardly be imagined by the medical students of today who dissect in well-equipped laboratories cadavers that have been preserved in refrigerators and carefully disinfected. It is better perhaps not to describe the conditions [16] and to assume that Leonardo has done the preliminary work and is now sitting near the table, has taken a sheet of paper, and is trying to draw what he sees as exactly as possible.

This entailed new difficulties of a very different order. Drawings of bones are relatively easy, but it is very hard to make a clear drawing of inside anatomy, of the entrails mixed with blood and other liquids; the outlines are vague and the perspective confusing. Leonardo excelled in this, and some of his anatomical drawings have never been surpassed. This was scientific-artistic work implying judicious selection and elimination as well as the ability to reproduce the chosen details faithfully.

Leonardo's anatomical curiosity was not a passing fancy; the large number of anatomical drawings which have come to us prove that he must have devoted almost as much time to them as if he had been a professional anatomist and naught else. That curiosity was scientific as well as artistic. He wanted to know how the human body was built and how it functioned; the descriptive part was accomplished by him astonishingly well, but he never put his observations together in the form of a treatise, and his drawings were far more elaborate than the notes which he added to them.

Artistic anatomy, that is, the study of anatomy as much as may be needed by artists who try to reproduce the human form, was a peculiarly Florentine subject. It concerned not only the sculptors, but also the painters, especially those of Florence, more interested in contours, lines, and shadings than in color. The great tradition begun by Donatello and Luca della Robbia was carried to excess by Antonio Pollaiuolo, then brought back to golden moderation by Verrocchio and

---

[16] In the course of my Harvard lectures, I tried to explain the conditions under which Leonardo and Vesalius did their work. I felt it necessary to do so in order to illustrate the heroism and the devotion of those men; on one occasion, I did it so vividly that one of the students was nauseated and was obliged to leave the classroom as fast as he could.

Leonardo. The artist, whether sculptor or painter, must know the superficial muscles of the body, and his drawing must be so accurate and sensitive that it suggests the muscles under the skin, whether at rest or moving, yet he must not emphasize them. The spectator should be unconsciously aware of their presence.

From time immemorial another kind of artistic anatomy had developed under mathematical and mystical influences. Some philosophers, anxious to reveal the harmonies of nature, tried to discover mathematical relations between parts of the body. Such preoccupations existed in Egypt, Greece, and India.[17] They exercised the mind of Leonardo and also that of his younger contemporary, Albrecht Dürer.

Leonardo was a student of one book, the book of nature. His studies were largely centered on the human body, but they ranged all over the whole field of natural history; he was always examining and drawing flowers and animals, and studying what would be called today physical geography, mineralogy, and geology. He was one of the first to interpret fossils in a rational way; he concluded that shells found high up in the hills were the remains of creatures which had been living on the sea floor, had been buried in the silt, then lifted up. He was one of the first to climb in the high mountains and to look at the wonders of the alpine world with the eyes of an artist as well as with those of a man of science. This is more remarkable than most people imagine, for they do not realize that Western people were generally afraid of the high Alps, which they believed to be tenanted by goblins and devils. Christianity had not been able to dispel these superstitions, while Buddhism, on the contrary, had favored opposite ones. The Buddhists of China and Japan associated high peaks with godlike powers; many temples were built on the way up and at the very tops and attracted innumerable pilgrims. In this respect (as in many others) Leonardo was an oriental.[18] His sayings on art and nature would delight Hindu, Chinese, and Japanese readers.

Leonardo was more rational than most people of his time, and remarkably free from superstitions, but he was not free from prejudices.

[17] Sarton, *Introduction to the History of Science* (3, 1584, 1948). Leonardo's interest is illustrated by his design of a man of perfect proportions (Accademia, Venice).
[18] *Introd.* (3, 511, 1171).

Nobody is, not even in our own "enlightened" day. Men of genius see further than other men, and their vision is not only deeper, it is generally clearer, much clearer. Yet, for all that, their vision is restricted and its sharpness limited. Leonardo's was extraordinarily broad and clear, but the knowledge available in his day was not sufficient to ensure his intellectual freedom. He was dominated by two sets of prejudices which we may call respectively Platonic and Galenic.

From Plato, the Neoplatonists, and the Qabbala, he had inherited the idea of microcosm *versus* macrocosm: there is a correspondence between the little world represented by our own body and the great world, the Universe. This misled him, as it had misled innumerable people before him, into all kinds of false analogies. Man's bones are like the earth's rocks; there is in him a lake of blood even as there are oceans; the tides of the sea are comparable to a man's pulse, the "circulation" of blood in the body is like the circulation of water in the earth; hair and feathers are like the grass in meadows or leaves on the trees; earthquakes are like disagreeable rumblings and eruptions in our own belly; rhythms and cycles can be observed on a small scale as well as on a large one. Where did Leonardo get these fanciful notions? He may have got them from many sources, he could not escape them. Artists are very fond of analogies, perhaps because these can be easily visualized, and the man of science in Leonardo was not rebuked because this set of analogies was so vast and complex, and because its truth was taken for granted by the majority of thinking men. I imagine that many "intellectuals" of Leonardo's time would have thought that one of the best proofs of their superiority over the uneducated mob was just that: their realization that the microcosm (their own body) is a reduced image of the greater world.

The Platonic prejudice colored almost everything, the Galenic one was more restricted. Though Leonardo did not con Galen's treatise as did the professors of anatomy, nor blame a corpse if it did not conform to the master's description, he could not help being influenced by certain dicta. How did he account for the heartbeat and the pulse? Galen did not believe that the blood circulated in the body but rather that it ebbed and flowed in the veins. Leonardo seems to have accepted that opinion, which tallied with the Platonic prejudice. In order to justify his views Galen had been driven to assume that the blood entering the right ventricle passed through the septum and thus reached the left part of the heart. How did the blood pass through the septum? One cannot see any openings in the latter. That is easy: it passed through invisible holes. Leonardo was so much blinded by the confluence of Platonic and Galenic prejudices that he, the wonderful observer and impeccable draftsman, drew a portion of the septum in which invisible holes had become visible.[19] It would be difficult to find a better example of the obnubilation of the human mind by an overpowering prejudice. For here we have a man of genius, one of the greatest of all times, a free mind, and yet he had been bamboozled by Plato and Galen to the extent of being able to see things that were not so; he was able not only to see invisible pores but to show them to others.

This raises a troublesome question. Was Leonardo really a scientific discoverer, a creative man of science? Does he deserve to be listed among the great men of science of the past?

My asking these questions may shock his admirers. His scientific genius is not questioned, nor his devotion to scientific subjects. That much of his work was essentially that of a man of science or technician, rather than that of an artist, cannot be denied. Then you may ask why I raise that question at all.

It is simply this. The process of scientific discovery is very complex. The beginning, of course, is to *see* something new and true, to see it clearly; this may be simply the result of good observations or experiments; in most cases, it implies the bringing together of different ideas, and enabling the one to fertilize the other. All this is complex enough and may involve long meditation; yet it is only a beginning. Having made his discovery, the man who was fortunate enough in making it must prove it first to himself, then to others. One may well claim that a discovery is not completed until it has been vindicated in public (it does not really exist as long as it exists only in your mind or in your own cryptic notes); in practice, the battle has not been won until the invention or the discovery has been made acceptable to competent judges.

The fundamental discovery, the bright idea which crosses a man's

[19] For sources, see *Isis* 35, 186.

138

brain, is as essential as the seed of a plant; yet like the seed it is only a commencement. If the seed is not allowed to develop, it is as if it had never been.

Leonardo had many of the qualities of a man of science: he was insatiably curious about all the secrets of nature, and his curiosity was disinterested; he fully realized the need of correct and prudent observations, and, when such were not available, the need of experiments which would permit of new observations.

"Experience, the interpreter between formative nature and the human race, teaches how that nature acts among mortals; and being constrained by necessity cannot act otherwise than as reason, which is its helm, requires it to act" (no. 1149). "Wisdom is the daughter of experience" (no. 1150). His general understanding of nature was that of a rationalist. "Necessity is the theme and the inventress of nature, the curb and law and theme" (no. 1135). "First I shall test by experiment before I proceed further, because my intention is to consult experience first and then with reasoning show why such experience is bound to operate in such a way. And this is the true rule by which those who analyse the effects of nature must proceed; and, although nature begins with the cause and ends with the experience, we must follow the opposite course, namely (as I said before), begin with the experience and by means of it investigate the cause" (no. 1148A). He expressed the same ideas in different terms repeatedly. He rejected the possibility of miracles, had no use for wonders, and despised superstitions.

His literary education had been neglected in his youth; he had hardly studied Latin, if at all; like every Italian he could read in a pinch simple Latin sentences, but the Latin books which contained the best scientific literature were closed to him. Florentines as well as Lombards are constitutionally jealous; [20] those who were jealous of Leonardo's prestige could whisper, "*Un uomo senza lettere!* What could one expect from such a one?" The individuals who were aware of his superiority but were too petty to acknowledge it had two weapons against him: he was illegitimate and illiterate, two good reasons for disposing of him a priori. Yet he knew his strength and was not afraid

[20] Leonardo was fully aware of the jealousy he was exposed to; witness this maxim, "A body may sooner be without its shadow than virtue be without envy" (no. 1183A).

of asserting his own knowledge derived not from books but from experience. "Any one who in discussion relies upon authority uses, not his understanding, but rather his memory" (no. 1159).

Of course, the word "illiterate" must not be taken literally; Leonardo must have read some books or listened to quotations from them, but it is very unlikely that he ever was a good reader. In his notes he very seldom quotes "authorities." I found some nine vague references to Aristotle, six to Vitruvius, five to Archimedes and as many to Ptolemy and to Pliny, two to Avicenna's anatomy. It may be that these numbers are not quite accurate, but they give one a general view of the situation.

And what a paradoxical situation that was! By way of contrast, consider the pedantic idiots who published books chuckfull of references and quotations. How learned they must have thought themselves to be, and how ignorant Leonardo. Who would pay any attention to his sayings? The most highly educated man of Florence was an "uomo senza lettere." Unfortunately, Leonardo's thoughts were not published, except centuries later, and thus he could not be vindicated. He had few opportunities of teaching his contemporaries, but he is teaching us, and we accept many of his lessons with humility and gratitude.

Being used to think of nature and of men in a general way, he was not historically minded, and very few of his innumerable notes are dated. That does not matter, except in those cases in which his opinions varied in the course of time. How did they vary? We would like to know which of many opinions is the latest and final one, and this is made impossible. The result of that is that we cannot give him full credit for one opinion against the opposite one. He cannot have it both ways. For example, he says somewhere, "The sun does not move" (No. 886), and one might be tempted to call him a forerunner of Copernicus, but that would not be right, for he generally claims that the sun does move, as our everyday observations seem to prove. A statement of his may be construed as affirming the circulation of the blood, but other quotations and drawings confirm the opposite theory. In this case, the discovery was not reiterated and completed by him, because he was inhibited by Platonic and Galenic prejudices. He spoke of gravitation and impetus but in the same way as many medieval doctors had done before him. In short, we cannot give him credit for

LEONARDO DA VINCI

any scientific discoveries, except, perhaps, such as are implied in his anatomical and mechanical drawings.

Such drawings oblige us to reconsider the matter from another point of view. Suppose a man made a very good drawing proving that he has observed an anatomical peculiarity (for example, Leonardo was the first anatomist to represent accurately the five fused vertebrae of the sacrum).[21] Would this suffice to call him the discoverer of it, if he did not explain it, as if he expected other people to remake the discovery as it were in the drawing? (It is undoubtedly easier to see the thing in the careful drawing than in reality.) In addition, we must remember that Leonardo's drawings were kept in his own portfolios and were not published until our own day. They were not shown to his contemporaries except to his familiars and to a few others, such as Marcantonio della Torre, and at the end of his life to the Cardinal Luigi of Aragon, who visited him in Cloux. Can one give credit to a man for discoveries which are hidden away?

To return to our former contention, it is not enough to make a discovery — one must interpret it and be ready to vindicate it against the people who deny or doubt it. Strictly speaking, no single discovery can be credited to Leonardo, and yet we must recognize that he was one of the great discoverers of all times.

He was one of the greatest men of science but remained unknown as such, except that he was considered a kind of wizard indulging in scientific research, and that his familars spoke of his various scientific activities. The fault for his being unappreciated rests entirely with him; he did only a part of the work which should have been done and stopped halfway.

One might say that Leonardo failed in his undertakings; that might be said even of the artist in him as well as of the man of science. He bequeathed to us a relatively small number of masterpieces, which represent only a part of his activity. His efforts to create an equestrian statue that would emulate the Colleoni proved abortive.[22] Nothing

[21] J. Playfair McMurrich, *Leonardo da Vinci, the Anatomist* (Baltimore, 1930; *Isis 15*, 342–344), p. 120, fig. 24.

[22] This particular failure was partly independent of Leonardo's will. The casting of the "gran cavallo" would have been immensely expensive and could not have been accomplished without the financial help of Lodovico Sforza. What had been done was destroyed by Gascon soldiers when they took Milan.

141

remains of the heroic horse except a few sketches. Many of his paintings have completely disappeared or else they have been jeopardized by Leonardo's experiments; for example, the marvelous Last Supper in the refectory of Santa Maria delle Grazie in Milan is but a shadow of itself. We know, however, that he exerted a deep influence upon many artists, especially during his second Milanese period and the years of wandering which followed it. In the scientific field, his influence was minimal, because nobody knew exactly what he was doing. He may have influenced such men as Marcantonio della Torre or Luca Pacioli, but the results of that are not tangible. His real influence as a man of science and thinker dates only from the nineteenth century.[23]

His technical activities are perhaps more astonishing than all the others, in what they included and in what they rejected. Here was a man who was interested in machines and gadgets of every kind, especially in war engines. It is as if a great artist of today were spending part of his time designing armored tanks or a new atomic bomb. Can you imagine that? The most paradoxical feature of all is that he paid no attention whatsoever to the two greatest inventions of his age — typography and engraving. The latter will be dealt with presently. Typography had been reinvented in Western Germany shortly before Leonardo's birth and by the time of his maturity it was already well established in many Italian cities; the first Italian printing press was started in Subiaco in 1465; printing began in Rome in 1467, in Venice in 1469; the year 1471 saw the beginning of it in Florence and in Milan. By the end of the century a large number of books had already been printed in Italy, and the new art had become one of the most important industries of Venice. Leonardo must have handled many printed books; yet he never referred to them as such.[24] There are no references to printing in his notes. How is that possible? Intelligent as he was, could he have failed to realize the importance of that invention, its *double* importance, for it made possible and even easy the multiplication of copies, and also their standardization? Moreover, the invention was not complete: there were many possibilities of improvement

[23] With the exception of his views on painting and art, which were made partly available in early editions of the *Trattato della pittura* (Paris, 1651; etc.).

[24] He refers to many books (Richter, 2, 366 ff.), but one cannot be certain that each or any reference is to a *printed* book.

which challanged the ingenuity of technicians. Did Leonardo share the prejudices of the rich bibliophiles against the new art which was jeopardizing the old art of hand copying? Human nature is so strange that the victim of snobs may well become a snob himself. We simply do not know but are very puzzled.

It is possible also that Leonardo was not interested in printing because he was not interested in books. He was neither a reader nor a writer. The abundance of his notes should not deceive us. His note-taking was not that of a scholar and potential author but of a craftsman and diarist. He wanted to be able to refresh *his* memory but was not thinking of other people. He collected notes and in some cases *planned* to write a treatise but that was about as far as he got. This special laziness or inertia was almost certainly induced by the absence of literary education in his youth. He did not like to compose a book and as a consequence there grew in him a kind of contempt for such work; his contempt was naturally increased by the fact that so much contemporary writing was scholastic and rhetorical — empty. On the other hand, he was able to coin sentences (or short paragraphs) of singular clearness and strength. His reluctance was similar to that of the majority of artists, who prefer to work with their brushes or chisels rather than with a pen; it might be compared also to that of the majority of men of science who have endless energy for their own investigations but find the writing of reports so dull that they procrastinate indefinitely, and thus fail to explain the very purpose and meaning of their efforts.

That was exactly Leonardo's case; it is not simply that he could not write a book, but he could not explain himself except in the form of aphorisms. He was satisfied with his observations and intuitions and did not wish to amplify them. This accounts for his relative failure in art, science, technology, and writing. He never gave his full measure except in painting, where a few masterpieces are sufficient to immortalize his name.

We all know people whose talents are limited, but who have the ability to capitalize and to exploit them to the limit; a new subject having excited their enthusiasm, they begin the writing of a book about it and learn as they go. Then there are others, at the other end of the gamut, who cannot husband their qualities; if they be scholars, they never cease to investigate; they accumulate mountains of notes and their magnum opus is seldom begun and never completed.[25] Leonardo was nearer to the second group than to the former, but this was due, perhaps, less to his defects than to his exceptional magnanimity. This was observed, strangely enough, by one of the worst rascals of a time rich in them, the satirist Pietro Aretino (1492–1556). In a moment of decency, Aretino remarked, "I say to you that Leonardo was equal to the greatest. His limitation was that he had so elevated a genius that he was never satisfied with what was done."

He lived in troubled times, in the midst of wars and revolutions, when there was little tranquillity and no security, when leading men were devils like Lodovico Sforza and Cesare Borgia (Machiavelli's Prince) or violent ascetics like Savonarola — an age of bravura, cruelty, and treachery. How did he preserve his own equanimity? He remained steadfast and well balanced because of his creative genius, but he did not produce as much as he could have done in happier circumstances. He was an artist and a poet, a contemplator, a dreamer. How much greater such a man, how much nearer to perfection, than if he had been more active, more "efficient."

This is so significant for the understanding of the essential, Leonardo's soul, that we must insist upon it, and the best way of doing so is to contrast him with another great artist, his younger contemporary, Albrecht Dürer.[26] I would be foolish to claim that Leonardo was a greater artist than Albrecht or vice versa; both men were very great artists, but Leonardo was certainly a greater man. While Leonardo was a dreamer, inhibited by his genius, Dürer was more practical, more "efficient." Let me illustrate this with a simple example. If you made a contract with Dürer for your portrait, you might be reasonably sure to obtain it in good time (we have more than fifty portraits painted by

[25] It is of such men that La Rochefoucauld wrote, "Ce n'est pas assez d'avoir de grandes qualités; il faut en avoir l'économie" (Réflexion no. 159).

[26] Albrecht Dürer (1471–1528) was 19 years younger than Leonardo, but he lived 10 years less (57 vs. 67) and thus survived the older by only 9 years. They might have met, but there is no reason to believe that they did. Dürer made woodcut copies of some of Leonardo's drawings (the Six Knots); Leonardo does not refer to Dürer.

144

him, not counting those included in religious compositions); if you made a contract with Leonardo, the chances are that the Master would find something more interesting to do and that the portrait would never materialize.

To put it bluntly, there are people who can be depended upon to deliver the goods and others who cannot. Dürer belonged to the first group and Leonardo to the second. Administrators and men of substance prefer to deal with the first and thus to advance their common interests; they leave the others alone.

Like Leonardo, Dürer jotted down a great many notes (text and figures), but unlike him he was anxious to put them together and to publish them. Three treatises of his were actually *printed*, the first dealing with mensuration by means of compass and square ruler (1525), the second, with fortifications (1527), the third, with proportions of the human body (1528). Leonardo had investigated all those subjects (geometry and perspective, proportions, fortifications, artistic anatomy) himself, but he had published nothing.[27] These subjects could not be explained without figures. Dürer's books were duly illustrated with his own engravings. While Leonardo paid no more attention to engraving than to printing, Dürer realized at once the immense commercial possibilities of both. Instead of producing a single painting or drawing, a woodcut or copper engraving would enable him to manufacture easily a great many copies. Not only that but, good business man that he was, he saw that it would be advantageous to produce *series* of engravings or woodcuts, and thus he would be able to sell an album of them instead of individual items.

Dürer established himself as a printer, engraver, publisher, bookseller. His three books bear the imprint "Printed at Nuremberg by Albrecht Dürer the Painter." There was a Dürer stall at the great commercial fairs of Frankfort and Nuremberg.

When he visited the Netherlands in 1520–21, he brought with him a whole "line" of his engravings and woodcuts; [28] these were very easy to carry in one's baggage and extremely profitable. Many of them were used by Dürer to ingratiate himself with powerful men; most of them

---

[27] In justice to Leonardo one must bear in mind that Dürer was much younger and that his three books appeared after Leonardo's death.
[28] Dürer produced some 100 copper engravings and about 200 woodcuts.

were sold. We are very well informed about that, for he included in his diary a full account of his sales and expenditures.[29] Another differential trait is afforded by the use of dates. Dürer signed every work of his and dated many; his instincts were those of a good accountant or annalist. Leonardo seldom dated anything; very few dates are found in his abundant notes. He was not more historically minded than a Hindu, and for the same reason; he was viewing everything sub specie aeternitatis.

I am not surprised that Leonardo failed to notice the commercial advantages of printing and engraving, but it is odd that, intelligent as he was, he did not perceive the immense value of both arts for scientific purposes. It was not too troublesome to copy a plain text, but very annoying and risky to copy astronomical tables or diagrams, and it was very difficult to reproduce exactly the illustrations needed in herbals, or in treatises of chemistry, anatomy, and surgery. Not only did printing and engraving make all these things easy, but, what matters even more, it made it possible (for the first time) to produce standard editions of every text, table, diagram, or figure.[30] Science could not progress without reliable standards.

Dürer was a good businessman, a "grand bourgeois"; he could get "interested" in scientific topics, but he was not a man of science in the higher sense; Leonardo was just that, a man of science, an impractical inventor, a cogitator, a bohemian. The first became quite rich, a substantial citizen of Nuremberg with a great house of his own; Leonardo impoverished himself, spent the end of his life homeless, not in the independence which he would have craved but as a guest of the king of France. The artistic genius of the former cannot be denied, but it was not so strong that Dürer could not always keep it under control with an eye open to the main chance; Leonardo's genius was deeper and more complex, unpredictable and unmanageable. Leonardo did not control it but was at the mercy of it.[31]

[29] It is not suggested that Dürer was avaricious or greedy, but his wife was, and it is hard for a man to be more generous than his spouse. Leonardo was never married.

[30] The figures of Luca Pacioli's book *Divina proportione* have been ascribed to Leonardo (the figures but not the engraving of them). Luca's knowledge was derived from Piero della Francesca rather than from Leonardo (*Isis 42*, 47).

[31] This reminds me of a profound saying recorded by André Gide in his *Journal* (5 Feb. 1931): "Avec du talent on fait ce qu'on veut, quand on a du génie on fait ce qu'on peut."

LEONARDO DA VINCI

Let us take a final look at the grand old man as he stands in the courtyard of the castle of Cloux, or as if we see him in the beautiful self-portrait, the red chalk drawing of Torino. His face is that of a very old man and yet he was then less than 67, perhaps less than 65, but he had suffered many vicissitudes, because of the world's cruelty and of his own anguish. He was a man of noble presence and, what matters more, of noble mind in the midst of ignoble circumstances, a great artist trying to do his very best as a painter, a perfectionist; a man of science, anxious to find the truth, to understand God and nature, himself, and other men.

His activities help us to realize the profound unity of knowledge and also its continuity, for in spite of his originality, which was unequaled, the sources of almost every one of his thoughts can be traced in the writings of antiquity or of the Middle Ages. This does not mean that he had copied them or memorized them unconsciously; in certain cases (for example, Chinese art theories), he could not possibly have had any knowledge of them.

His outstanding contribution was the proof in his own person that the pursuit of truth and the pursuit of beauty were not by any means incompatible. Many have equaled or surpassed him in the pursuit of either, no one in the pursuit of both. Therefore, he remains the paragon, and, as it were, the patron saint of all men who love beauty and truth with equal fervor.

He was a defender of reason, full of disdain for the superstitions which were flourishing in his time even more than in ours,[32] but he was essentially a spiritualist, realizing that the essence of man is in his soul, and that the essence of nature also is spiritual.

Think of him as a builder of bridges — the one between science and art and the other between the inchoate medieval thought and modern rationalism.

Vasari remarks, "Marvelous and celestial was Leonardo, the son of Ser Piero da Vinci. He would have been very proficient in learning and in the elements of science (*lettere*) had he not been so variable and unstable. He set himself to learn many things and after having begun, abandoned them."

---

[32] "O speculators on perpetual motion, how many vain projects in this search you have created! Go and be the companions of the searchers for gold" (no. 1206). Many other maxims of his condemn superstitions and irrationality.

"Variable and unstable," yes. He was the tool of his restless curiosity and implacable genius. He was intelligent, too intelligent, and, you add (as Vasari did), too unstable for the continuation of profitable undertakings. Curiously impartial in an age of unbridled passions, he was often allured by his imagination; yet his genius kept him under control. There was in him the instinct of a modern man of science, but of one who was also an artist and a poet. He remained serene in the midst of catastrophes, partly because he was so deeply immersed in his own thoughts. To say that he was unstable is petty, however; he was unstable with regard to little things but not with regard to the essential ones. "He who is fixed to a star does not change his mind" (no. 682).

I am not a very practical man; yet, when I think of Leonardo, I cannot help being ashamed of being as practical as I happen to be. He was unable to "plan" anything or to stick to his plans, because his was a creative, not an administrative, genius. Individually and socially we are planning too much, acting like busybodies and muddling things in the name of "order." In science, and even more in art and letters, the less planning the better. Let there be a minimum of administration and a maximum of freedom. Leonardo did not express these views as has just been done, but they were writ deep in his heart.

The supreme discipline is that of love; "the love of anything is the offspring of knowledge, the love being the more fervent in proportion as the knowledge is more certain . . ." (no. 1210). One might add that without love true knowledge is out of the question.

Simon Stevin of Bruges

(1 5 4 8 - 1 6 2 0)

INTRODUCTION

1.   I HAVE TAKEN pains to give an account of Stevin's life and works which should be as accurate and as complete as the scale of this memoir would permit, and I trust that historians of science will find it useful and that some of my brief statements will challenge criticism. However, we need considerably more: Stevin's personality is such a great one that a very full biography should be eventually devoted to it. Investigations in the Dutch and Belgian archives may clear up moot points. Some additional light may be expected from Isaac Beeckman's diary, of which our learned colleague of Vlissingen, Mijnheer Cornelis de Waard, has been preparing an edition for many years. And let us hope that when the *Hollandsche Maatschappij der Weten-schappen* has finally completed its magnificent edition of Huygens' works and correspondence,[1] begun almost half a century ago, it will undertake the building of a similar monument to the memory of Stevin. This might be done with the cooperation of a Belgian society, for Stevin's fame belongs equally to both countries.

The present memoir is hardly more than an introduction to the study of this subject which, if we would try to follow all of its ramifications, would involve a survey of almost every aspect of scientific thought in a critical and fascinating age.

A complete bibliography of Stevinian publications would be exceedingly difficult and tedious, for his works were often issued in strange ways. There are plenty of bibliographical irregularities and niceties to enchant bibliomaniacs, and to disgust the historians who

---

[1] See *Isis 21*, 213–215.

are more interested in ideas than in the accidents of printing and publication. I have tried to give enough information to identify and date exactly each work, and not much more.

My main purpose has been to state Stevin's main achievements and I have tried to do so as clearly and concisely as I could.

2. The Flemish mathematician Simon Stevin was perhaps the most original man of science of the second half of the sixteenth century. I say "perhaps" only because of his contemporary Galileo (1564–1642), who was at least as original. However, the latter was sixteen years younger than Stevin and outlived him twenty-two years; though some of his discoveries were made at about the same time as Stevin's, they were published much later; the fundamental works upon which his fame is based appeared only in the seventeenth century; the two most important many years after Stevin's death. Hence it is not quite proper to compare both men: they belong to two succeeding generations. Moreover, the great Fleming is distinctly a man of the second half of the sixteenth century, while his Italian peer represents admirably the first half of the seventeenth century.

If we leave Galileo "hors concours," Stevin was undoubtedly the most original man of the second half of the sixteenth century, but he has not yet received the full fame he deserves. This may seem strange, for his greatness is conspicuous and not only in a single domain but in many. On the other hand it may be argued that he has been neglected because of his very originality and that such neglect thus becomes a sort of confirmation of his genius. It can be shown that one of his fundamental ideas set forth by him in 1585 — three centuries and a half ago — has not yet been grasped by a very large section of the civilized and intelligent people of our own time. And how could people truly admire one whom they do not understand, how could they consider great a man whose greatness they have not yet been educated to appreciate?

I. STEVIN'S LIFE

3. Stevin's life has not yet been thoroughly investigated and there are many obscure points relative to it which further studies might possibly elucidate. The little we know may be summed up as follows. He was born in Bruges in 1548, and was active for a time in Antwerp

as cashier and bookkeeper; later he was employed in the financial service of his native city. Sometime after 1571 he left Bruges because he had failed to obtain a franchise from taxes on beer. He traveled in Prussia, Poland, Sweden, and Norway and finally established himself in the northern part of the Netherlands, which had then already shaken off Spanish domination. In 1581, we find him in Leiden; in 1582, his first book appeared in Antwerp; and on the 16th of February 1583 he was matriculated as a student of the University of Leiden. Later he taught mathematics at that University and the prince Maurice of Nassau [2] was one of his pupils. By 1590 he was living in Delft, where he had undertaken to establish a new model of windmills for which he had received a patent (*octrooi*) from the States-General in 1586; in 1592, he was put in charge of the "waterstaat" (waterways) of Delft.

4. He had been in communication at least since 1585 with the Delft patrician Johan Hugo Cornets de Groot,[3] for in that year he dedicated the *Arithmétique* to him. This Johan Hugo de Groot was deeply interested in mathematics and physics, and is many times mentioned by Stevin (e.g., in the *Weeghconst* and the *Waterwicht* of 1586). During the latter's residence in Delft they had more opportunities of discussing scientific subjects together. It was probably then that they made experiments on falling bodies, disproving the Aristotelian idea that heavier bodies fall faster than lighter ones.[4]

5. In January 1593, upon the recommendation of the stadhouder Maurice of Nassau, he was appointed by the States-General "castrametator," i.e., quartermaster general of the Dutch armies, a position which he held until the time of his death.

However, toward the end of his life, as he complained of the un-

[2] Maurice, count of Nassau, later prince of Orange and stadhouder of the United Provinces (born 1567, died 1625; stadhouder 1585–1625).

[3] Or Janus Grotius. Born near Delft 1554; died in Delft 1640. Father of the more famous Hugo Grotius (1583–1645). Burgomaster of Delft 1591–1595, curator of Leiden University 1594. See Cornelis de Waard in *Nieuw nederlandsch biografisch woordenboek* (vol. 2, 528–9, 1912).

[4] This is said by W. van der Woude and P. J. Blok (*N.n.b.w.*, 5, 816, 1921), I do not know on what grounds. They further claim that Stevin and the burgomaster de Groot made those experiments before Galileo. I am not able to confirm either the anteriority or even the reality of their experiments. Galileo's experiments took place while he was living in Pisa, 1589–1592. It is not possible I believe to date them more accurately. See Vincenzo Viviani's account in *Opere di Galileo* (Favaro's edition, vol. 19, 606, 1907).

gratefulness of the States-General, Maurice of Nassau appointed him a member of his council and superintendent of financial matters.

In 1600, he organized the mathematical teaching at the engineering school attached by Maurice of Nassau to the Leiden University [5] — that teaching being given in the national language, as opposed to the University itself where it was presumably given in Latin.

Prince Maurice had a very genuine interest in mathematics [6] and his relationship with his tutor and technical adviser was as intimate as it could be. A number of Stevin's scientific writings were the fruits of that relationship. The Prince used to carry the manuscripts of them with him in his campaigns. Fearing that he might lose them, he finally decided to have them published, not only in the original Dutch text (*Wiscontighe ghedachtenissen,* 5 vols., 1605–1608) but also in a Latin translation by Willebrord Snel (*Hypomnemata mathematica,* 5 vols., 1605–1608) and in a French translation by Jean Tuning (*Mémoires mathématiques,* only 3½ vols. published, 1605–1608). It is true these memoirs might have been saved by the preparation of other manuscript copies, yet the printing of the Dutch text seemed advisable for three reasons clearly set forth in the preface which may be found in the three editions. As the French text is easier to read for most readers than either the Dutch or the Latin ones, I quote these three reasons from it:

La premiere, que quelques uns, és mains desquels viendroient ces escrits, se pourroient attribuer nostre labeur & inventions; comme c'est chose qu'on voit bien arriver: A quoy le meilleur remede a semblé de les mettre en lumiere par le moyen de l'impression. La seconde, qu'il y auroit aussi cest avantage à attendre, que si quelques uns y rencontrent des fautes, ils les pourront corriger, et y joindre d'autres nouvelles inventions, profitables au public, & tendantes à plus grande satisfaction de celuy pour qui ces livres sont escrits. La troisiesme que, comme je declareray ci apres mon opinion estre que les grands arts & sciences ne peuvent parvenir à la perfection du siecle sage, si ce n'est que de grands peuples & nations s'y exercent en leur propre langue; puis que le present œuvre est formé avec esgard visant à telle fin, sans doute le recellement de ces livres n'accorderoit pas avec leur contenu, ni avec mon intention.*

[5] After W. van der Woude and Blok.
[6] Cappelle (1821).
* [The first, that some of those into whose hands these writings may come might attribute them to our labor and invention, a thing that one can well see might happen; the best remedy for it has seemed to be bringing them into the light by means of the printing press. The second, that it would also have this attendant

6. Late in life — he was then 64 years old — he married a young woman, named Catharina Craey. On March 28, 1612, he bought a house in The Hague; the house was not yet completely built when he acquired it but according to the contract it had to be delivered to him at the end of April. That house still exists in the Raamstraat no. 47 and is now marked with a bust of the great scientist. He obtained it presumably for the reception of the young wife whom he married in the same year. She gave him four children who were born in that house: Frederik, in 1613, Hendrik, in 1614, and two daughters, Susanna and Levina. Stevin died in 1620, presumably in The Hague and in that very house wherein we know that he spent the last years of his life. It is strange that the death of so great a man, a familiar of the Prince, should have been almost unnoticed. However, the place, The Hague, is mentioned on an anonymous portrait . . . and if he had died away from his home his death would have been probably more conspicuous.

Catharina did not remain a widow very long, for on February 28, 1621 she married Maurits de Viry (or de Virieu), bailiff of Hazerswoude. They sold Stevin's house on May 6, 1623 and established themselves in Leiden, where she died half a century later on January 5, 1673.

To return to the children. The eldest son Frederik was a student in Leiden and became a jurist; he died in Leiden in 1639, at the age of twenty-six. The second son Hendrik, born a year after his senior in 1614, studied mathematical sciences in Leiden and became an engineer. He traveled in Bohemia, Italy, Belgium, Saxony — observing engineering matters everywhere. He was for a time quartermaster and engineer in the Dutch armies, until a wound obliged him to withdraw from such strenuous activities and to return to his studies. He established himself in Alphen (near Breda) where he was lord of a manor (*ambachtsheer*). His interest in his father's work was much stimulated by the latter's eulogy in Adrianus Romanus' book, *Ideae mathematicae*

---

advantage: if anyone found errors in them, he could correct them and also add other new inventions useful to the public and giving the greatest satisfaction to the one for whom these books were written. The third, as I will show here, that according to my opinion the great arts and sciences cannot attain to the perfection of the age of wisdom [see below, 20(b)] unless great peoples and nations practice them in their own tongue; since the present work is shaped looking toward such an end, without doubt the withholding of these books would not accord with their contents nor with my intention.]

pars prima (1593). He took considerable pains to collect his father's dispersed manuscripts and to publish them (see below, 28–29). He shared his father's enthusiasm for the Dutch language and carried it to the point of fanaticism, for he was anxious not only to promote its study but also to exclude the teaching of Latin from the Dutch schools (a very bold proposal in his day). He claimed that every subject should be taught in the mother tongue and that foreign languages were of no use except to people who wanted to travel abroad and to study foreign cultures. He spent the end of his life in Alphen. He was in correspondence with Constantijn and Christiaan Huygens and with other mathematicians. He died after 1668.

7. In July 1846 a modest but beautiful monument was erected to Stevin's memory in his native city, Bruges. This was the occasion of a long and heated controversy as to his loyalty to his fatherland and religion.[7] Looking at it from a distance that controversy seems particularly futile. When he was serving the Prince of Orange, Stevin was helping him to fight not Belgium, but Spain. Did he become a Protestant? This is possible but unproved. In the *Vita politica* he recommends that one should practice one's own religion in secret if it be different from the Prince's, and not to disturb the public order. If he remained faithful to the Church of his baptism, he was a crypto-Catholic according to his own definition. If so, he would deserve some measure of blame, because Prince Maurice was revolting not only against Spain but also against the Roman Catholic Church. Considering the general bent of his mind, it is probable that he had little interest in theological differences. Moreover, had he not witnessed the intolerable excesses committed by Spain in his native land in the name of orthodoxy? In any case it is not true that he made a legacy to the church of Westkerke to pay for masses,[8] the man who made that legacy being a namesake who died in 1434.

---

[7] An account of it will be found in the *Bibliotheca Belgica* (vol. 23, note on the *Vita politica*, S. 132, Ghent, 1880–1890, with bibliography).

[8] A denial of this fact is necessary because it was adduced by no less an authority than Moritz Cantor in his articles on Stevin in the *Allgemeine deutsche Biographie* (vol. 36, 158–160, 1893) and in the *Encyclopaedia Britannica* (11th. ed. 1910, 1½ col.). It is no longer found in the 14th ed., the Editor having decided that Stevin did not deserve so much space and telescoped Cantor's article to one third of its original length.

SIMON STEVIN OF BRUGES

8. (S. 124).[9] *Tafelen van Interest, midtsgaders de constructie der seluer* (Tables of interest, together with their construction). 92 p. Antwerp, 1582. (In Dutch).

Pp. 9–34 contain an account of the different kinds of interest and explain the composition of the tables; p. 35–59, tables of compound interest and notes relative to them; p. 60–92, applications. According to the author's own statement in his preface (dated Leiden, July 16, 1582), the inventor of these tables was Jean Trenchant, who gave a specimen of them in his *Arithmétique* (Lyon, 1558).[10]

A French translation of Stevin's tables was published in his *Pratique d'arithmétique* (Leiden 1585, 1625) mentioned below, and reprinted in Girard's edition (1634), though without the preface.

Judging from Girard's publication (for I have not seen the original Dutch book), there are sixteen tables of interest from 1 percent to 16 percent each for n years ($n = 1$ to 30). Each table is divided into three columns, of which the first gives the number n, the second the capital which will be worth, together with the compound interest, 10,000,000 after n years, the third the value of n annuities of 10,000,000 at the beginning of the first year (of course the numbers of the third column are simply the totals of the numbers of the second column down to that year).

These tables are followed by seven others entitled "Table d'interest du denier n" ($n = 15$ to 19, 21, 22). The "table du denier 20" is not given as it is identical with the table of interest for 5 percent.

Stevin's tables were the first to appear in print but of course manuscript tables of the same kind had been used by bankers long before his day. The earliest we know of were compiled c. 1340 by Francesco Balducci Pegolotti for the great commercial firm Bardi of Florence, and

[9] This number and the corresponding ones below refer to the notices in vol. 23 of the *Bibliotheca Belgica* (Gand, 1880–1890), where additional information may be obtained. I have tried to give all the information which is of real interest to the historian of science, as opposed to the bibliographer and the bibliophile.

[10] *L'Arithmétique de Ian Trenchant départie en trois livres. Ensemble un petit discours des Changes, avec l'art de calculer aux getons.* This work was very popular, being printed at least 16 times within a century. The author is otherwise unknown. See my query no. 38 in *Isis 21*, 207–209, 1934.

included in his treatise *Libro di divisamenti di paesi e di misure di mercatanzie* (or *Pratica della mercatura*) and edited by Gian Francesco Pagnini, *Della decima e di varie gravezze imposte dal comune di Firenze* (4 vols., Lisbona and Lucca, 1765–66; in vol. 3). The use of such tables was transmitted from Italy to other countries, chiefly those like the Netherlands where the commercial activity was greatest, but their diffusion was probably slowed up by the fact that bankers having them would be likely to consider them as secret tools of their trade, and at any rate would have no interest in communicating them to their rivals.

9. (S. 125). *Problematum geometricorum libri V* (118 p.), Antwerp (s. a., 1583).

Collection of geometrical problems arranged in the following order: Book I. Division of polygons (*a*) by a line passing through a point of the perimeter or (*b*) by a parallel to one of the sides. Book II. Application of the *regula falsi* to mensurations. Book III. Regular polyhedra and semi-regular polyhedra which can be inscribed in a sphere (quinque corpora regularia, quinque aucta corpora regularia, novem truncata corpora regularia). Book IV. Construction of a solid similar to another, and equal in volume to a third. Book V. Construction of a solid similar to two others and equal in volume to their sum or difference. Stevin's references to Euclid are to the Clavius edition of Cologne 1574. An elaborate analysis of this work was published by Gravelaar in 1901.

10. (S. 126 and 127). *Dialectike ofte bewysconst. Leerende van allen saecken recht ende constelick oirdeelen; oock openende den wech tot de alderdiepste verborghentheden der natueren* (12 l., 172 p.), Leiden 1585 (in Dutch).

This is a treatise on "dialectics and the art of demonstration" which the author composed in the form of a dialogue between Pieter and Jan (Pierre et Iehan). Stevin was deeply convinced of the actual or potential superiority of the Dutch language over all others, yet he realized the temporary insufficiency of the Dutch scientific terminology, and tried to remedy it. The *Bewysconst* includes (p. 134–140) a Latin-Dutch glossary of logical terms.

The need of technical books in Dutch at that time is illustrated by the contemporary publication of two other ones. Nicolas Petri of Deventer, *Practique om te leeren rekenen, cijpheren ende boeckhouwen*, Amsterdam 1583 (arithmetic including bookkeeping), and the anonymous *Ruyghbewerp vande redenkaveling ofte nederduytsche dialectike*, Leiden 1585 (on dialectics). Such books were in demand because there was a group of people, constantly increasing in numbers and importance — merchants, bankers, etc. — who did not know Latin yet were keen to obtain useful knowledge.

Stevin's book was published a second time in Rotterdam 1621. This edition does not seem to differ at all from the first, except with regard to the orthography.

Stevin refers to the *Bewysconst* in his *Thiende*.

11. (S. 128). *De Thiende*, 36 p., Leyden 1585. The tithe . . .

12. (S. 129, 130). *L'Arithmétique et la Pratique d'Arithmétique* (2 vols., 9 l. + 642 p. + 7 l., 203 + 12 p.), Leiden 1585.

Vol. 1 contains the arithmetic in two books; then a French translation of the first four books of the algebra of Diophantos (free version from Xylander's Latin text, 1575). This was the first translation of Diophantos in any European vernacular.

Vol. 2 (*Pratique*) contains rational computations, then proportional computations. Then: rule of three, rule of five, rule of company (i.e., compound proportion), rule of alligation, rule of interest and tables of interest (translation of item in § 8), rule of false position, the tithe (translation of item in § 11), surds and explanation of book X of Euclid's Elements.[11]

At the end of the *Pratique*, the author mentions two friends of his, Johan Cornets de Groot (father of Hugo Grotius) who is helping him for his statics, and Ludolph van Ceulen, with whom he is constantly discussing mathematical subjects.

This work, though very original, is based to a large extent upon the writings of Cardano, Tartaglia, Bombelli, and to a lesser extent upon those of Rudolf, Stifel, and Pedro Nuñez.

A revised edition of the *Arithmétique* was prepared by Albert Girard (Leiden 1625). Girard added to it a translation from the Greek of books 5 and 6 of Diophantos and Stevin's *Appendice* quoted below (§ 15); he made also a few other changes of no importance. Girard's edition was reprinted without ulterior modification in the *Œuvres* of 1634 (vol. 1).

13. (S 131). (a) *De Beghinselen der Weeghconst* (18 l., 95 p.), Leiden 1586. Treatise on statics divided into two parts dealing respectively with principles and the determination of centers of gravity.

(b) *De Weeghdaet* (43 p.), Leiden 1586. Praxis artis ponderariae. Statical applications.

(c) *De Beghinselen des Waterwichts* (81 p.), Leiden 1586. Principles of hydrostatics.

These three booklets are quoted together as they were published together by the same publisher with the same woodcut and motto, "*Wonder en is gheen wonder.*" Though independent they may be considered three parts of the same book, sold separately for commercial or other reasons.

The three pamphlets were reprinted by Stevin under the single title *Weeghconst* in his *Wisconstighe ghedachtenissen* (vol. 4, 1605). He was planning to write two others, including one on aerostatics, but failed to do so.

[11] A propos of this last part see M. Mersenne, *Traité des quantités incommensurables . . . Les erreurs de S.S. réfutées* (anonymously published in Paris 1640).

In the first and third Stevin reiterates his conviction of the excellence of the Germanic languages. According to him Dutch is the best language for scientific purposes because it combines briefness with clearness. He maintains that in that respect Dutch is superior to Greek and Latin, and in proof of his assertion quotes the Latin translation by Federico Commandino of two propositions of Apollonios of Perga covering no less than 36 lines and adds a Dutch translation covering only 9 lines. He announces his intention of translating Apollonios into Dutch, a purpose which he could not fulfill.

According to him the superiority of Germanic languages, and particularly of the Dutch, was due not only to their brevity and richness in monosyllables, but also to their lending themselves so well to the creation of intelligible compound words,[12] to their convenience for technical purposes, and finally to their moving power. As an illustration of the latter he mentioned the existence of so many religious sects in the Germanic lands! Stevin was arguing in a strangely egocentric way, and did not realize that the power of the Dutch language to move him was essentially due to the fact that it was his mother tongue, his very own. He came back to this question in his Geography, and also in the Preface to his *Hypomnemata*.[13] He was a poor philologist — and not in any sense a humanist but rather the opposite — yet he discovered the fundamental argument for the justification of any language, however unimportant that language may seem as compared with other ones: that the full spiritual development of a people can only be accomplished by means of its own language (see end of the French preface quoted above in § 5).

It may be added that Stevin's claims for the Dutch language were also justified in his day by the political and economic leadership of the Dutch people — that is, not Stevin's own countrymen but those who had freed themselves from Spain and Rome: this was the true Golden Age of the Seven United Provinces.

14. (S. 132, 133, 134). *Vita politica. Het burgherlick leuen* (56 p.) Leiden 1590 (in Dutch).

Treatise on civics which the author composed 1° because he considered it more necessary than ever in those troubled times that every

---

[12] E.g. hoekmaet for sine; aardrijkskunde for geography; wiskunde for geometry.
[13] See *Praefatio* and *De renovatione eruditi seculi* (2 membrum, etc.).

citizen should know his duty, 2° because it gave him a new opportunity of using the Dutch language and enriching it. He had to solve problems of terminology similar to those of his *Dialectike*. In some cases he puts in the margin the Greek and Latin equivalents of the Dutch terms used by him.

The *Vita politica* is divided into eight chapters: 1. Definition of civic life; 2. What is the foremost authority of the state; 3. How to determine the political party which one should join; 4. Civic duties of people in authority; 5. How should the citizen behave with regard to the laws which are not considered obligatory, but rather doubtful or contradictory; 6. Whether religion is necessary or not; 7. Rules of conduct in religious matters; 8. Civic life in general.

This table of contents, naked as it is, helps us to realize how difficult it was to be a good citizen in those days, for many issues were uncertain, and there were many conflicting duties. The main difficulties — the religious ones — are discussed in the two final chapters. It is in those chapters that Stevin recommended that people who did not share the Prince's religion should conform outwardly and avoid any disturbance of the public peace (see our § 7). It is very easy to criticize that theory to-day, but it was probably the wisest in Stevin's time and place.

The *Vita politica* was reprinted many times: Delft 1611, Middelburg 1658 (with a long appendix), Amsterdam 1684 (without the appendix; reimpression of the first two editions); again in the *Materiae politicae* edited by Stevin's son (with the appendix).

15. (S. 135). *Appendice algébraique contenant règle générale de toutes Equations* (3 l.), Leiden 1594.

Supplement to the *Arithmétique*.

This is one of Stevin's most important publications: it includes a general rule to solve numerical equations of every degree. Expressed in modern language: if $f(a) > 0$ and $f(b) < 0$, there is between a and b at least one root of the equation $f(x) = 0$. At the end of this short paper Stevin announced that his friend Ludolph van Ceulen had also found a general rule for the same purpose and that he had promised to publish it. Ludolph van Ceulen has not kept his promise but judging from his treatise *Van de circkel* (Delft 1596) he could solve numerical equations of any degree. Another friend of Steven's, Adrian Romanus, could also solve them (see his *Idea mathematica*, Antwerp 1593). Stevin was the only one who published his method, and he thus deserves full credit for it.

The unique copy of the *Appendice*, kept in the University Library of Louvain, was lost when that library was destroyed by the Germans in 1914.

159

However, the text has been preserved for it was reprinted in the second edition of the *Arithmétique*, in the Dutch, Latin, and French editions of the *Hypomnemata mathematica* (see *Hypomnemata*, vol. 5, p. 7–9, *Datis tribus* etc.); and in Girard's *Œuvres* (Arithmétique, p. 88).

16. (S. 136, 137). *De Sterctenbovwing* (4 l., 91 p.), Leiden 1594 (in Dutch).

Treatise on fortification which the author composed in Dutch because he was anxious to serve his countrymen, and also because (so he said) the Dutch language was especially adequate for technical purposes. His opinion on the subject is fortified by some remarks of Cardan (*De subtilitate*, book 2). This treatise was much praised by the famous Belgian military engineer Henri Alexis Brialmont (1821–1903) in an appendix to Steichen's *Mémoire* (1846).

Reprinted, Amsterdam 1624. German translation, *Festung-Bawung*, by Gotthard Arthus (1570-after 1630) of Danzig (Frankfort a.M., 1608, again 1623). French translation by Girard in the *Œuvres mathématiques*.

17. (S. 138, 139). *De Havenvinding* (28 p.), Leiden 1599.

The States-General gave the printer, Christoffel van Raphelengen, by privilege dated March 18, 1599 the exclusive right for six years to print and sell this book in any language. The printer himself expressed his intention of publishing it in Latin, French, Dutch, and other languages.

Treatise explaining to sailors how to determine their landings by means of the compass. According to the preface, Maurice of Nassau had ordered all the sea captains to make observations of magnetic deviation and to report them to the admiralty.

The treatise includes a table (*Tafel der naeldwijsinghen*) giving the deviation, latitude, and longitude of some 43 places. The longitudes are very erroneous, the average error amounting to 6° 5.[14] The table is arranged in a curious manner. The places quoted are divided into four regions: first "percx" on the north side, second "percx" on the north side, first "percx" on the south side, second "percx" on the south side (excepting Goa, Cochin, and Canton). In the first, the deviation is easterly, it increases from 0 to 13.24 then decreases to 9.30; in the second, it is westerly and increases from 0 to 33 then decreases to 26; in the third, it is easterly and increases from 0 to 19 then decreases to 2.30; in the fourth it is westerly and increases from 0 to 22 [15] then decreases to 0. According to Stevin himself (Definition 1), the data were collected by Petrus Plancius [16] and credit for this invention (*havenvinding*) should thus be given to the latter. After perusing this little book I cannot help feeling that Stevin had at first greater hopes in the practical value of deviation than later experiments known to him justified; he then restricted the scope of his method: the determination of deviation

---

[14] Marguet, 1931, 60.

[15] With one irregularity: 13, 16, 15, 22.

[16] Pieter Platevoet, Dutch preacher and geographer (1552–1622). See elaborate biography by A. A. van Schelven in *Nieuw Nederlandsch biografisch woordenboek* (4, 1077–1086, 1918), wherein the *Havenvinding* is wrongly ascribed to Plancius. This Plancius is said to have drawn a map on Mercator's (or rather Wright's) projection in 1594, but that map is lost (Mottelay, 1922, 560).

could not replace that of longitude in general navigation; yet it would be useful to identify one's landings. Even that modest hope had to be abandoned later on.

Stevin's moderation will be better appreciated by reference to the contemporary theories attempting to establish a regular connection between variation and longitude: thus Giambattista della Porta in his *Magia naturalis* (see edition of Naples 1589, p. 143) and others leading to the extravagant treatises of the Languedocian Guillaume le Nautonier, *Mécographie de l'eymant. C'est à dire la description des longitudes trouvées par les observations des déclinaisons de l'eymant* (Venes 1603) and *Mécométrie de l'eymant. C'est à dire la manière de mesurer les longitudes par le moyen de l'eymant* (Paris 1602, Venes 1603) (or both books together dated 1604).[17] That intrepid theorician did not hesitate to draw a magnetic chart of the world *a priori!*

Stevin published *De havenvinding* anonymously but included a revised edition of it in his *Wisconstige gedachtenissen* (1, 163-175). A part of the original text is included in the *Rara Magnetica* edited by Gustav Hellmann in his *Neudrucke von Schriften und Karten über Meteorologie und Erdmagnetismus* (no. 10, Berlin 1897). Hellmann's reprints contain a facsimile of the Dutch title-page, the *"Tafel der naeldwijsinghen"* and *"Hoemen het noortpunt en naeldwijsing vindt,"* 2 figs. (the text is not a facsimile reproduction).

A Latin translation by no less a person than Hugo Grotius was published by the same publisher in the same year:

Λιμενευρετικη *sive, Portuum investigandorum ratio.* Metaphraste Hug. Grotio Batavo (6 l., 21 p., 1 p.), Leiden 1599.

This text was reprinted in the *Hypomnemata* after revisions bringing it into agreement with the revised Dutch text published in the *Wisconstige gedachtenissen.*

An English version was made by Edward Wright (1558?-1615) on August 23, 1599:

The haven-finding art (cover, 7 l., 27 p.), London 1599. There is a copy of this book in the Library of Congress and I examined another one in the Huntington Library in San Marino, California. This translation was reprinted in the third (posthumous) edition of Wright's *Certain errors in navigation detected and corrected* (London 1657, 20 p. at end), but not in the first and second editions of that book (1599, 1610).

The *Haven-finding art* of 1599 begins with an *Epistle dedicatorie* to the Lord High Admiral of England, which includes a reference to the discovery of the inclination by Robert Norman (1576, published in his *Newe attractive,* 1581).

A French edition had been planned from the beginning, but was not published separately. It is included under the title *Du Trouve-port, ou la manière de trouver les Havres,* in Girard's *Œuvres* (vol. 2, 171-176, 1634).

---

[17] Marguet, 1931, 98. This question — variation vs. longitude — is very interesting but equally intricate. See Mottelay, 1922, 63. Mme Paul Tannery, *Correspondance du* P. Marin Mersenne (vol. 1, 202, 207, 1933).

18. (S. 140, 141, 142, 144). *Wisconstige Gedachtenissen, inhoudende t'ghene daer hem in gheoeffent heeft . . . Maurits Prince van Oraengien* (2 vols. folio, very complicated pagination), Leiden 1605–1608 (in Dutch).

This contains the substance of the lessons which Stevin gave Prince Maurice on a great variety of mathematical subjects; it is a sort of mathematical encyclopaedia. The Prince used to carry manuscript copies of these lessons with him in his campaigns and on one occasion he almost lost them. He then decided to have them published not only in the original language, Dutch, but also in Latin and French translation. This was done except that the French translation, or at any rate its publication, remained incomplete.

The titles of the Latin and French editions are:
Hypomnemata mathematica, hoc est eruditus ille pulvis, in quo se exercuit . . . Mauritius princeps auraicus . . . A Simone Stevino conscripta, & e Belgico in Latinum a VVil. Sn. *conversa* (4 vols. folio, very complicated pagination),[18] Leiden 1605–1608.
Mémoires mathématiques, contenant ce en quoy s'est exercé Maurice Prince d'Orange . . . Descrit premierement en Bas Alleman . . . translaté en François par Iean Tuning (4 parts in one vol.),[19] Leiden 1605–1608.
The French translator, Jean Tuning, was secretary to Prince Frederik Hendrik of Nassau (1584–1647), Maurice's young brother; he was born in Leiden and matriculated at the University of Leiden in 1593.

It is remarkable that on the Latin title page Stevin's language is called "Belgian" [20] — a term new to me in that acceptation — and on the French title page, "Low-German." The second designation is not incorrect, and tallies with the official name "Netherlandish." The first is stranger. Of course Stevin's mother tongue was Flemish, but it is possible that it had been somewhat Dutchified during his long residence in Holland: this question might interest philologists but I cannot stop to consider it. It will suffice to remark that Flemish is a dialectical

---

[18] The copy I used in the Harvard Library is bound in one thick volume (30 x 20 x 10 cm).

[19] The copy available to me in the Harvard Library is incomplete. It contains only vol. 1, 1608, Cosmographie, 180 p. (incomplete), and vol. 2, 1605, Practique de géometrie, 132 p.

[20] Adriaan van Roomen, speaking of Stevin's language in his *Idea mathematica* (1593), also calls it "lingua belgica." Hendrik Stevin, Simon's son, translating this very passage into Dutch, calls it "nederduytsche taal." "Lingua belgica" is Latin purism, just as "lingua sarmatica" to mean Russian.

form, or rather a collection of dialects, closely related to the Dutch dialects. Flemings and Dutchmen use the same grammars and dictionaries; the Flemish and Dutch languages are not more different than the American and the English languages. In other words, — for almost every purpose we may consider them as a single language. One wonders then what was the intention of the Dutchman who called Stevin's language "Belgian"; or maybe he had none.

The Latin translation was made by Willebrord Snel van Royen,[21] Dutch mathematician, geodesist, and physicist. According to Huygens it was Snel who first discovered and discussed in his lectures at the University of Leiden the fundamental law of refraction later published (without experimental proof) by Descartes (1637). Snel translated the whole of Stevin's *Wisconstige gedachtenissen*, except that the text of the *Liber quintus geographiae De limenheuretica* is simply a revision of Hugo Grotius's version.

For scientific purposes the Dutch and Latin texts are equivalent. As the Dutch text is not available to me, and the Latin text is easier to consult by the majority of readers, I shall take the latter as the basis of my analysis. It must be understood that each treatise exists not only in Dutch, but also in French, unless I state the contrary.

19. With regard to the date it should be noted that the publication of the three editions — Dutch, Latin and French — was begun in 1605 and completed in 1608. In each case the title of the first volume bears the date 1608, which simply means that that title page was printed last. I have examined more closely the Latin edition, the only one which was completely available to me (I used also a part of the French one), and in that edition the main title pages of vols. 1 and 5 bear the date 1608, and those of vols. 2 to 4, the date 1605, but vol. 1 is divided into three parts of which the first and third are not dated, but the second is dated 1605. Hence vols. 1 to 4 of the Latin edition were probably printed in 1605, except two parts (Parts 1 and 3 of vol. 1), which may have been printed at any time between 1605 and 1608; while volume 5 — which is in the nature of a general supplement — was probably issued in 1608. After the work had been kept on the stocks almost four years the printer became impatient and the publication was completed somewhat abruptly. This is explained at the end of it (see vol. 5, 205 of Latin edition, also end of my § 24).

20. The *Hypomnemata* are divided into five volumes which we shall now examine in due order.

---

[21] Willebrord Snellius (1580–1626). The original Dutch name is Snel, not Snell. See elaborate biographical notice by Cornelis de Waard, *Nieuw nederlandsch biografisch woordenboek*, 7, 1155–1163, 1927.

Vol. 1. Cosmography (*Tomus primus de Cosmographia*, 1608). This is subdivided into three parts (each with its own pagination!): (*a*) Trigonometry in four books (343 p.); (*b*) geography in six books (188 p.); (*c*) astronomy in three books (335 p.); that is, in all 866 p. not counting many unnumbered leaves.

(*a*) Trigonometry (*Pars prima cosmographiae de triangulorum doctrina*). No date on separate subtitle page. Book 1. De sinuum canonibus fabricandis. Construction of tables of sines, tangents and secants, together with such tables. The tables were not reprinted in Girard's *Œuvres*, Girard having published independent tables (The Hague 1626) which were far more convenient. Book II. De triangulis planis (plane trigonometry). Book III. De sphaericis triangulis (spherical trigonometry). Additamentum. De sphaericis multangulis. Appendix doctrinae triangulorum. Book IV. De cœlestium sphaerarum problematis, quae ex calculo sphaericorum triangulorum solvuntur (trigonometrical applications to astronomical problems).

Stevin's trigonometry was partly translated and published in German (S. 144):

Simonis Stevini Kurtzer doch grundlicher Bericht von Calculation der Tabularum Sinuum, Tangentium und Secantium . . . (Nuremberg 1628).

This translation was made by, or under the auspices of, Daniel Schwenter (1585–1636), professor of oriental languages and mathematics in Altdorf, who wrote an introduction to it. It covers only the first book of Stevin's trigonometry, less the tables, and the beginning of book II. Apparently Schwenter (or the translator) did not have access to a complete copy, for he quotes in his preface four axioms of Bartholomaeus Pitiscus concerning spherical angles, because (so he says) Stevin has entirely neglected that subject. It would thus seem that Schwenter knew only of the first two books, and this would suggest that the publication of Stevin's works was even more fragmentary than we realize otherwise. The second part of Schwenter's edition contains tables of sines, tangents, and secants, calculated with reference to a radius divided into 10,000,000 parts, by Johannes Praetorius.

(*b*) Geography, 1605 (*Secunda pars cosmographiae de geographia*). Not translated into French except book V, but there is a complete French translation in Girard's *Œuvres* (vol. 2, 104–183, 1634). Book I. De geographiae definitionibus generatim (p. 1–45, general definitions).

This includes some extraordinary developments on the "*eruditum seculum*," a mythical age of learning and wisdom.[22] Stevin's belief in the existence of that golden age is justified by arguments largely drawn from the history of ancient science (p. 8–14), and is bolstered

---

[22] "Eruditum seculum dicimus, quo mirabilis quaedam scientia hominibus nota fuit, quod certis quibusdam signis certo quidem, sed nec apud quos, aut ubi locorum, aut quando extiterit cognoscimus" (p. 8). See also end of the preface to the *Mémoires* quoted above (§ 5).

up by a series of testimonies culled out of the ancient literatures by Hugo Grotius.[23] Finally he draws up a program of efforts which may lead to the restoration of that time of wisdom, and manages to introduce into this a new vindication of his own beloved language — together with tables of Dutch, Latin, and Greek monosyllables, to illustrate what he considered to be one of the chief merits of the Dutch language, its great richness in monosyllables and its concision.[24]

The idea of a primordial golden age is one of the oldest conceits of the human mind. Our Edenic belief or dream is but one of its forms, and that particular form can be traced back to Sumerian times.[25] The fact that such strange ideas may be found alongside others of the purest scientific kind is but another illustration of the infinite complexities of the human mind. No man is always consistent, certainly no man of genius; or to put it otherwise, when consistency exists it is more often than not combined with mediocrity.

Book II. De hylocinesi terrestris globi (p. 47–67; on material changes of the earth). Much of this would be classified today under the heading of geology. Book III. De terrestri atmaeoria [26] (pp. 69–81; on the height of clouds). Dealing with the height of the atmosphere with reference to Ibn al-Haitham as translated by Gerard of Cremona and to Pedro Nuñez (1492–1577). Book IV. De histiodromia [27] (p. 83–159; on the road followed by a sailing boat). Problem of the loxodromic line and tables ad hoc, Canones loxodromicorum. Book V. De limenheuretica,[28] metaphraste Hug. Grotio (p. 161–173). See our § 17. Book VI. De theoria maritimorum aestuum in accessu et recessu (p. 175–183; on tides).

(c) Astronomy (Cosmographiae pars tertia de cœli motu). No date on separate subtitle page. Not available in French, except later in Girard's Œuvres. Book I. De investigatione motus planetarum syderumque coelo affixorum ex observationum Ephemeridibus stante et quiescente terra (p. 1–114; Study of stellar and planetary motions on the hypothesis of the fixity of the earth). Book II. De investigatione motus planetarum ex ratiocinio mathematico ad commentitiam stantis terrae hypothesin derivata (p.

[23] Testimonia aliquot perantiqui et sapientis cujusdam aevi a Hugone Grotio collecta (p. 15–16). A French version of Stevin's lucubrations on the age of wisdom may be read in Girard's Œuvres (2, 106–125) together with Girard's strange commentary. Girard's attack on the French language in a French book is certainly curious.

[24] Another example of a similar incongruity (irrelevant defense of the Dutch language in a scientific argument) may be read in the Thiende.

[25] G. Contenau, Manuel d'archéologie orientale (Paris 1927, 315; Isis 20, 474–478).

[26] Vaporium altitudine.

[27] De velificationis cursu quam dixeramus Nausiporiam.

[28] Portuum investigandorum ratione.

115–231). Mathematical calculations on the same basis. Book III. De investigatione motus planetarum ex ratiocinio mathematico ad veram et naturae rerum consentaneam motae Terrae hypothesin derivata (p. 233–335). Same study on the correct Copernican hypothesis. Additamentum motus latitudinis quinque planetarum, Saturni, Iovis, Martis, Veneris & Mercurii secundum stantis Terrae hypothesin (p. 297–309). Appendix de ignorato planetarum motu ab Ptolemeo notato & animadverso: deque Copernici theoricis inde constitutis (p. 310–335). This ends the Tomus primus, which is somewhat larger than the four other tomi put together.

21. Vol. 2. Geometry (*Tomus secundus de geometriae praxi*, 184 p., 1605). In six books of which only books I to IV are translated into French (the French translation of books V and VI was added later by Girard in the *Œuvres*). This work is different from the *Problemata geometrica* and inferior to it; it is also a collection of geometrical problems but it is not as logically as the former; it was chiefly made to complete the Prince's geometrical training.[29] Book I. De magnitudinum descriptione. (p. 5–44). Book II. De magnitudinum dimensione (p. 45–89). Book III. In magnitudinum additione, subductione, multiplicatione et divisione (p. 91–109). Book IV. In magnitudinum proportione (p. 111–122). Book V. De sectione proportionali (p. 123–153). Book VI. De magnitudinum in alias 'ὁμογένεας transformatione (p. 155–184).

22. Vol. 3. Optics (*Tomus tertius de optica*, 100 p., 1605). The Dutch original text is entitled *Van de deursichtighe* (perspective); this illustrates an equivocation which can be traced back to mediaeval times.[30] Stevin planned to write three books which are announced at the beginning of this volume,[31] yet only two appear in the Dutch and Latin editions. As to the French edition, it includes only the first book, and this book was not even translated until the end (there is a French version of book II in Girard's *Œuvres*). It would seem that the work was suddenly interrupted during the printing of it; according to Tuning's testimony, the printer was anxious to be through with it and became very impatient.

Book I. De sciagraphia (p. 3–85). This is what Vitruvius or Hero called scenographia, and corresponds more closely to modern perspective. According to Stevin's first definition, "Sciagraphia est rerum exstantium plana imitatio quae tamen eminens quoque videatur." Book II. De primis elementis catoptricae (p. 87–100). Theory of mirrors. Appendix: Discussion of virtual images on the basis of propositions of Euclid, Ibn al-Haitham and Witelo. The absence of book III, which was to deal with refraction, is very remarkable and the more so because the translator Willebrord Snel was destined to immortalize his name a few years later by his successful investigation of that very subject.

23. Vol. 4. Statics (*Tomus quartus de statica*, 196 p., 1605). Not available in French (except in Girard's *Œuvres*). Stevin's three books on statics

[29] Argumentum (p. 3) : Cum mecum geometriae πράξιν scribere constituissem, ut in ea Illustrissimum meum Principem exercerem . . .

[30] Sarton, *Introduction* (vol. 2, 23).

[31] Optica tribus libris comprehendimus: primo sciagraphiam, secundo radiorum reflexionem, tertio refractionem exposituri.

and hydrostatics are here reprinted but divided into five books, and supplementary materials form the substance of a sixth part. Book I. De staticae elementis (p. 3–51). Book II. De inveniendo gravitatis centro (p. 53–77). Book III. De staticae praxi (p. 79–108). Book IV. De hydrostatices elementis (p. 109–141). Book V. De initiis praxis hydrostatices (p. 143–149). Appendix statices, ubi inter alia errores quidem Στατικῶν ἰδιωμάτων refelluntur. Refutation of Aristotelian mechanics (p. 150–155). (Part VI). Additamentum staticae (p. 157–196). The summary announces that this supplement contains six parts, but only four were published. (a) De spartostatica (funium statica, statics of strings or ropes). (b) De trochleostatica (study of pulleys). (c) De fluitantibus acrobaricis (equilibrium of floating bodies, such as ships, of which the emerging part is high and heavy). (d) De chalinothlipsi (i.e., fremorum pressu), on the pressure of bits! The two other parts which were announced but not completed in due time and not included are (e). De hydatholcia (aquae attractu). (f) De aërostatica (aerostatics).[32]

24. Vol. 5. Varia (*Tomus quintus de miscellaneis*, 1608). In the preliminary announcement six parts are announced, but only the first two were actually published. Part I. De annotationibus arithmeticis (6 p.) (a) Discussion of a problem of Diophantos "19 Zetema 2 libri."[33] (b) Latin version of the *Appendice algebraique*, for which see section 15 above. Part II. De apologistica principum ratione italica (204 p.). This is a translation of the *Livre de compte de prince* (section 25). The four unpublished sections would have been entitled: III. De musica theoria, IV. De architectura, V. De polemica, VI. De variis. A part of them was published by Hendrik Stevin.

P. 205 of vol. 5 contains a list of all the parts which had to be omitted though their publication had been announced, eight in all, i.e., the four just mentioned, one in optics, two in statics, and more arithmetical notes than the two named above (part 1 of vol. 5), — and gives an explanation of their absence: the printer's impatience; he was tired of keeping indefinitely the sheets already printed and suggested that additional materials could be published independently later when the author had completed their redaction. Table of contents of the five volumes (p. 206–210). Errata (p. 211–214).

25. (S. 143). *Livre de compte de prince à la manière d'Italie, en domaine et finance extraordinaire, estant aux Mémoires mathématiques la deuxiesme partie des meslanges, contenant ce en quoy s'est exercé . . . le prince d'Orange* (in all 204 p.), Leiden 1608.

Reprint from the last part of Stevin's *Mémoires*. Originally written in Dutch it is said that there was also a separate Dutch edition but no copy of the latter has yet been found. It is probable that that separate edition

[32] The learned editors of Mersenne's correspondence (Mme. P. Tannery and Cornelis de Waard) make a puzzling reference (vol. 1, 596, 1933) to "un traité spécial que Stevin composa avant 1585 sur la pesanteur de l'air." No further explanation is given, nor is any source indicated, but I assume that the information is taken from Isaac Beeckman's diary of which de Waard is preparing an edition.

[33] In reality it is problem 18 of Book II (Tannery's edition, 1, 110–113, 1893.)

was simply a reprint with separate title page of the second part of the fifth volume of the *Wisconstighe ghedachtenissen*. A revised edition of the Dutch text appeared in the *Materiae politicae* (1649). A Latin version by Snel is included in the *Hypomnemata*. The French translation was made by Jean Tuning. It was not reprinted in Girard's *Œuvres*.

This treatise on bookkeeping "in the Italian manner" (i.e., in partita doppia, double entry) was composed by Stevin at the request of Prince Maurice, and aptly dedicated to Sully, the great French economist and minister to Henri IV. It is divided into two parts: The merchant's account book, and the prince's account book, and the latter part is subdivided into three others: Livre de compte en domaine, livre de compte en dépenses, livre de compte en finances extraordinaires.

For another work of Stevin's on the same subject see the note below on the *Materiae politicae*.

The earliest treatise on double-entry bookkeeping was the *De computis et scripturis* (36 chapters) included in the *Summa de arithmetica* of Luca Pacioli (Venice 1494) and this was the fountain head of all ulterior publications, but if Pacioli was the first expositor of the subject he was by no means the inventor of it. It is probable that that method was invented in northern Italy. In any case the earliest examples of it have come down to us from that country: accounts of the stewards of Genoa 1340; Medici accountbooks, Florence 1395; ledgers of the firm Donado Soranzo and brothers, Venice 1410.[34] These methods were perhaps somewhat different; Pacioli said he explained the "Venetian" one.

The Italian method was introduced into the Low Countries, Germany, and England by means of a number of sixteenth-century books written in Dutch, German, French, English. The bibliography of these books is full of difficulties because the authors were generally insignificant, and because the books themselves were used rather than treasured.[35] For example, the oldest English treatise on the subject, an incomplete but literal translation of Pacioli by Hugh Oldcastle, was printed in London 1543, but no copy of it is extant. It was reprinted in London 1588 by John Mellis: it is Mellis himself who tells us that Oldcastle's book was printed in London on August 14, 1543 and

[34] For Genoa and Venice, see Brown (1905, 99). For Florence, see Alberto Ceccherelli, *I libri di mercatura della banca Medici* (Florence 1913).

[35] Much information may be found in Brown (1905); also, less completely but with additional facsimiles, in Geijsbeek (1914).

that he used it for thirty years! These matters being of antiquarian rather than of scientific interest, we may pass them over.

Suffice it to say that Stevin was not the introducer of double-entry bookkeeping into northern Europe, not by any means. On the contrary he had many obscure predecessors. His interest in the subject was natural enough for did he not begin his career as cashier and book-keeper in Antwerp? An analysis of the sixteenth-century literature on bookkeeping would show that Antwerp played an important part in the diffusion of the Italian method, as might well be expected considering her commercial supremacy in that century.

It is not even correct to say that Stevin was the first to make a distinction between personal and impersonal (princely, municipal, or national) accounts — for this had been done all along in Italy — but he emphasized the need of separating these accounts and of applying the same methods to both, and he was able to draw attention to his views in the proper places thanks to his intimate relationship with prince Maurice and his dedication to Sully. Apparently he was the first man to perform duties comparable to those of a public accountant and to rationalize those duties. He was keenly aware of the necessity of introducing internal checks into the accounts in order that the auditing might be easier and deeper.

The origin of his treatise is clearly explained in the dedication to Sully and in two preliminary dialogues. He recalls his experience as a bookkeeper and cashier in an Antwerp firm and his work in the financial administration of his native city. While doing this work he was struck by the fact that the domanial and financial accounts were kept so badly that princes were always at the mercy of their intendants and receivers, who could deceive them with impunity. It was very soon clear to him that the only way to put a stop to those abuses was to introduce into the public or princely administration the very methods used by merchants, but he had no chance to set forth his views to a competent person until the day came when Maurice of Nassau asked for his advice in that very matter. Stevin explained his ideas of reform to him, and composed the first part of his work; Maurice then asked him to compose the second part (i.e., the prince's accountbook). The Prince understood at once the advantage of Stevin's method and introduced it in his own domains (1604).

169

26. (S. 145, 146, 147, 148, 149). *Castrametatio, dat is Legermeting* (4 l., 56 p.), *Nieuwe maniere van sterctebov door spilsluysen* (2 l., 62 p.), Rotterdam 1617.

These two parts are meant to go together as a single book, but they are sometimes found separate. Each has its own pagination, title page, and preface; the first preface is dated The Hague, November 4, 1617, and the second, The Hague, December 21, 1617.

The first part deals with castrametation, that is the art of laying out a military camp, with special regard to the customs and needs of the Prince of Orange. The second is devoted to the construction of sluices and the deliberate use of sluices in fortifications for defensive purposes. Sluices were useful also to maintain a proper level of water in the moats. These moats were important in peace as well as in war time for ships took refuge in them in bad weather or when the river was made unsafe by floating ice. Of course sluices had been known for centuries, but Stevin may have improved their construction and at any rate his treatise was one of the earliest on the subject, and contained the very first explanation of their use for tactical purposes, that is, for flooding the country and thus causing it to become inaccessible to the enemy. It is interesting to recall that during the great war the Belgian army availed itself near Nieuwpoort of the very method which their illustrious countryman had been the first to expound three centuries before. This treatise was much praised by general Brialmont.

Both parts were reprinted in the same style (i.e., with separate paginations) and with the same figures in Leiden 1633.

French translation in the same style entitled *La Castramétation . . . Nouvelle manière de fortification par écluses*, Rotterdam 1618. There is a copy of this edition in the Harvard Library. This translation was published by the same printers as the Dutch original edition and it includes the same illustrations, notably the portrait of Prince Maurice. The translator is not named; in fact the book is not called a translation, and both prefaces are signed by Simon Stevin, and bear the same date, The Hague, March 12, 1618. It is possible that Stevin made the translation himself.

There were two other French editions in the same year: one in Leiden, by the Rotterdam printer, the other in Leiden, by the Elzeviers, — both editions bearing the Elzevier imprint. The text was reprinted in Girard's *Œuvres mathématiques*.

There is also a German translation at least of part two: *Wasser-Baw. Erstlich in Niederländischer Sprach beschrieben . . . Anjetzo aber durch einen Liebhaber ins Hoch Teutsch ubersetzt*. Franckfurt, 1631.

170

This completes the list of the books published by Stevin and of their later editions; we shall now consider the *Œuvres* published by Girard and other posthumous publications.

27. (S. 150). (Bastard title). *Les Œuvres mathématiques de Simon Stevin augmentées par Albert Girard.*

(Title page). *Les Œuvres mathématiques de Simon Stevin de Bruges où sont insérées les Mémoires mathématiques esquelle s'est exercé le . . . Prince Maurice de Nassau . . . Le tout reveu, corrigé et augmenté par Albert Girard, Samielois,[36] Mathématicien* (folio, 4 1., 224 + 680 p.), Leiden, Elzevier, 1634.

Albert Girard was born at Saint Mihiel, Lorraine, in 1595; he spent a good part of his time in the Netherlands and died at The Hague, 1632.[37] The *Œuvres* were thus posthumous with regard to the editor as well as to the author. The dedication to "Messeigneurs les États Généraux de Païs Bas Unis" and to "Monseigneur le Prince d'Au-renge"[38] is signed by Girard's widow and children. He left behind eleven children. Girard was himself a great mathematician, and he added many observations of his own to the Stevinian text: these observations can be easily distinguished from the rest. Some works were translated by Tuning or Stevin, others were translated by himself and abbreviated; his own additions are always specifically mentioned as such. Hence the *Œuvres* can be used to study Stevins own thought, but one must be careful not to ascribe Girard's unmistakable interpolations to Stevin.[39]

It will suffice to indicate briefly the contents of the *Œuvres*. They are divided into six volumes, generally bound in one; vol. 2 to 6 have a continuous pagination.

Vol. 1. Arithmétique. This includes the Appendice algebraique, p. 88–89 (see § 15). Vol. 2. Cosmographie: Doctrine des triangles (Tuning's translation in *Mémoires*, minus the tables). Geographie et Astronomie, translated by Girard. Vol. 3. Practique de géométrie. Books 1 to 4 are Tuning's translation, books 5–6, Girard's. Vol. 4. Art pondéraire ou statique. Girard's translation, which is not quite as faithful as Snel's Latin version. Vol. 5. Optique. Book I was translated by Tuning, book II by Girard. Vols. 2 to 5 are a

---

[36] That is, of Saint Mihiel.

[37] For Girard's life see Cornelis de Waard's article in *Nieuw Nederlandsch biografisch woordenboek* (vol. 2, 477–481, Leiden 1912).

[38] Not Stevin's patron, Maurice, who died in 1625, but Maurice's younger brother, Frederik Hendrik, stadhouder from 1625 to 1647.

[39] For a more detailed discussion of the differences between the Stevin text and the Stevin-Girard text see Bosmans (1926, p. 5–9).

French translation of the *Wisconstighe ghedachtenissen*, that translation being either the one already published by Tuning in the *Mémoires mathématiques*, or Girard's own version. Vol. 6. Fortification. In three parts. Parts 1 and 2 are the items of § 26; part 3, Girard's version of the item of § 16. There is nothing new in Girard's *Œuvres* except his own notes, but it it is a very convenient edition of Stevin's works, and probably the one which is used by most scholars.

28. (S. 151). *Materiae politicae. Burgherlicke stoffen. Vervanghende ghedachtenissen der oeffeninghen des . . . Prince van Orangie. Beschreven deur zal. Simon Stevin . . . En uyt sijn naghelate Hantschriften bij een ghestelt deur sijn soon Hendrik Stevin* (2 vols., very complicated pagin.), Leiden n.d. (1649).

After Stevin's death his manuscripts were not handled with sufficient care by his widow and his elder son, Frederik (1613–1639). When his second son, Hendrik, inherited them he found them in great disorder. Some of them had found their way into other hands, for example, in those of Isaac Beeckman (1588–1637) [40] who had made copies of them. Hendrik obtained these copies (or the originals?) through Isaac's brother, Abraham. He tried to put all these papers in order and began a publication of them in 1649. Only these two volumes have appeared. Their dedication is dated Alphen, February 1649. As the *Materiae politicae* do not contain much which would be of direct interest to the historian of science, my description will be very brief. All these writings are in Dutch, but for the sake of simplification I shall not quote the Dutch titles except in one case.

Vol. 1 contains a series of eight memoirs on administrative and military matters. 1. Description of a model town and a model house (128 p.) 2. New edition of the *Vita politica*, 1590 with the appendix included in the Middelburg edition of 1658 (p. 1–45). 3. Organization and hierarchy of different administrative bodies and authorities (p. 47–86). 4. Administrative ethics; means of selecting good officials (p. 87–121). 5. Rules for diplomatic correspondence and records (p. 123–141). 6. Retaliations in peace time (p. 143–152). 7. Necessity of moving garrisons frequently, and the keeping of adequate records to facilitate periodical movements of that kind (p. 153–173). 8. Non-mathematical parts of the military art (p. 175–273).

Vol. 2. Sometimes found separately with the title *Verrechting van domeine mette contrerolle en ander behouften vandien.* Leiden, "In 't tweede Iaer des Vredes" (In the second year of the peace,[41] i.e., 1649). This contains only two items, both dealing with financial matters. The first is the *Ver-*

---

[40] On Isaac and Abraham Beeckman, see notes by Cornelis de Waard, *Nieuw Nederlandsch biografisch woordenboek* (vol. 7, 84–88, 1927).

[41] Reference to the Treaty of Münster (Jan. 1648) between Holland and Spain, wherein the latter finally recognized the independence of the United Provinces.

rechting van domeine. Reform of the domanial administration (4 l., 156 p.). The second, *Vorstelicke bouckhouding in domeine en finance extraordinaire op de italiaensche wyse* (complicated pag., total 274 p.). This second part is a revised and enlarged edition of the Dutch version of the *Livre de compte de prince* in the *Wisconstighe ghedachtenissen.*

Parts of this vol. 2 have been reproduced in facsimile in Geijsbeek (1914, 114–136).

Another "title" edition of the *Materiae politicae* was published by the same printers, but by another publisher in Leiden 1649 (S. 152). A real second edition appeared in The Hague 1686.

29. (S. 153). Hendric Stevin, *Wisconstich filosofisch bedryf* (one vol. quarto, very complic. pagin.), Leiden 1667. *Plaetboec* (folio atlas accompanying the vol. of text), Leiden 1668.

The author of this work is not Simon, but his son Hendrik. However, the latter refers frequently to the former and quotes fragments from his unpublished writings, e.g., on the construction of windmills,[42] on the keeping in repair of harbors and waterways, on the impossibility of perpetual motion.

I have not seen this work and only know it through the description given in the *Bibliotheca belgica*, wherein the Dutch titles of each part are given. However, these titles are not always sufficiently clear to warrant translation without the context. Brief and incomplete as my analysis is, it will suffice to indicate the nature of this collection.

1. Explanation of the publication of this work, including biographical information. 2. Resistance of solid bodies, such as cords, beams, columns, axles. 3. Statics. 4. Cinematics. Includes an exchange of letters (1618) between Simon Stevin and I. L. Hoste, mathematician to the Duke of Lorraine: Hoste thought he had found a means of creating a perpetual motion, and Stevin proves that he is wrong. 5. Van de schampige beweging. 6. Van alder volmaecste cammen en staven (on the best materials for the construction of windmills). 7. Van rechtschape reetschap van gewelt. 8. Vant onfeylbaer uyrwerk te water en te land (on an infallible clock for use on land or at sea). 9. On an unsinkable ship. 10. On windmills. This seems to be Simon's own work; in any case it refers to his own inventions patented in 1586 or 1588. Another treatise on windmills by Simon as preserved by A. Beeckman. 11. Documents and remarks concerning the works to be undertaken in various cities to improve their harbors and waterways. Much of this concerns Simon directly. The cities involved are Danzig, Elbing, Braunsberch, Deventer, Rheinberg, Schiedam, Lingen, Calais, Leiden. 12. More hydraulic projects. This includes two chapters by Simon on pumps. Some of Hendrik's schemes were very bold (see prop. 25); he suggested drying up the sea of Haarlem, building a dam in the Ij and draining part of it, digging a canal from Amsterdam to the North Sea, draining the Zuiderzee. Some of these projects have actually been realized, the last one is in the process of realization in our own days. 13. Theological and philosophical

---

[42] They are called "watermolens" (watermills) but they are really windmills used for pumping water. The Dutch term refers to their function, the English to the driving power.

topics. 14. Van de wisconstige burger en crychvolcstier. 15. Appendix, containing various corrections.

30. *De spiegeling der singconst* (Mirror of the art of singing). Edited by David Bierens de Haan (1822–1895), in the latter's Bouwstoffen voor de geschiedenis der wis- en natuurkundige wetenschappen in de Nederlanden, no. XXVI (*Verslagen en mededeelingen der koninklijke Akademie, Afd. Natuurkunde*, 20, 102–195, Amsterdam, 1884).

This is the treatise on music which Stevin had planned to publish in vol. 5 of his *Wisconstighe ghedachtenissen* (see § 24). In fact it is entitled "Derde deel der ghemengde stoffen vande spiegeling der singconst" (third part of the miscellanea, etc.).

31. *Van de molens* (about windmills). Edited by the same in same series no. XXVII (*Ibidem*, 197–232).

This treatise by Simon Stevin was revised by one Professor Golius in 1634. Calculations concerning 19 windmills.

Both items 30 and 31 have also been reprinted by Bierens de Haan in a separate volume. Simon Stevin, *Deux traités inédits* (Amsterdam 1884), wherein he has replaced his Dutch prefaces of the original academic edition by French prefaces.

32. *Unpublished manuscripts.* For information on Stevin's MSS. see *Bibliotheca belgica*, note S. 151, p. 8–15 and the end of Bosmans' notice in the *Biographie nationale de Belgique* (1924). Some of Stevin's texts will eventually be published in Beeckman's Diary to be edited by Cornelis de Waard. However, it would seem that the essential of Simon Stevin's abundant production is already available in print. In fact the very best was already available in Stevin's time, and the posthumous publications which we owe to the piety of his son and of Bierens de Haan have added but little to his fame.

III. STEVIN'S ACHIEVEMENTS

His mathematical sources

33. Before dealing with Stevin's mathematical discoveries, it is well to say a few words of his mathematical learning. We may assume that he was tolerably well acquainted with the Greek masterpieces available in Latin. He knew especially well Euclid and Diophantos. Among the Arabic mathematicians, he knew al-Khwārizmī, as translated by Robert of Chester. He was familiar with the writings of his older contemporaries the Italians Cardano, Tartaglia, and Bombelli, and the Portuguese Pedro Nuñez, but apparently not with those of the German mathematicians except Michael Stifel and perhaps Christoff Rudolff.[43]

[43] Florian Cajori, *History of mathematical notations* (vol. 1, 157, 1928).

Arithmetic

34. First systematic explanation of decimal fractions and extension to them of the fundamental operations (1585).[44] Unfortunately the beauty of this innovation was hidden by cumbersome notations.

First suggestion of the extension of the decimal idea to weights and measures (1585).

These two very important items will be fully discussed in a separate paper [*Isis 23*, 121–153 (1935)].

35. Publication of the earliest printed tables of interest (1582).

36. Insistence on the separation of princely or government accounts from the personal ones and application of the Italian methods, i.e., double-entry bookkeeping, to both (1608). Stevin was not the first to do this,[45] but he worked out these ideas in great detail and recommended their adoption to Prince Maurice and to Henri IV's minister, Sully.

Algebra

37. Rules relative to equations can be generalized if signs are attached to the numbers: e.g., one can then speak of adding $(-b)$ to a instead of subtracting b from a. They can be generalized as well if one admits that some coefficients may be null (incomplete equations).

That the addition of $(-b)$ is the same as the subtraction of b had already been stated by Stifel (*Arithmetica integra* 1544) and Cardano (*Ars magna* 1545), but Stevin was the first to make use of this for the generalization of the solution of equations.

On that basis Stevin generalizes the rules relative to the solution of quadratic, cubic, and biquadratic equations. However, the cubic equation must first be reduced to the form $x^3 = px + q$.

---

[44] These dates refer to Stevin's publications which can be easily identified by reference to the list given above. In 1585, and also in 1594 he published more than one book but on such different subjects that no ambiguity is possible. For subjects dealt with in the *Hypomnemata* the date is sometimes given as 1605, sometimes 1608 (see note in section 19).

[45] Not to speak of the Byzantine financial administration which was highly technical, sound ideas on state accounts and budgets had been developed by Oriental authors many centuries before Stevin. See for example the *Siyāsatnāma* composed in Persian by Nizām al-mulk in 1092. Extract translated into French by Carra de Vaux, *Les penseurs de l'Islam* (vol. 1, 314–315, 1921). Sarton, *Introduction* (vol. 1, 1780).

The treatment of equations must be purely algebraical, i.e., free from geometrical considerations (1585).

38. Interpretation of negative roots of equations as the positive roots of the equation obtained by the substitution of $(-x)$ for x. Hence every equation of the second degree whose roots are real has two roots (1585).

That interpretation was already expressed by Cardano with respect to cubic equations (*Ars magna*, 1545). For Stevin's views see Girard's edition, p. 77.

39. Rule for the solution of numerical equations of any degree.[46] Given the equation $f(x) = 0$, if $f(a) > 0$ and $f(b) < 0$, there is at least one root between a and b.

Stevin shows how the decimals of the root can be obtained by successive approximations, and he remarks that in some cases the true value cannot be reached though one can obtain as many decimals of it as one may wish and come indefinitely near to it (1594).

40. Modern definition of polynomials (*Arithmétique*, book 1, def. 26). Solution of the problem: to find the greatest common divisor of two polynomials (ibidem, book II, problem 53) (1585).

Geometry

41. Generation of an ellipse by lengthening the ordinates of a circle in the same proportion (1605).

Scénographie, article VI (Girard, p. 549).

42. Solution of particular cases of the inverse problem of perspective: Given two figures in a plane which are perspectives of one another, place them in space and determine the eye's position (1605).

Scénographie, Invention de l'œil (Girard 550, etc.) See Michel Chasles, *Aperçu historique* (Bruxelles, 1837, 347).

If the perspective (or picture) plane rotates around the ground line and the spectator rotates around his basis, remaining all the time parallel to the plane, the perspective will not be disturbed; it will still exist when the perspective plane is horizontal (1605).

Scénographie, Theor. V, Prop. VII (Girard, p. 533). Gino Loria, *Storia della geometria descrittiva* (Milano 1921, 21, 215).

---

[46] Needless to say no equations are meant other than rational and integral polynomials equalled to zero.

Trigonometry

43. Reduction of the trigonometrical formulas relative to right-angled spherical triangles to six, and an explicit statement that these six formulas are sufficient to solve all problems (1608).

A. v. Braunmühl, *Vorlesungen über die Geschichte der Trigonometrie* (vol. 1, 227, 1900).

Analysis

44. The method of exhaustion as applied by Archimedes, involving a *reductio ad absurdum*, is replaced by a direct passage to the limit, e.g., in the determination of centers of gravity (1586).

Thus Stevin is one of the links in the gradual transformation of the Greek method of infinitesimal analysis into the modern one, the chain being as follows: Archimedes, Commandino, Stevin, Grégoire de Saint Vincent, Guillaume Boelmans, André Tacquet, Pascal, Leibniz. Another chain was Archimedes, Luca Valerio, Kepler, Cavalieri, Leibniz. These chains were not independent for there were contacts between Valerio and Saint Vincent, and perhaps between Stevin and Kepler.

Stevin's mechanical sources

45. Stevin was acquainted with the Μηχανικὰ προβλήματα ascribed to Aristotle; with Archimedes, Pappos; Jordanus Nemorarius — the *Liber Jordanis de ratione ponderis* was printed in Venice 1565;[47] Leonardo da Vinci (via Cardano), and Tartaglia. He was probably acquainted with Giambattista Benedetti's early work through Jean Taisnier, but it is unlikely that he knew already in 1586 Benedetti's main work, the *Diversarum speculationum mathematicarum et physicarum liber* (1585), wherein some of his hydrostatic ideas were anticipated: a year is but a very short time for a work printed in Torino to reach the Low Countries in the midst of war. He may have known the *Mechanicorum liber* of Guido Ubaldo del Monte (Pisauri 1577).

Statics

46. Simple demonstration (different from the Archimedean) of the condition of equilibrium of a horizontal lever with unequal arms

[47] Sarton, *Introduction* (2, 615).

(1586). It is true this demonstration had been known implicitly [48] for a considerable time, — perhaps already in Hellenistic days. A similar demonstration reappears in Galileo's *Discorsi e dimostrazioni* (1638), and in later writings.

It should be noted that Stevin's demonstration is not essentially better than that of Archimedes, for he makes use of the center of gravity, the determination of which implies the principle of statical moment. However, his attempt to improve the epistemological foundation of statics is significant.[49]

47. Very simple and original demonstration of the law of equilibrium on an inclined plane based upon the postulate of the impossibility of perpetual motion (1586).

Hence are implicitly deduced: the general law of composition of concurring forces (parallelogram of forces), the decomposition of a single force (e.g., the weight of a body) into two normal components (see also *Spartostatica*, 1605).

48. Stevin did not actually recognize the principle of virtual velocities, already vaguely expressed in the Peripatetician physics and developed during the Middle Ages by Muslim and Christian mechanicians, but he accepted a principle somewhat differently represented by these two Latin lines:

Ut spatium agentis, ad spatium patientis:
Sic potentia patientis, ad potentiam agentis.[50]

These two principles were often confused in the sixteenth century but Stevin was very clearly in favor of virtual displacements as against virtual velocities; in this he was followed by Descartes. On the contrary Galileo continued in this respect the Peripatetician line of thought.

49. Representation of forces by vectors. (Was Stevin truly the first to do this?).

---

[48] It is found explicitly in a thirteenth century MS. (Bibl. Nat. Paris, fonds latin, 7377B) quoted by Duhem (1905, 1, 287–289).

[49] For another criticism of Archimedes see V. F. Lenzen, Archimedes' theory of the lever (*Isis 17*, 288–289, 1932).

[50] Quoted in his *Trochleostatica* (1605, p. 172) and called by him a "staticum axioma." [As the space of the body acting is to the space of the body acted upon, so is the force of the body acted upon to the force of the body acting.]

SIMON STEVIN OF BRUGES

Hydrostatics

50. Restatement of the fundamental principle of hydrostatic equilibrium — "Aquam datam, datam sibi intra aquam locum servare" [51] established upon the postulate of the impossibility of perpetual motion.

Hence are deduced the laws of hydrostatic pressure and their application to the study of communicating vessels and floating bodies and finally the hydrostatic paradox (1586).

Similar conclusions with regard to communicating vessels and even to the principle of the hydraulic press were published a year earlier by Giambattista Benedetti in a letter, "De macina quae aquam impellit et sublevat," included in his *Diversarum speculationum mathematicarum et physicarum liber* (Torino 1585, 287–288) but Stevin's work was in all probability independent of this.[52]

51. There has been some discussion as to whether Stevin was the discoverer of the hydrostatic paradox or not. It has been claimed, on the one hand, that it was already implied by Archimedes, who discovered the general law of which the hydrostatic paradox was but a paradoxical consequence; on the other hand (by Schor) that for a clear recognition of it we must wait until Pascal (*Traitez de l'équilibre des liqueurs*, Paris 1663). I believe that both claims are wrong: one cannot give credit to anybody for implications, but only for explicit statements, especially not when the implication is somewhat paradoxical. On the other hand though Stevin did not understand the paradox as deeply as Pascal, nor express it as neatly (as far as expression is concerned Stevin was but a stammerer as compared with Pascal), — yet he was clearly aware of it and suggested experimental verifications of it.

An excellent vindication of Stevin was made by no less a person than Lagrange in his *Méchanique analitique* (Paris 1788, première partie, section 6).[53]

---

[51] I quote the Latin translation from the *Hypomnemata* (vol. 4, 114). The original text was in Flemish (1586). [A given volume of water remains in the place in the water given to it.]

[52] The most elaborate study on Benedetti is Giovanni Bordiga, Giovanni Battista Benedetti, filosofo e matematico veneziano del secolo XVI (*Atti del R. Istituto Veneto*, t. 85, p. 2da, 585–754, 1926; see p. 718).

[53] *Œuvres de* Lagrange (vol. XI, 191–2, 1888). According to Duhem, Stevin

Let us read Stevin. I cannot refer to the Dutch text of 1586 which is not available to me, but see *Hypomnemata*, t. IV, p. 119.

"8 Theorema 10 Propositio. Aquae fundo horizonti parallelo tantum insidet pondus quantum est aquae columnae cujus basis fundo, altitudo perpendiculari ab aquae superficie summa ad imam demissae aequalis sit." [54]

Then see *Hypomnemata*, t. IV, p. 145.

"Exemplis pragmaticis 10 propositionis hydrostatices veritatem comprobare." [55] In this place there is a good statement of the hydrostatic paradox, and of the experimental verification of it, and the application of it which led later to the hydraulic press [56] is unmistakably indicated. For the French translation of these texts see the *Œuvres mathématiques* edited by Girard (vol. 2, 487, 498).

Stevin's priority over Pascal with regard to the hydrostatic paradox is also established by the testimony of contemporaries: see the memorandum prepared by Descartes for Isaac Beeckman in 1618 and preserved in the latter's diary and Mersenne's remarks in his *Vérité des sciences* (Paris 1625, p. 231) concluding that under certain circumstances "un sceau d'eau peut autant peser comme fait toute l'eau de la mer." [57]

52. Approach to the notion of metacentrum in his treatise on topheavy floating bodies (De fluitantibus acrobaricis) added to the second edition of the Statics (*Hypomnemata*, vol. 4, 177–180, 1605).

The metacentrum was first defined and named by Pierre Bouguer

---

deserves even more credit than Lagrange was willing to give him; he should be considered "the inventor of the true foundations of hydrostatics." P. Duhem, *Archimède connaissait-il le paradoxe hydrostatique?* (*Bibliotheca mathematica*, 1, 15–19, 1900). D. Schor, Stevin und das hydrostatische Paradoxon (*Ibidem*, 3, 198–203, 1902).

[54] [As much weight of water rests upon the bottom parallel to the horizon as there is to a column of water whose base is equal to the bottom, and whose altitude is equal to the perpendicular dropped from the topmost surface to the bottom.]

[55] [By pragmatic examples to prove the truth of the tenth proposition of hydrostatics.]

[56] Or "Bramah" press, patented by Joseph Bramah (1748–1814) in 1795.

[57] For Descartes, see *Œuvres* (Adam et Tannery, vol. 10, 67–74, 1908). For Mersenne, his *Correspondance publiée par Mme. Paul Tannery* (vol. 1, 313, 1933). Mersenne quotes Stevin, Descartes does not, but the source of his reflexions was undoubtedly the same. [A seal of water can weigh as much as all the water in the sea.]

(1698–1758) in his *Traité du navire, de sa construction et de ses mouvemens* (Paris, 1746, 257).

Navigation

53. Scientific comparison of the two fundamental methods of navigation: sailing along a great circle and sailing along a loxodrome [58] (De histiodromia, 1608).

The history of the loxodromes (curves cutting all the meridians under the same angle) begins with Pedro Nuñez, who was the first to have a clear idea of them and to show that they were spirals coiling round but never reaching the poles (1537). Nuñez was not able to draw correctly a loxodrome on a map, and there is no Portuguese map with correct loxodromes anterior to Mercator. The latter's globe of 1541 was the first correct application of them to cartography.[59]

The use of the Mercator projection made the drawing of loxodromes very easy, as these were projected as straight lines. The earliest known example of the Mercator projection is Mercator's planisphere of 1568–69, but it was only approximately correct up to the latitude of 40°. The construction was empirical: Mercator probably noted where the loxodromes cut the meridians on a sphere and placed his parallels on the map accordingly. The first attempt to solve the problem mathematically (as much as this could be done without the resources of the calculus) was made by Edward Wright (1558?–1615): Wright's principles were applied with acknowledgment by Thomas Blundeville in London 1594 and without acknowledgment by Jodocus Hondius in Amsterdam, c. 1597; Wright finally published them together with tables ad hoc in his *Certaine errors in navigation* (London 1599).[60]

The loxodrome was at first called linea rhombica, rumbus, rhumb, or rhumb line. Cantor says that the word loxodrome was introduced by Willebrord Snel in his *Tiphys Batavus* of 1624.[61] This statement is not correct. We find that word already in Stevin's treatise on the

[58] S. Günther (1879, 345, 363, 395).
[59] Hermann Wagner, Die loxodromische Kurve bei Mercator (*Nachrichten, Kgl. Ges. d. Wiss., Göttingen*, 254–267, 1917; *Isis 4*, 591).
[60] M. *Blundeuille his Exercises containing sixe treatises* (London 1594). Jodocus Hondius' map called *Typus totius orbis terrarum* (c. 1597). Mottelay 1922, 559–564).
[61] *Tiphys batavus sive histiodromice, de navium cursibus et re navali* (Leiden 1624). Cantor, *Vorlesungen* (II2, 707, 1900).

Histiodromia (1605), — but the Latin translator of that treatise was Snel himself. Hence Snel may have been the introducer, instead of Stevin (I have no access to the Dutch text), but in any case he introduced them in Stevin's work, and the date is 1605, not 1624. The word loxodrome is opposed to the word orthodrome, referring to a great circle.

"Histiodromiae subjectum quatuor definitionibus et undecim propositionibus expedivimus, earum duae priores ὀρθοδρομίαν seu rectas velificationis lineas, caeterae λοξοδρομίαν seu curvas explicabunt" [62] (*Hypomnemata*, vol. 1, part. 2, 84, 1605).

This treatise includes "canones loxodromici" enabling the navigator to construct loxodromes point by point on a globe. These tables were an improvement upon the tables of meridional parts compiled by Edward Wright (who is duly named in the introductory statement,) and they were considerably elaborated by Snel in his *Tiphys Batavus* of 1624.

Stevin suggested the use of metallic "curves" (curved rulers) for the drawing of loxodromes on a sphere. (De loxodromicarum cuprearum helicum fabrica. *Ibidem*, p. 138).

54. Method of identifying harbors by the determination — in addition to the latitude — of magnetic declination, the direction of the true north being found by the observation of two equal altitudes of the sun (1599).

According to Stevin's own statement credit for this method should be given in the first place to the geographer Petrus Plancius (see above section 17); in any case Plancius it was who obtained the data collected in *De Havenvinding*. Stevin quotes in the same book (1599) one Regnier Pieterszoon (Reginaldus Petraei) as the inventor of a special model of quadrant, but he makes no reference to anybody else, not even to William Borough (1536–1599), English navigator who appended to the *Newe Attractive* by Robert Norman (London 1581) a *"Discourse of the variation of the cumpas, or magneticall needle, wherein is mathematically shewed the manner of the observation, effects, and application thereof."* Borough gave many observations of variation and remarked that nearly all the contemporary charts,

---

[62] [We have explained the subject of histiodromia by four definitions and eleven propositions; of these the first two will explain *orthodromian* or sailing in straight lines, the rest will explain *loxodromian* or sailing in curved lines.]

including Mercator's famous planisphere of 1569, were full of errors because the cartographers had failed to take variation into account. The *Discourse* was reprinted at least three times: 1585, 1596, 1611, 1614 (?). Thus three editions appeared before the *Havenvinding*. However, it is possible that Stevin had not heard of it.

Theory of tides

55. General theory of tides in the sixth book of the geography: De theoria maritimorum aestuum in accessu et recessu (*Hypomnemata*, vol. 1, part II, p. 175–188, 1608.)

Stevin and later Kepler expressed their belief in the importance of lunar attraction as a tidal factor. Stevin tried to develop a mathematical theory of this; he was more cautious in his conclusions than Kepler. The latter's belief in the magnetic influence of the moon was an object of derision to Galileo whose fear of astrological explanations led him to deny the possibility of any lunar influence on the tides. Stevin's and Kepler's theories, imperfect as they are, constitute the most important progress in the theory of tides before Newton's *Principia*.

Stevin indicates a rough means of calculating the beginning of ebb and flow from lunar observations. At the end of his book (Prop. 9. Quomodo aestuum maritimorum cognitio planius indigari possit) he insists upon the necessity of obtaining abundant experimental data in order to be able to improve the mathematical theory of tides and their prediction in definite places. He also suggests (*ibidem*) making an experimental study of tides in a small and remote island, such as St. Helena, where the general phenomena would not be disturbed by continental influences.

Geology

56. The second book of Stevin's geography printed in the *Hypomnemata* (vol. 1, part II, p. 47–67, 1605) entitled "De hylocinesi terrestris globi" is truly a geological treatise. According to the first definition (p. 51), "Terreni globi hylocinesis, est variarum materiarum, è quibus coagmentatus est, motus in suo loco, figura totius manente sphaerica."

In plain English the term "hylocinesis" refers to the internal changes of the materials constituting the earth. Stevin's treatise is a summary of physical geology discussing the changes in the surface of the earth and the forces which produce them.

His views might be roughly described as uniformism (as opposed to catastrophism): he explains past changes by the action of forces which we may observe with our own eyes. His account of the formation of mountains is incorrect because he had but little if any knowledge of them; he was very familiar with dunes and was deceived by a false analogy between dunes and mountains. He gives accounts of many physical actions which modify the face of the earth: wind, rain, snow, running waters, evaporation, alluvions, sedimentations (and how these are affected by the varying speed of a stream), water infiltrations, incrustations, petrifications. He had noted the difference in the profiles of the two banks of a river, and the gradual development of its meanders; the alternations of lands and sea; he makes curious remarks on the dissolution of all kinds of earths and minerals in water, on the destruction and "growth" of rocks and metals, etc. Correct interpretation of fossil shells. His explanation of peat desposits is incorrect.

Similar ideas are found in the Arabic and Latin writings of the Middle Ages.[63] A more detailed inventory of them than has yet been attempted would be needed to determine exactly the amount of novelty of Stevin's views. According to Zittel,[64] Stevin's book was the first systematic treatment of the subject, but such a statement remains doubtful and meaningless, until a comparative analysis has been made of that book and of various mediaeval summaries.

Technology

57. Improvements in the construction and use of sluices (canal locks) and application of sluices to the defense of fortified places (1617). See my preliminary discussion of this in my account of Stevin's *Castrametatio* in § 26.

Sluices were possibly invented as early as the time of Ptolemaios II (middle of the third century B.C.), and we may expect their development to have been especially rapid in countries such as Holland, where the need of them was greatest. According to Darmstaedter

[63] Sarton, *Introduction* (vol. 2, 48).
[64] Zittel (1901, 186).

184

and Feldhaus [65] a sluice with gates at both ends (lockchamber, Kammerschleuse, kolksluis) was built in Spaarndam, 1253, by Willem of Holland (this would then be Willem II, count of Holland and Zeeland, born 1228). The existence of such a sluice in Holland by the middle of the thirteenth century is plausible; yet I have found no documents confirming it. We have more definite evidence concerning the locks constructed in 1439 by Fioravante of Bologna and Filippo degli Organi of Modena.[66] The first clear description of locks was given by Leone Battista Alberti (1404–1472) and excellent drawings were made sometime later by Leonardo da Vinci.

To return to Stevin, we find the following information in his treatise of 1617 (I have used the French translation of 1618 published by himself and presumably equivalent to the Dutch original). It is divided into four chapters:

1. De la nouvelle invention d'escluses; 2. De l'affermissement des fonds d'escluses et dodanes; 3. Règle générale de la nouvelle manière de la fortification des villes par escluses; 4. Exemples comment aucunes villes consistantes en effect, se pouvent fortifier par les règles générales du 3 chapitre.

Stevin's improvements were relative to three purposes: the deepening of harbors, the drying up of low lands, and the transfer of ships with high masts. Smaller improvements concern the construction of foundations, and gates and other technical details. However, the main novelty of his effort consists in its application to fortification.

58. Stevin improved the windmills which were so extensively used in his country for pumping water out of the polders. In 1586, he received a patent concerning their construction from the States-General. I do not know the exact nature of the improvements which he introduced.

59. He invented a kind of chariot equipped with sails, by means of which a party of 28 people including Prince Maurice were taken from Scheveningen to Petten along the shore of the North Sea in two hours, the distance being fourteen Dutch miles (a distance of more than

[65] Ludwig Darmstaedter's *Handbuch* (Berlin 1908). F. M. Feldhaus, *Die Technik* (Leipzig, 1914, 962).
[66] I shall discuss this in vol. 4 of my *Introduction to the history of science*. [This volume was never completed.]

fourteen "hours"); this occurred probably about the end of the year 1600.

This unimportant invention seems to have given him more popularity with his contemporaries than all the rest of his work! It is known through an engraving by Jacques de Gheyn representing the chariot, with a text in Dutch, French, and Latin, and a poem by Hugo Grotius celebrating it. These engravings were first published c. 1612, and many times published and imitated afterwards. A complete set is exceedingly rare.

I have never seen them and know them through a description in F. Muller, *De Nederlandsche geschiedenis in platen. Beredeneerde beschrijving van Nederlandsche historieplaten* enz. (vol. 1, 139–141, Amsterdam 1863–1870) and through photostats of a late copy in the British Museum. The title of the copy described by Muller is "Currus veliferi illustrissimi principis Mauritii volitantes duabus horis Scheverina Pettenum ad quatuordecim milliaria hollandica, quae singula justae horae iter excedunt."
The British Museum copy, dated Amsterdam 1652, is oblong, the three pages of the French text being printed side by side, the three pages of the Dutch side on another sheet, and the two pages of the Latin text on still another. Considering the great rarity of that publication and its relative shortness I reproduce in appendix [omitted] the French text, entitled "Les artificiels chariots à voiles du comte Maurice." The Latin text is entitled "Comitis Mauritii Currus artificiales vento acti" and the Dutch text "Sijn Excell. Graef Maurits kunst-rijcke Windtwagens" . . .

To return to Stevin's sailchariot, it was used again in 1606 by the French savant Nicolas Claude Fabri de Peiresc (1580–1637), who admired it exceedingly. According to Jacques de Gheyn's illustration there was also a smaller chariot; the latter was tried as late as 1790, the experiment being unsuccessful, and it could still be examined in Scheveningen in 1802.

60. It is not correct to say as is done in Darmsttaeder's *Handbuch* [67] (1908, under year 1605) that Stevin was the first to illustrate surveying chains. These were first described and illustrated by Melchior Sebiz, *Siben Bücher von dem Feldbau* (Strassburg 1579, p. 472).

Franz M. Feldhaus, "Zur Geschichte der Messkette," *Geschichtsbl. für Technik und Industrie*, vol. 6, 71–72, 1 fig., Berlin 1919.

61. To conclude, Stevin's main achievements concern the extension of the decimal idea to fractions, and to weights and measures, the

[67] The dates concerning Stevin in that *Handbuch* are generally incorrect.

186

SIMON STEVIN OF BRUGES

theory of algebraic equations, and above all the principles of statics and hydrostatics. He was one of the greatest mathematicians of the sixteenth century and the greatest mechanician of the long period extending from Archimedes to Galileo.

IV. BIBLIOGRAPHY

62. This bibliography is by no means complete, but it contains the essential. For the earlier writings see the *Bibliotheca belgica* (vol. 23, Ghent 1880–1890), Father Bosmans' notice in the *Biographie nationale* (Brussels 1924), or W. van der Woude's notice in the *Nieuw Nederlandsch biografisch woordenboek* (Leiden 1921). General reference books such as Cantor, Darmstaedter, Tropfke, Sarton are not quoted. There are a few additional references in the footnotes . . .

Almagià, Roberto, La dottrina della marea nell'antichità classica e nel medio evo (*Acc. dei Lincei, Memorie, sci. fis.*, vol. 5, 377–513, see p. 510, Roma 1905).

Bosmans, Henri, Notes sur l'arithmétique de S.S. (*Ann. soc. scient. 35*, mém. 293–313, Bruxelles, 1911).

—— Sur quelques exemples de la méthode des limites chez S.S. (*Ann. soc. scient. 37*, mém. 171–199, 1913).

—— La Thiende de S.S. A propos d'un exemplaire de l'édition originale qui a échappé à l'incendie de Louvain (*Rev. quest. scient. 27*, 109–139, Bruxelles, 1920; *Isis 4*, 142).

——Remarques sur l'arithmétique de S.S. (*Mathesis 36*, 23 p., 1922; *Isis 5*, 223).

—— Le calcul infinitésimal chez S.S. (*Mathesis 37*, 18 p., 1923; *Isis 6*, 155).

—— La résolution des équations du troisième degré d'après S.S. (*Mathesis 37*, 246–254, 304–311, 341–347, 1923).

—— La Thiende de S.S. Facsimile de l'édition plantinienne de 1585 (*Éditions de la Société des bibliophiles anversois*, no. 38, 41 + 37 p., Anvers, 1924; *Isis 7*, 543).

—— Henri Stevin et S.S. (*Biographie nationale*, vol. 23, col. 884–938, Bruxelles, 1924; *Isis 7*, 542).

—— La résolution de l'équation du 4e degré chez S.S. (*Mathesis 39*, 49–55, 99–104, 145–153, 1925).

—— Le mathématicien belge S.S. (*Periodico di matematiche 6*, 231–261, Bologna, 1926).[68]

Brown, Richard, The history of accounting and accountants (Edinburgh, 1905).

Cappelle, Johannes Pieter van, S.S. en over de wiskundige verdiensten van Prins Maurits (*Bijdragen tot de geschiedenis der wetenschappen in Nederland*, 1–59, 125–166, Amsterdam, 1821).

[68] Father Bosmans has written many other papers which ought to be considered though they do not deal specifically with S.S. See A. Rome, Le R. P. Henri Bosmans, S.J. (*Isis 12*, 88–112, 1929).

Dijksterhuis, Eduard Jan, S.S. und seine Bedeutung für die Geschichte der Mathematik und Naturwissenschaften (*Unterrichtsblätter für Mathematik und Naturwissenschaften 38*, 148–150, Frankfurt, 1932).

Duhem, Pierre, Les Origines de la statique (2 vols., Paris, 1905–1906). Chiefly vol. 1, 1905.

—— Études sur Léonard de Vinci (3 vols., Paris, 1906–1913). Chiefly vol. 1, 1906.

Geijsbeek, John Bart, Ancient double-entry bookkeeping (182 p., published by the author, Denver, Colorado, 1914).

Goditsky-Tsvirko, A. M., An outline of the history of the funicular polygon (*Publications of the Institute of communication engineering*, 26 p., 23 figs., Leningrad, 1929.

    In Russian. See *Isis 15*, 295.

Gravelaar, N. L. W. A., S's Problemata geometrica (*Nieuw archief voor wiskunde*, vol. 5, 106–191, Amsterdam, 1901).

Günther, Siegmund, Geschichte der loxodromischen Curve (*Studien zur Geschichte der mathematischen und physikalischen Geographie*, 333–408, Halle a.S. 1879).

Kokomoor, F. W., The distinctive features of the seventeenth century geometry (*Isis 10*, 367–415, 379, 1928).

Loria, Gino, Storia della geometria descrittiva (Milano, 1921; *Isis 5*, 181–182).

Mach, Ernst, The science of mechanics (third revised ed., Chicago, 1907).

Marguet F., Histoire générale de la navigation du XVe au XXe siècle (Paris, 1931; *Isis 19*, 235–237).

Mottelay, Paul Fleury, Bibliographical history of electricity and magnetism (London, 1922; *Isis 6*, 104–107).

Schor, D., S.S. und das hydrostatische Paradoxon (*Bibliotheca mathematica 3*, 198–203, 1902).

Steichen, Michel, Mémoire sur la vie et les travaux de S.S. (Bruxelles, 1846).

Tesch, J. W., Waar is S.S. geboren? (*Nieuw archief voor wiskunde 3*, 94, Amsterdam, 1898).

Vincent, Jean, Le système géologique de S.S. (*Annuaire météorologique de l'Observatoire Royal pour* 1901, 355–361, Bruxelles, 1901).

Vivanti, Giulio, I principali trattati di algebra dalle origine della stampa al 1800 (*Periodico di matematica 4*, 277–306, 1924; *Isis 7*, 314).

Wieleitner, Heinrich, Über die Fortschritte, die S.S. in der Lösung der quadratischen Gleichung erzielte (*Sitzungsber. der physik.med. Sozietät zu Erlangen*, vol. 58–59, 177–180, 1926–27).

Woude, W. van der; Blok, P. J., Articles on Hendrick and S.S. (*Nieuw Nederlandsch biografisch woordenboek*, vol. 5, 815–818, 1921).

Zittel, Karl Alfred von, History of geology and palaeontology (London, 1901, p. 186).

[The section on Iconography and the Appendix are omitted.]

Cambridge, Mass.
    [1934]

Rumphius, Plinius Indicus
[the East Indian Pliny]

(1 6 2 8 - 1 7 0 2)

AFTER having obtained his B.S. in Harvard in 1864 under Louis Agassiz, Albert Smith Bickmore,[1] a son of Maine with a fine enthusiasm for natural history, started for a long journey to the Far East. He visited the Malay peninsula, the Dutch Indies, and Japan, being back in Boston in December 1867. According to the account in his book, *Travels in the East Indian Archipelago*,[2]

On the 19th of April, 1865, I was fifty miles east of Christmas Island, floating on the good ship "Memnon" toward the Strait of Sunda.

I was going to Batavia, to sail thence to the Spice Islands, which lie east of Celebes, for the purpose of collecting the beautiful shells of those seas.

I had chosen that in preference to any other part of the world, because the first collection of shells from the East that was ever described and figured with sufficient accuracy to be of any scientific value was made by Rumphius, a doctor who lived many years at Amboina, the capital of those islands. His great work, the *Rariteit Kamer*, or Chamber of Curiosities, was published in 1705, more than sixty years before the twelfth edition of the

[1] A. S. Bickmore, born at Tenant's Harbor, Maine in 1839, died at Nonquitt, Massachusetts in 1914. He studied in Dartmouth and Harvard and was soon appointed assistant in the Harvard Museum of Comparative Anatomy. He travelled to the Far East in 1864–1867. He was not a prominent naturalist, but is sure of immortality as the "father of the American Museum of Natural History." Indeed he it was who conceived the plan of it soon after his return from the East, and having enlisted a sufficient number of influential friends, he secured the initial organization of the Museum in 1869. He was the first superintendent of it from 1869 to 1884. Then having understood ahead of most people that the educational possibilities of the Museum were not sufficiently utilized he conceived a new plan of adaptation of the Museum to public education. In this he was I believe a pioneer, at least in America. He was the first curator of the Museum's Department of Public Education. See article by Eleanor Robinette Dobson (*DAB*, 2, 238–239, 1929).

[2] London 1868, but I quote from the New York edition of 1869. Both editions are apparently identical.

189

Systema Naturae was issued by Linnaeus, "the Father of Natural History," who referred to the figures in that work to illustrate a part of his own writings. When Holland became a province of France, in 1811, and it was designed to make Paris the centre of science and literature in Europe, it was said that this collection was taken from Leyden to that city, and afterward returned, and that during these two transfers a large proportion of the specimens disappeared; and that, finally, what was left of this valuable collection was scattered through the great museum at Leyden. It was partly to restore Rumphius's specimens, and partly to bring into our own country such a standard collection, that I was going to search myself for the shells figured in the *Rariteit Kamer*, on the very points and headlands, and in the very bays, where Rumphius's specimens were found . . . (p. 13–14).

At first I bought them by the basketful, until all the more common species had been obtained, and then I showed the natives the figures in Rumphius's *Rariteit Kamer* of those species I still wished to secure, and at the same time offered them an extra price for others not represented in that comprehensive work. One species I was particularly anxious to secure alive. It was the pearly nautilus. The shell has always been common, but the animal has seldom been described. The first was found at this place, and a description and drawing were given by Rumphius. Afterward a dissection and drawing were given by Professor Owen, of the British Museum, and his monograph probably contains the most complete anatomical description that has ever been made of any animal from a single specimen. He worked, as he himself described it to me, with a dissecting knife in one hand and a pencil in the other. So little escaped his pen and pencil, that very little information has been added by later dissections. I was so anxious to secure one of these rare animals, that I felt that, if I should obtain one and a few more common species, I could feel that my long journey had been far from fruitless. Only the second day after my arrival, to my inexpressible delight, a native brought me one still *living* (p. 134–135).

It was my desire not only to obtain the same shells that Rumphius figures, but to procure them from the same points and bays, so that there could be no doubt about the identity of my specimens with his drawings. I therefore proposed to travel along all the shores of Amboina and the neighboring islands, and trade with the natives of every village, so as to be sure of the localities myself, and, moreover, get specimens of all the species alive, and thus have ample material for studying their anatomy (p. 141).

Who was this Rumphius whose ancient book had caused a young American zoologist to travel so far away from home and had fired his soul with so much enthusiasm for natural history? Bickmore visited the tomb of Rumphius in Amboina and apropos of that gives a short account of the latter's life (p. 251–252), but that account as well as his description of the tomb contain so many inaccuracies that it is better to disregard them.[3] Let us tell Rumphius' story again. It is such

[3] I would not conclude that Bickmore's book is bad. Its value can only be

a good story, and to my mind at least such a cheering one, that it cannot be told too often.

George Eberhard Rumpf or Rumphius [4] was born in or near Hanau on the River Main (a few miles from Frankfort) in 1627 or 1628 (the date of birth is uncertain; it was sometime between May 15 and July 7). The town of Hanau is famous for two other sons, the two brothers Grimm, Jacob (1785–1863), the founder of Germanic philology, the discoverer of "Grimm's law" of consonant shiftings (1822), and Wilhelm (1786–1859), the main creator of "Grimm's tales," one of the founders of folklore. It is hardly possible for the inhabitants of Hanau or for its careful visitors to ignore the brothers Grimm for a statue is dedicated to them, but how many know that that little city gave birth also to a third man at least as great as the two others? How many of the Hanauers themselves know of him I wonder?

Georg Rumphius was the son of a prosperous architect and he was educated in the local gymnasium. He soon developed a very adventurous spirit which must have disturbed the family and their anxiety was perhaps mixed with a feeling of relief when he was enlisted by the count Ludwig von Solms-Greifenstein (Braunfels) so-to-say in the Venetian army, but in reality in the service of the Dutch West India Company. Those were golden days for the German princelings who could sell their subjects or dispose of them like heads of cattle. If the boy was in search of adventures he made a good bargain for he had plenty of them — adventures and catastrophes!

Catastrophe no. 1. — The boy boarded the "Swarte Raef" (Black raven) in Texel, sailing to Brazil, but the ship was captured by the Portuguese and every soldier which she carried was impressed into the Portuguese army. However, he turned this grievous accident into a new opportunity. While serving in Portugal he heard so many stories of the wonders of the East Indies that his imagination was inflamed.

---

determined by a naturalist. Scientific books which are good in other respects often contain inaccurate historical data; indeed conscientious scientists often lack historical feeling and have no appreciation of historical truth. Natural history they seem to think must be told accurately, but for human history anything goes!

[4] It is better to use the Latinized form Rumphius which he always used himself, in his Dutch writings as well as in his Latin ones. However, in a letter to the directors of the Dutch East India company, dated August 20, 1663, he signed: "Jeuriaen Rumph van Hanau," also "Georgius Everhardus Rumphius van Hanau" (*Gedenkboek* 1902, p. 13).

In 1649, he was allowed to return to Hanau where he remained a few years, years of final preparation about which we would like to know more. At the end of 1652 — Aet. 24–25 — he took service as a warrant officer in the Dutch East India Company. He sailed again from Texel, the day after Christmas of that year — on the ship Muyden, arrived in Java in June 1653, and soon proceeded to Amboina where he landed toward the end of the same year.

Amboina [5] is one of the smaller islands of the Moluccas (or Spice Islands) but one of the most important, and the town in that island bearing the same name is the capital of the Moluccas. That archipelago had been conquered by the Portuguese about 1525, but the Dutch lured by the precious spices — nutmeg and clove — were soon hovering about it, full of covetousness, and their influence began to be felt early in the seventeenth century — at first in the southern part where Amboina is located.

To return to our hero the authorities soon realized that he had no taste for warfare and soon after his arrival he was transferred from the military to the civil service. He was appointed an under-merchant (onderkoopman) in 1657 and a merchant (koopman) in 1662. He seems to have done what was expected from him and to have been throughout a very faithful and helpful servant of the Company though his main interest was obviously in another direction. Whatever his training may have been, he was a born naturalist and one can easily imagine the impact of tropical nature — fantastic and equally alluring in its luxuriance and diversity — upon a young mind thus oriented. No sooner was he settled in Amboina than he began making a systematic survey of the flora and fauna of the Moluccas, describing carefully everything that lived and grew in his island and the neighboring ones, collecting as well geographical and mineralogical information, in short preparing, with increasing consciousness, what might be called the Natural History of that region. It is much to the credit of the Dutch authorities that they favored his efforts outside of the commercial field, and allowed him to devote to his hobby more and more time. The governor-general Joan Maetsuyker (1608–1678, gov. 1653–1678) in Batavia, a man of considerable influence who could have harmed as

---

[5] Amboina or Amboyna is the Malay name internationally used. The Dutch call it Ambon. Position 3°40′ S, 128°20′ E.

well as helped him, chose the latter course and deserves our gratitude. In 1669, Rumphius was planning to go to Batavia to discuss his work with Maetsuyker and to arrange for the publication of his writings, but various circumstances obliged him to delay his journey from month to month, and then Fate struck him a second time.

Catastrophe no. 2. — In May 1670, Rumphius lost his sight! Just try to imagine what such a misfortune, terrible enough for any person, meant for a man who wanted to see everything with his own eyes. However by this time he had acquired so much experience in the accurate description of natural objects that he could guide the efforts of others, and use other eyes than his own for the development of his knowledge. In this eventuality the Dutch Company was generous to him, and permitted him not only to continue in its employ, but to devote much of his energy to science rather than to business. This is the more remarkable because the Dutch Company was as hardheaded a corporation as ever was, for which business and still more business was the supreme rule of life. Much may be forgiven them because of their generous treatment of Rumphius! Thus the blind man of forty-two now bound to remain in Amboina until the end of his days continued courageously the immense task which he had begun with open eyes and youthful enthusiasm.

Catastrophe no. 3. — However, Fate would not leave him alone, or rather would try his mettle to the limit and thus enable us to see how great he was. On February 17, 1674, an earthquake visted Amboina; Rumphius's wife, Susanna, and his youngest daughter were killed. Still he continued his scientific investigations as well as the fulfilment of his commercial duties.

By that time, Rumphius' main work was already well advanced. That was a herbal of the Moluccan flora, to be published later, much later, under the title of *Herbarium amboinense.* He seems to have begun it as early as 1655. After thirty years of intermittent but perseverant labor he had accumulated splendid collections of drawings and descriptions.

Catastrophe no. 4. — On January 11, 1687, Amboina was almost completely destroyed by a conflagration. All of Rumphius's drawings (or the drawings made under his direction) were lost, but the manuscript itself was largely saved. The old man continued! He arranged for the preparation of a new set of drawings. These were made by his son Paulus Augustus and other draughtsmen controlled by his good judgment and his vast experience, by all the ingenuity of an eager and resourceful mind.

Catastrophe no. 5. — After five years of labor, the text and abundant illustrations of half the *Herbarium* (books 1 to 6) were finally completed. The manuscript was sent to Holland in 1692 in the ship Waterland, which was sunk by the French — everything on board being lost. Happily before sending the precious manuscript the new governor-general Joannes Camphuys had caused a copy of it to be made. Rumphius continued his work.

Catastrophe no. 6. — Four more years of labor amidst all the discomforts of tropical life (as hard and cruel as it is glamorous) — far away from every library and university — and the new manuscript of the whole work (12 books) was ready. In 1696, the Heeren Zeventienen [6] had it in their hands — one of the masterpieces of botanical literature — but they did not consider it worth publishing. It was to remain forty years hidden in their archives.

In the meanwhile the indomitable Rumphius had found the master whom all must obey. Death overtook him in Amboina on June 15, 1702.

At the time of his death he had written at least two capital works, but neither was published. To these works, his main titles to immortal fame, I shall come back presently. When Rumphius died very few people outside of the Dutch Company were aware of their existence, let alone of their exceptional merit. Rumphius himself however was not unknown. From distant Amboina he corresponded with many scientists of the Indies and of Europe. He made a collection of "rarities" for the cabinet of the Grand Duke of Tuscany, Cosimo III de' Medici (now apparently lost). Best of all, many letters of his were communicated by the German botanist Christian Mentzel (1622–1701) to the *Academia naturae curiosorum* and published in its *Miscellanea curiosa sive Ephemerides* from 1682 to 1698. That *Academia* (the very one which exists to this day under the name of *Kaiserlich-Leopoldinisch-Deutsche Akademie der Naturforscher zu Halle*) had honored itself greatly in

---

[6] I quote them after the article in NNBW. I have not been able to find additional information on Messrs. Zeventienen, the executive board (17 members) of the Dutch East India Co., but perhaps the best they deserve is oblivion and mercy.

1681 by appointing this unknown Moluccan naturalist to its membership, and calling him *Plinius indicus*.[7]

After a long period of oblivion, Rumphius's *"magnum opus"* the *Herbarium amboinense* was rescued from the Zeventienen archives by the Amsterdam professor Johannes Burman (1707–1779) who decided to edit it, to translate it into Latin, to add various notes, and to publish it with the original illustrations. The work was so enormous and so expensive to produce that no single Dutch firm would assume the whole risk. It was finally issued by a consortium of eight Dutch publishers, in six folio parts appearing in Amsterdam from 1741 to 1750.[8] A new "title edition" of the whole work appeared in 1750. An *Auctuarium* or supplement was published in 1755. The *Herbarium amboinense* was not simply the first herbal of the Moluccas; it was the first large herbal of the eastern and tropical world. And not only that but the descriptions were remarkably accurate and the illustrations splendid. To his careful descriptions of plants and the unequivocal attribution of various traditional names to the described specimens, that is, to the complete identification of the plants, Rumphius added information concerning their habitats and their flowering seasons, and explained how to cultivate them. That information, or at least much of it, is still valuable today.

Rumphius' monumental work was not completely given to the world until more than half a century had elapsed since his death. We cannot help feeling, what a pity he could not enjoy a fame so richly deserved, but Rumphius would probably have said that the thing that really mattered to him was not the fame but the deed.

The other great work which we owe to him, the very one which caused a young Yankee to travel to the Far East in the sixties of last century, was revealed much earlier though not early enough to appear within his lifetime. I am now referring to his *Amboinsche Rariteitkamer*, the manuscript of which was sent by him in 1701 to his friend Dr. Hendrik D'Acquet, burgomaster of Delft. This was a collection of beautiful plates with brief descriptions of the objects illustrated, — mostly shells. Such a book was likely to be appreciated by the collec-

[7] Every member received a nickname at the time of his election, but they were not often as adequate as in this case. See *Isis 16*, 144.

[8] The original MSS. are preserved in the Library of the University of Leiden.

tors of "rarities" and by the other scientific dilettanti, who were surprisingly numerous at that time, in the quiet, prosperous, and studious Holland perhaps more than anywhere else. That, and also its smaller size, explains its earlier publication in 1705,[9] — that is, half a century before the herbal, though the manuscript of it reached Europe many years later. It is one of the classics in the history of malacology.

Rumphius is one of the great naturalists of the seventeenth century and indeed of all times. In addition to that, he was a man of heroic size — and it is for that reason above all others that I love him and celebrate him. He deserves to be better known especially to young naturalists, and I hope that an elaborate biography of him may soon become available to them.

S. S. *Excalibur*

(*June* 13, 1936 *off the Azores on the way from New York to Marseilles*).

BIBLIOGRAPHY

In 1902, the Colonial Museum of Haarlem commemorated the second centenary of Rumphius' death and published on that occasion in the Dutch language a memorial book which is the main source of information available to-day.

Rumphius Gedenkboek, 1702–1902. Uitgegeven door het Koloniaal Museum te Haarlem, 15 Juni 1902 (folio viii–222 p., illus.).

This contains a series of studies on his biography (by J. E. Heeres), on his work as a historiographer, botanist, zoologist, mineralogist, etc., and a very elaborate bibliography by G. P. Rouffaer and W. C. Muller (56 p.). Indeed that bibliography is so complete that it would seem almost impossible to improve upon it except by the suppression of many futilities. The *Gedenkboek* is the foundation for a complete biography of Rumphius, a biography which is still unwritten.

See also J. Sirks's short notice in the *Nieuw nederlandsch biografisch woordenboek* (vol. 3, 1104–1107, 1914).

[9] A Latin edition, *Thesaurus imaginum piscium testaceorum,* etc. including the same plates, was published in Leiden 1711. There are various other editions in Dutch, Latin, and German.

Montucla

(1 7 2 5 - 1 7 9 9)

His Life and Works

MONTUCLA'S LIFE

1. Jean Etienne Montucla [1] was born in Lyon on September 5, 1725. His father was a business man (négociant). The best schools of that time were those directed by the Jesuit fathers, and the Jesuit College of Lyon was one of the best of its kind. It is there that Jean received his first education, and this implied as thorough a mathematical training as was available anywhere in those days, and a far deeper training in Greek and Latin than would be available anywhere in our own days. His solid knowledge of the ancient languages made it relatively easy for him later to pick up a sufficient understanding of foreign languages such as Italian, English, German, and Dutch. The Jesuits of Lyon educated two other mathematicians, who were Montucla's younger contemporaries: the astronomer Lalande (1732–1807) and the historian Charles Bossut (1730–1814). Bossut became himself a Jesuit; as to Montucla, and even Lalande, in spite of his virulent atheism, they remained exceedingly grateful to their Jesuit teachers; and the latter went so far as to write in the *Bien Informé* of February 3, 1800, apropos of the Jesuit foundation, "Ce fut le plus bel ouvrage des hommes, dont aucun établissement n'approchera jamais, l'objet éternel de mon admiration, de ma reconnaissance, de mes regrets." [2]

In 1741, Montucla lost his father, and four years later the grandmother who had taken charge of his education. He then proceeded to

---

[1] The name Montucla is rare. There is a place named Montusclat in Saint-Julien-Chapteuil, arr. du Puy (Haute-Loire). Montucla's family may have originated there.

[2] Quoted by Le Blond (663, 1802). Text revised by Lalande. ["It was the men's best work which no other institution will ever approach, forever the object of my admiration, of my gratitude and of my yearning."]

the law school of Toulouse, and after having completed his law studies went to Paris.

There were then fewer meeting places for students and scholars, literati and dilettanti, than there are now. On the other hand some of the booksellers seem to have been more educated than their fellows of today, and their shops were sometimes promoted to the dignity of small literary clubs. Thus Lalande owed much information and inspiration to the bookseller and publisher Desaint, and Montucla found a similar asylum in the bookshop of Jombert,[3] who was to be later the publisher of his main books. There he had occasion not only to browse among the mathematical and artistic books of Jombert's stock but to meet congenial souls, such as Lalande, Diderot, d'Alembert, Gua de Malves, the architect Jacques François Blondel, the Le Blonds, the Cochins and the Coustous. He was for many years a contributor to the *Gazette de France.*

2. We do not know when he began his investigations on the history of mathematics. Yet his great book devoted to the subject contains such an abundance of materials that its preparation must have taken many years. It was already sufficiently advanced in 1754 to be announced by the publisher. Indeed Montucla's first book, *Histoire des recherches sur la quadrature du cercle,* appeared in that year, and it includes a *Privilège du roi* (Paris, Nov. 5, 1754) granted to Charles Antoine Jombert for the publication not only of itself but of various other books, notably Montucla's *Histoire des mathématiques*[4] and Pierre Estève's *Histoire de l'astronomie* (3 vols., Paris 1755). However, the larger work came out of the presses only in 1758 and in the meanwhile Montucla edited together with Pierre Joseph Morisot-Deslandes the collection of documents concerning inoculation which was issued by another publisher in 1756 but was already privileged in 1754. His main work was probably delayed by this strange medical intermezzo, or quite as likely by the necessity of additional investigations, for we have evidence that the author continued to correct and polish it until the last moment.

[3] Charles Antoine Jombert (1712–1784), bookseller and man of letters. See NBG (26, 874, 1858).

[4] It was against the publisher's interest to obtain such a privilege too early for it was valid for only nine years (sometimes less), counted, not from the date of publication but from the date of the privilege itself. Thus in this case the publisher's monopoly was reduced to five years instead of nine.

When the *Histoire des mathématiques* finally appeared (1758) its author was not by any means unknown to the public. Indeed he had been appointed an associate of the Academy of Berlin as early as July 3, 1755, in recognition of his history of the quadrature. The two quarto volumes of his *Histoire* were very favorably received, and he was much encouraged to prepare the publication of a third volume to be devoted to the eighteenth century and for which he had aleady gathered abundant materials.

It is said by his biographer that he was a good geometer [5] but we have no proof of it. It is clear that most of his time from 1754 to 1761 must have been devoted to his historical researches. In 1761, he was appointed secretary of the intendance of Dauphiné, and during his residence in Grenoble he married in 1763 Marie Françoise Romand.

3. Soon after his marriage Montucla was obliged to absent himself from France for fifteen months (1764–65) as a member of a mission to Cayenne. This episode, lightly dismissed by Le Blond, suggests that if it is wise to refer as much as possible to contemporary biographies this must always be done with great caution. To be sure, the early biographers knew facts which would necessarily escape later ones, but they are also more likely to be prejudiced, and they may have many reasons of giving one piece of information and withholding another. The facts relative to the mission to Cayenne are, as far as I have been able to reconstruct them, as follows:

On the eve of signing the treaty of peace of 1763 consecrating the abandonment of Canada to England, the French government thought of compensating that loss by the colonization of French Guiana. A vast and unlimited territory ending near Cayenne, and extending between the rivers Kourou and Maroni, was granted to the Dukes of Choiseul and Choiseul-Praslin (the Duke of Choiseul was then minister of the army and navy).[6] The direction of the colony was intrusted to the

[5] "Il étoit d'ailleurs très bon géomètre, les *Sections coniques* de la Hire l'avoient familiarisé avec la géométrie ancienne; et l'on a vu de lui des mémoires d'analyse qui prouvoient du talent, mais qu'il n'a jamais publiés" (Le Blond, 667). Philippe de la Hire (1640–1718) wrote treatises on conics, the main one being his *Sectiones conicae in novem libros distributae* (folio, Paris 1685), which exerted a strong influence as long as geometry was not displaced by the calculus. He made ancient geometry intelligible and popularized the synthetic methods of Desargues and Pascal. Montucla does not give him his due (*Histoire*, vol. 3, p. 6).

[6] "Ces terres leur furent accordées en toute propriété, seigneurie et justice, tant pour eux que pour leurs successeurs, avec droits de pêche et de chasse, dans

chevalier Turgot,[7] who remained in Paris and appointed Thibaut de Chanvalon intendant general. A large number of settlers were recruited, particularly in Alsace and Lorraine, and being deluded with fantastic hopes of wealth without work and prosperity without pains were sent to Cayenne. Hardly anything was done to favor their efforts and the colonization was a tragical failure. The first settlers arrived in Cayenne on July 14, 1763, and many shiploads followed in 1763 and 1764; the abundance of the emigration combined with the lack of organization, produced chaotic conditions, misery, revolts, and diseases, and the emigrants died like flies. Finally the chevalier Turgot felt obliged to proceed to the Guiana for investigation. He arrived at Cayenne toward the end of December 1764, proved himself timorous and incapable, and did hardly more than imprison the intendant Chanvalon and increase the chaos. A census begun on January 10, 1765 by the chevalier de Balzac established the existence of 918 survivors (out of more than 10,000).[8] Turgot left Cayenne on April 5, 1765; it is said that during the three months of his residence in Guiana he had never left the town!

According to Le Blond, Montucla was appointed first secretary of the chevalier Turgot for this project, and astronomer royal. Le Blond's statement [9] is very unclear. I have not been able to find any trace of Montucla in the many publications, relative to the history of French Guiana and the ill-fated Kourou expedition, which I have consulted. No mention of his departure, or arrival, or of his stay in Guiana; no

toute l'étendue de la contrée et toute la profondeur des terres; avec privilège de nommer les commandants, les officiers municipaux et de justice, dans les villes, bourgs et villages qui se formeraient dans leurs concessions respectives, et permission de donner leurs noms et ceux de leurs familles aux lieux principaux. La seule condition qui fut mise au don de cette propriété était de la défendre." (*Précis*, p. 15). Notice the strong feudal nature of that grant.

[7] Etienne Francois, marquis Turgot (1721–Paris–1789), one of the founders of the Société royale d'agriculture, and brother of the famous economist Turgot (1727–1781).

[8] The total number is quoted very differently by different sources, 14,000 being the maximum, 2,361 the minimum. The correct number seems to be much closer to the maximum than to the minimum (*Précis*, 72).

[9] "Le chevalier Turgot ayant été chargé en 1764, par le duc de Choiseul, de former une colonie, avec Thibaut de Chanvallon [sic], à Cayenne, il demanda comme premier secrétaire Montucla, qui joignit à ce titre celui d'astronome du roi. Les malheurs de cette expédition ne laissèrent pas à l'astronome le temps de joindre ses propres travaux à tous ceux qu'il avoit si bien décrits" (Le Blond, 668). See notice on Thibaut de Chanvalon in NBG (9, 683, 1854).

mention of him whatever in this connection, except by Le Blond and those who have copied him.

After having examined rapidly many shelves of books on French Guiana, I selected the following for further study:

Ministère de la Marine et des Colonies, *Précis historique de l'expédition du Kourou (Guyane française)*, 1763–65 (79 p., Paris, Imprimerie royale, 1842). This is the official account based on the colonial archives, however these archives may contain documents concerning Montucla which have not yet been utilized.

H. Ternaux-Compans, *Notice historique sur la Guyane française* (viii + 190 p., Paris, Firmin Didot, 1843). Includes a bibliography (p. 169–190) of 166 items relative to (French) Guiana, in chronological order, from 1557 to 1842.

Frédéric Bouyer, *La Guyane française*. Notes et souvenirs d'un voyage exécuté en 1862–63 (folio 316 p., illust., Paris, 1867).

If the date 1764 and other facts quoted by Le Blond are correct,[10] it is possible that Montucla went to Cayenne only with Turgot, though this does not tally with another statement according to which Montucla was absent from France for fifteen months. Considering that Turgot's project was such a dismal failure it is not surprising that Le Blond has so little to say about it. It is highly probable that Montucla and other survivors were ordered to keep their mouth shut after their return. I must add that Cayenne's atrocious fame was still blackened within Montucla's lifetime by the deportation of 18 fructidor an V (September 4, 1797). On that date the Directoire exiled its leading opponents to the Guiana (Conamana and Sinnamary). Some 328 royalists were deported to Sinnamary, and this sentence, cruel enough under any circumstances, became truly inhuman because of the absence of preparations to receive the exiles, most of whom were literary men and clerics unable to provide for themselves and to bear the discomforts and dangers of the tropics.[11] No wonder that the name of Cayenne became almost synonymous with hell, — a comparison which the penal settlement established in 1852 did its best to perpetuate.

Le Blond's obituary of Montucla was originally read at the Société

[10] These facts seem to be correct.

[11] We are better informed with regard to this episode than with regard to the Kourou one, because some of the exiles survived and wrote elaborate accounts: Jean Pierre Ramel (London 1799), Jean Jacques Aymé (Paris 1800), Louis Ange Pitou (Paris 1805), François, marquis de Barbé-Marbois (Paris 1835). Needless to say those accounts were highly colored and far from impartial. For a more judicial statement, see Bouyer (1867, p. 77).

de Versailles [12] on January 15, 1800, and in those days most people did not know of the horrors of Kourou and Sinnamary and the few who did know found it safer to be silent. Hence Le Blond's laconism is natural enough. To the paragraph already quoted he adds:

Je n'ai pu me procurer la relation qu'il fit sous le nom du gouverneur, et dans laquelle se trouve la liste des plantes qu'il rapporta aux serres de Versailles. De ce nombre étoient le cacao et la vanille, qu'il présenta à Louis XV à son arrivée. Un haricot sucré: *le gros perlé*, cultivé depuis cette époque dans le potager.[13]

I do not know anything about the "gros perlé," but cocoa and vanilla were not novelties, for the conquistadores had brought them from Mexico to Europe two centuries earlier.

4. It would seem that when Montucla had been appointed royal astronomer in Guiana he had been promised to receive after his return a post of professor of hydrography in one of the naval schools . . . but that hope did not materialize. After having spent some time with his wife's family in Grenoble, he finally obtained a subordinate post in the superintendence of royal buildings, gardens, manufactures, and academies, and moved to Versailles. He kept that post for some twenty-five years, that is, until every bureau of the royal administration was swept away by the triumphant Revolution. During that quarter of a century of peaceful activity, Montucla devoted his leisure to historical studies, chiefly to the preparation of an entirely new edition (1778) of Ozanam's mathematical recreations, and to the translation (1784) of Jonathan Carver's travels along Lake Superior and in Minnesota; it is highly probable that he also accumulated materials for the continuation of his history of mathematics.

His was the quiet and domestic life of a scholar. It is said that even when friendly groups gathered in the evening in his house, according to the custom of Versailles, he would appear only for a few moments, then return to his studies, and not show himself until supper time. He

---

[12] More exactly, Société libre d'agriculture de Seine-et-Oise.

[13] Le Blond, p. 668. ["I could not obtain the statement which he made under the name of the governor and in which is found the list of the plants he brought back for the conservatories at Versailles. In this group were cocoa and vanilla, which he presented to Louis XV on his return. A sugar bean, *le gros perlé* [has been] cultivated since this period in vegetable gardens."]

spoke easily, without pretense, told stories with much naïvety, and his manners were suggestive of virtue and good taste.[14] His income had never been large and he had been obliged to spend it in order to provide the humble comforts and elegance of his home, the education of his children, and to satisfy his own intellectual needs. When the Revolution suppressed his office, he lost everything.

5. Lalande persuaded him then to prepare a new edition of his *Histoire des mathématiques* and obtained for him some help from the publisher Panckoucke. However, the new edition was finally issued by another publisher, Henri Agasse, with whom Lalande was already negotiating in 1796.[15] The first two volumes, that is the revision of the original volumes, appeared on August 7, 1799. Montucla was able to supervise the publication of vol. 3, new material, to the p. 336.

Montucla was not a member of the Royal Academy of sciences; it is said that Lalande had been asked to offer him a place in it but that Montucla had declined as he did not feel he had enough free time to do justice to the opportunity. Having lost his position, the situation was different. The old academy was suppressed in 1793, and reorganized under the name of Institut national des sciences et des arts in 1795. Montucla was one of the original members of the Institut national for he was elected on 9 ventôse an IV (Feb. 28, 1796) and the first meeting occurred in the Louvre on 15 germinal an IV (April 4, 1796).

In spite of the fact that he had been a clerk in the royal administration, he must have had good friends among the revolutionaries, for we find his name in the first list of men of letters to whom the Comité de salut public distributed national rewards (1794). In the following years he was ordered by the government to examine the treaties deposited in the archives of the ministry of foreign affairs. His long career in the service of the superintendence of royal buildings had

[14] "Il respiroit dans toute son habitude la bonhomie de la vertu, et la délicatesse du bon goût" (Le Blond, 669).

[15] See Lalande's letter of 5 thermidor an IV (July 23, 1796) in the D. E. Smith Library. David Eugene Smith, Among my autographs. 6. The threatened loss of the second edition of Montucla's history (*American mathematical monthly 28*, 207, 1921). One of Montucla's letters in the same collection (20 vendémiaire an VI = 11 October 1797), also published by Smith (*ibidem 29*, 253–255, 1922), gives us a pathetic view of the old man's "closing years" full of disappointment and bitterness.

given him considerable knowledge not only of the industrial arts but also of agriculture. For example he had been one of the promoters of the great farm of Rambouillet, where his chief, the count d'Angiviller,[16] had taken great pains to acclimatize merino sheep.[17] Such practical knowledge more valuable than ever in a time of national crisis was now placed at the service of the Société de Versailles. Unfortunately it was not sufficiently appreciated to afford him a living. For two years the maintenance of his family was derived from his work in an office of the national lottery. During the last four months of his life he enjoyed a pension of 2400 francs which was granted to him by the minister N. L. François de Neufchâteau after the death of Horace Bénédict de Saussure.

6. He had been suffering for some time from retention of urine. On the 4th of November 1799 this old complaint took an alarming turn, and could not be subdued any longer. Montucla was aware of the efforts which were vainly made to save his life, but he did not lose his equanimity, and remained conscious almost until his last hour, which occurred at ten o'clock at night on December 19 of the same year (28 frimaire an VIII).[18] He was survived by his widow, a daughter married in 1783, and a son employed in one of the government offices.

For the appreciation of his character it is worthwhile to place on record his courageous defense of his benefactor Baudouin de Guemadeuc[19] when the latter was calumniated and exiled. According to his first biographer, Montucla was modest in spite of his merit and

[16] Charles Claude de Flahault de la Billarderie d'Angiviller, member of the Royal Academy of sciences, "Directeur et ordonnateur des bâtiments du Roi, intendant du Jardin Royal des plantes en survivance." Died in Altona, Holstein, 1810.

[17] The buildings of that farm still exist and have been used since 1871 for the School of shepherds. One may find a good summary of some of the efforts made in France before the Revolution for the improvement of agriculture in Edouard Grimaux, *Lavoisier* (2nd ed. 1896, 149–190), but there is no mention in it of Montucla or Angiviller.

[18] I quote the date given by the Académie des sciences (*Annuaire pour* 1928, 250), and by Lalande in the *Histoire* (vol. 3, 336). The date given by Le Blond (p. 672) is slightly different: Dec. 18.

[19] It was through him that Montucla had obtained his first appointment in Grenoble. Lalande joined in his defense. During the terrible days of the Revolution many friendships were forgotten, and gratitude more often than not was obliterated by fear. Witness Lavoisier's shameful abandonment by his friends and clients.

beneficent in spite of the smallness of his means to a degree which was truly admirable.

7. *Chronology of Montucla's writings and main events of his life.*
1725.09.05 Montucla's birth in Lyon (see § 1).
— Educated by the Jesuits in Lyon (§ 1).
1741 Death of his father (§ 1).
1745 Death of his grandmother, who had taken charge of his education after his father's death (§ 1).
c. 1745 Studies law in Toulouse, and a few years later establishes himself in Paris and contributes to the *Gazette de France* (§ 1).
1754 His first book: *Histoire des recherches sur la quadrature du cercle* (§ 8).
1755.07.03 Foreign member of the Berlin Academy. See Adolf Harnack, *Geschichte der kön. Preuss. Ak. d. Wiss.* (vol. 1, 477, 1900).
1756 *Recueil de pièces concernant l'inoculation de la petite vérole* (§ 13).
1758 *Histoire des mathématiques* [jusqu'à la fin du XVIIᵉS.] (2 vols.) (§ 18).
1761 Appointed secretary of the Intendance of Grenoble (§ 2).
1763 Marries Marie Françoise Romand, in Grenoble (§ 2).
1764–65 Mission to Cayenne as secretary to chevalier Turgot and astronomer royal (§ 3).
c. 1766 After his return and sojourn in Grenoble, is appointed a clerk in the Superintendence of royal buildings, Versailles (§ 4).
1775 Royal censor (I do not know how long he kept the office) (§ 25).
1778 Reedition of Ozanam's *Récréations mathématiques et physiques* (4 vols.) (§ 25).
1784 French translation of Jonathan Carver's Travels, *Voyage dans les parties intérieures de l'Amérique septentrionale* (§ 30).
After 1789 Loses his position in the Superintendence of royal buildings, probably when that administration itself was suppressed (§ 4).
1794 Receives a national reward from the Comité de salut public (§ 5).
1795 Ordered to examine the treaties deposited in the archives of the ministry of foreign affairs (§ 5).
1796.02.28 Elected "Associé non résident de la section de mathématiques de l'Institut national" 9 ventôse an IV (§ 5).
1799.08.07 Second edition of the *Histoire des mathématiques* (vols. 1 and 2) (§ 33).
1799.12.19 Death in Versailles, 28 frimaire an VIII (§ 6).
1800.01.15 A. S. Le Blond reads his obituary at the Société libre d'agriculture de Seine-et-Oise, 25 nivôse an VIII (§ 40).
1802.05 Posthumous publication of vols. 3 and 4 of the *Histoire des mathématiques* [XVIIIᵉ siècle] (§ 35).
1831 Second edition of the *Histoire de la quadrature* prepared by S. F. Lacroix (§ 11).

SARTON ON THE HISTORY OF SCIENCE

(In chronological order)

8. *Histoire des recherches sur la quadrature du cercle* (xlviii + 304 p., 161 × 95 mm., 8 folding plates. Paris, Ch. Ant. Jombert, 1754). Copy in the Harvard Library.

The author's name does not appear on the title page, nor at the end of the preface, nor in the censor's approbation signed by La Chapelle and dated May 1, 1754, but in the Privilège du Roi, the author is called M. de M.

This little book, Montucla's firstling, was published by him at the age of 29; he was induced to compose it because of his growing irritation against the many publications of the circle-squarers, a category of fools which was more frequent in the seventeenth and eighteenth centuries than it is now though it is by no means extinct. The quadrature of the circle, as he remarked at the beginning of his preface, is one of the stumbling blocks of the human spirit, and indeed, because of its relative simplicity, the most famous. There are other paradoxical problems in the field of mathematics but most of them are too technical and recondite to attract the public's attention. Unfortunately the problem of the quadrature of the circle can be explained to everybody, and becomes an easy trap to every person who knows enough geometry to be presumptuous, but who has not enough knowledge and common sense to be wary. In his preface Montucla shows that there are various kinds of circle-squarers but that they have generally in common a deep ignorance of the futile efforts of their forerunners. Hence he considered it worthwhile to write a history of the subject, hoping that this might help to prevent the incipiency of the disease and its contagion; as to the men who were already affected by it, their condition was generally hopeless.

9. He refers with special praise to the French mathematician Thomas Fantet de Lagny (1660–1734) who was one of the pioneers in the attempt to demonstrate the impossibility of the quadrature of the circle. The end of his preface is devoted to a gentle quizzing of the most persistent circle-squarer among his contemporaries, Joseph Louis Vincens de Mauléon, chevalier de Causans, who was governor of the

206

principality of Orange.[20] This eccentric personage deserves to arrest our attention, for he may well be considered the paragon of circle-squarers. He was a wealthy man who could afford to have a series of pamphlets beautifully published at his own expense. Moreover he offered a prize of three hundred thousand francs to whomever could prove the falsity of his demonstration. This involved him in various litigations, and caused the Royal Academy a good deal of trouble, the chevalier de Causans being presumably too powerful a person to be disposed of easily. The depth of his madness may be judged from his claim that his proof of the quadrature enabled him to explain the mysteries of original sin and of the Holy Trinity!

Ten publications of his are listed in the *Catalogue de la Bibliothèque nationale* (vol. 25, 100, 1906). *Le spectacle de l'homme*, 1751. *La vraie géométrie transcendante et pratique*, 1754. *Éclaircissements sur le péché originel*, 1755. *Au Roi*, 1757 (again 1759). *Mémoire pour la vérité contre l'erreur*, 1759. *Mémoire instructif*, 1760, etc. (extreme dates 1751–1760). However, that list is not complete, for it does not include the very pamphlet to which Montucla especially refers, under the title *Prospectus*.[21] Nor does it include a pamphlet in the Harvard Library entitled *La Quadrature de cercle*, démontrée à l' Académie Royale des Sciences le 14. Mai 1755. par M. le Chevalier de Causans, ci-devant Colonel du Régiment d'Infanterie de Conty. A Paris M.DCC.LV (24 p. quarto, 1 folding plate). I read enough of it to satisfy myself that it is pure nonsense.

10. Montucla's book is divided into six chapters which may be rapidly described as follows: Chapter 1. Definition of the problem. Differences between absolute and approximate quadratures. The determination of the longitude is independent from the quadrature of the circle! It was necessary to discuss such absurdities because of the extravagant claims made by circle-squarers.[22] Chapter 2. Efforts of the ancients. Chapter 3. Later investigations down to the invention of the calculus. Discussion of the many controversies which took place

[20] Including the city of Orange, near Avignon. For a short biography of the chevalier de Causans, see NBG (vol. 9, 261, 1754). No dates given, but his publications range from 1751 to 1760.

[21] According to NBG, *Prospectus apologétique pour la quadrature du cercle*, 1753.

[22] To illustrate, the (British) Board of longitude received in 1796 a letter from Dr. Woemen, "a native of Saxony, acquainting the Board that he can express π and the ratio of 1 to $\sqrt{2}$ integrals, and that this comprehends the discovery of the Longitude. He was informed that the Board do not receive proposals of this nature." Quoted from Rupert T. Gould, *The marine chronometer* (London 1923, p. 15; see *Isis 6*, 123).

in the seventeenth century, and to which James Gregory (1638–1675) gave a new turn, when he published in Padua 1667 his *Vera circuli et hyperbolae quadratura* (a little book of 62 p., c. 20 × 15 cm., of which only 150 copies were issued) in which he attempted to prove that these quadratures were truly impossible.[23] Considering his purpose the title of his booklet was rather paradoxical, but as Montucla remarks (p. 87), to show that a geometrical problem cannot be solved is a way of solving it. Gregory's paper was misunderstood even by so great a man as Huygens. He deserved to be criticized for his proof was not complete, yet incomplete as it was it was prophetic,[24] and from his time on, an increasing number of mathematicians had the intuition that the quadrature was impossible and academies paid less and less attention to the proofs of the quadrature which continued to be submitted to them. Montucla himself concluded (p. 95), "Les Géomètres admettent aujourd'hui d'une commune voix que la quadrature indéfinie du cercle est impossible." [25] Chapter 4 deals with the deeper knowledge obtained by means of infinite series and includes a history of the integral calculus. Chapter 5. History of the most famous circle-squarers ("quadrateurs," a term coined by the author to avoid the necessity of giving the fair name of "geometer" to people who were unworthy of it). The main personalities discussed are Nicholas of Cusa, Simon Duchesne, Oronce Finé, Joseph Scaliger, Longomontanus, Giambattista Della Porta, Thomas Hobbes, Olivier de Serres, Mallement de Messange, Mathulon, Basselin, Clerget, Liger. Chapter 6. Supplement containing a brief discussion of other famous problems, as the duplication of the cube and the trisection of the angle. Index.

11. Montucla's views on the quadrature of the circle are explained more briefly in his edition of Ozanam's *Récréations* (vol. 1, 355–366, 422–424, 1778, and — as revised by Lalande — in the *Histoire des mathématiques* (vol. 4, 619–643, 1802). A new edition of his monograph of 1754 appeared in 1831:

Histoire des recherches sur la quadrature du cercle . . . par Mon-

---

[23] A. M. Clerke, James Gregory (*Dictionary of national biography*, vol. 23, 98–99, 1890). Cantor (2, 717–718, 1900).

[24] The *Vera circuli quadratura* is remarkable in another respect, because it introduced the fundamental ideas of convergence and divergence of series.

[25] ["Geometers admit today with one voice that the unlimited quadrature of the circle is impossible."]

tucla. Nouvelle édition revue et corrigée (xvi+300 p., 21 × 13 cm., 4 folding plates. Paris, Bachelier, 1831).

The editor is not named on the title page, but the preface is signed L. c. The editor was Silvestre François Lacroix (1765–1843), who without being one of the giants was one of the most distinguished mathematicians of a century ago. He corrected carefully Montucla's text, revealed names unmentioned in it,[26] and added a number of footnotes (easily distinguishable from the original ones). For example we learn from one of these footnotes (p. 20), that the disease of "circle-squaring" was still as common in 1831 as in 1754, and the patients, as refractory. This may seem less excusable but in reality the situation was not essentially different in 1831 from that obtaining in 1754. The conviction that the quadrature of the circle was impossible was gradually increasing but it had not yet become a certainty. In 1767, Johann Heinrich Lambert proved *rigorously* that π is irrational;[27] and a few years later (1775) the Royal Academy (of Paris) decided that it would not consider any more solutions of the quadrature![28] In his *Eléments de géométrie* (Paris, 1794) Legendre simplified Lambert's proof and showed that π^2 was also irrational. He added: "Il est probable que le nombre π n'est pas même compris dans les irrationnelles algébriques, c'est-à-dire qu'il ne peut être racine d'une équation algébrique d'un nombre fini de termes dont les coefficients sont rationnels; mais il paraît très difficile de démontrer rigoureusement cette proposition . . . "[29] The proof was certainly difficult, and almost a century had to elapse before it was finally given. In his famous memoir

---

[26] E.g., François Nicole (1683–1758) anonymously praised in the first edition (p. xxiv); named in the second (p. 16).

[27] Johann Heinrich Lambert, Mémoire sur quelques propriétés remarquables des quantités transcendantes circulaires et logarithmiques (*Mémoires de l'Académie de Berlin*, année 1761, Berlin 1768, p. 265–322). Read in 1767.

[28] "L'Académie a pris, cette année, la résolution de ne plus examiner aucune solution des Problèmes de la duplication du cube, de la trisection de l'angle ou de la quadrature du cercle, ni aucune machine annoncée comme un mouvement perpétuel" (*Mémoires de l'Académie de Paris*, année 1775, Histoire, p. 61). The decision is justified in the following pages (p. 61–68).

[29] I think this statement occurs already in the first edition of 1794. However, the earliest edition available to me is the third (an IX, 1800) whence I derived my quotation (p. 327). ["It is probable that the number π is not even included in algebraic irrationals, that is, it cannot be the root of an algebraic equation with a finite number of terms the coefficients of which are rational; but it appears very difficult to give a rigorous proof of this proposition."]

of 1882, Über die Zahl π (*Mathematische Annalen*) Ferdinand Lindemann proved the transcendence of π. Lindemann's proof was rigorous but unnecessarily complicated, and it took more than ten years of competitive efforts to bring it down by successive stages to a more convenient level of simplicity.[30] I told this story at some length because it affords an excellent example of the fact that, even in the field of mathematics, conviction may be a relative matter. Since 1882, the impossibility of the quadrature is absolutely certain, but mathematicians had been morally convinced of it for more than a century before that date.

12. Lacroix added seven longer and valuable notes at the end of the text (p. 265–290); they prove that he had investigated a few of the main sources. These notes deal with Simplicius, the approximations of π from Archimedes to Metius, A. A. Kochansky, Lambert, John Machin, etc. He underlines the importance of Lambert's and Legendre's proofs of the irrationality of π and π^2, and wonders (as the latter did) whether higher powers may not be also irrational. In order to evidence the degree of approximation obtainable in actual computations, he remarks that while the value of π had been obtained with at least 126 decimals, 16 decimals would already suffice to express the length of a circle having for radius the average distance of the Earth from the Sun, with an error of less than a thousandth of a millimeter.

To conclude, Montucla's history of the quadrature is still a valuable book, but Lacroix's edition superseded completely the original one.

For a deeper study of the subject than was possible to Montucla, Lalande, and Lacroix, see Ferdinand Rudio, *Archimedes, Huygens, Lambert, Legendre, Vier Abhandlungen über die Kreismessung mit einer Übersicht über die Geschichte des Problemes von der Quadratur des Zirkels* (VIII + 166 p., Leipzig, 1892). For the anecdotic and pathological aspects see Augustus de Morgan, *A budget of paradoxes* (London, 1872; 2nd ed. by D. E. Smith, 2 vols., Chicago, 1915; errata in the *Monist* 27, 474–477, 1917; *Isis 3,* 117).

13. *Recueil de pièces concernant l'Inoculation de la petite Vérole & propres à en prouver la sécurité & l'utilité* (xii + 335 p., 16.5 × 10

[30] The best account of the proof and its genesis will be found in Felix Klein's famous textbook, *Vorträge über ausgewählte Fragen der Elementargeometrie* (1895) available in many languages. English edition by W. W. Beman and D. E. Smith; second edition revised by R. C. Archibald (New York, 1930; *Isis 16,* 547).

cm. 166 × 99 mm., Paris, Desaint & Saillant, Vincent, 1756). The copy used by me was borrowed from the Library of Congress.

No author's name appears on the title page, nor at the end of the preface, nor in the censor's approbation (dated July 18, 1754). The compilation was made by Montucla and Pierre Joseph Morisot-Deslandes. Of the latter I only know that he edited the posthumous publication of the *Traité des accouchements* (Paris, 1759) by Nicolas Puzos (1686–1753).

The practice of variolation (as opposed to the more scientific Jennerian inoculation or vaccination) was immemorial in Asia (India, China, Iran) and it has also been witnessed among primitive African tribes. It was introduced into Europe by two Greek physicians: Emanuele Timoni, who sent an account of it to the Royal Society, dated Constantinople, Dec. 1713, and Iacopo Pilarino (1659–1718), who published an account of it in Venice 1715, then — more effectively perhaps — by that strange character, Lady Mary Wortley Montagu (1689–1762), who brought it back from Constantinople to England in 1718. The practice spread in England, also in the American Colonies. Its subsequent introduction into France was largely due to Voltaire, Théodore Tronchin, and La Condamine. The latter's *Mémoire sur l'inoculation de la petite vérole*, read at the Académie des sciences on April 24, 1754,[31] was very influential; there are at least twenty editions of it in French and in other languages. From that time on the practice became more and more popular until it was superseded by Jenner's method (1798).

14. Montucla and Morisot-Deslandes prepared this little book soon after La Condamine's lecture, which one of them at least attended. They saw the value of confirming La Condamine's argument by placing a number of original documents in the hands of the French public. In this manner the results of English experience would become completely available to their countrymen and the havoc made by smallpox might be mitigated. Their book was soon ready, for it was approved by the Royal Censor on July 18, 1754, but various circumstances delayed its publication. It was finally published in 1756 when the authors took advantage of a revival of public interest due to the inoculation of two royal children.

[31] Printed in the *Histoire de l'Académie royale des sciences* (Année 1754, p. 615–670, Paris, 1759).

15. The best history of variolation was written by Arnold C. Klebs, Die Variolation im achtzehnten Jahrhundert. Ein historischer Beitrag zur Immunitätsforschung (*Zur historischen Biologie der Krankheitserreger*, 7. Heft, 78 p., Giessen, 1914). Shorter account by the same in the *Johns Hopkins Hospital Bulletin* (24, 69–83, 1913). In the Giessen paper Klebs does hardly more than mention Montucla (note 64, p. 70) but he should not be blamed for this, for Montucla's booklet was but a second-hand collection of documents . . .

17. I do [not] know how the two authors of this compilation arranged their collaboration. Morisot-Deslandes was presumably a physician, while Montucla had received no medical training. However, little medical knowledge was needed for their purpose, which was simply to enable the reader to solve the following problem:

> Une Maladie meurtriere, & que la plus grande partie des hommes doit subir, enlève une portion considérable du genre humain; une expérience que nous pouvons dire aujourd'hui d'un demi siècle, a appris que cette maladie contractée volontairement, dans certaines circonstances, & avec les préparations convenables, étoit d'une bénignité extrême, & préservoit à l'avenir de la prendre une seconde fois naturellement; est-il raisonnable de choisir ce dernier parti, ou vaut-il mieux s'obstiner à attendre le coup mortel sous le ridicule prétexte qu'on sera peut-être un des privilégiés? C'est là précisément l'état de la question concernant l'Inoculation" (Preface, p. v).[32]

It was also to show to the French people how this practical problem had been solved by their English neighbours.

This double purpose was nicely fulfilled. The readers of La Condamine's memoir and of this collection were undoubtedly well informed; and thanks to Montucla modern critics can obtain easily a fair picture of the progress of variolation by the middle of the eighteenth century.

18. *Histoire des mathématiques* . . . (2 vols. quarto, 25 × 19 cm., xxxvi + 638 p., 5 folding pls.; 680 p., 10 folding pls. Paris, Ch. Ant.

---

[32] ["A deadly disease, and one which the great majority of mankind must undergo, removes a considerable portion of the human race; experience, we can say today after half a century, has taught that this illness contracted voluntarily, in certain circumstances and with suitable preparations, is extremely mild and will prevent catching it a second time naturally: is it rational to choose this second alternative, or is it better to persist in awaiting the mortal blow under the ridiculous pretext that one will be perhaps one of the privileged [and escape it?] That is precisely the issue concerning Inoculation."]

Jombert, 1758). The censor's approbation is dated August 19, 1758, and signed Montcarville.

In spite of the fact that this work was the author's *magnum opus* and has remained his main title to fame, we shall not attempt to analyze it as elaborately as the earlier works, in the first place because it is far better known, in the second place because of its encyclopaedic nature. It will suffice to indicate its main peculiarities.

To begin with it is necessary to insist that this is not simply a history of mathematics, and that its title, long as it is, fails to indicate its true contents. Indeed the book deals not only with mathematics, but also (though less elaborately) with mechanics, physics, and astronomy. It is a history of the mathematical sciences, and might also be called a history of science written from the mathematical angle, even as many histories of medicine are to some extent histories of science written from the medical angle.

19. Montucla's preface shows that he had a very clear appreciation of the cultural value of the history of science and of the technical value of the history of mathematics. His interest in the subject went back many years but had been heightened by the *Encyclopédie* which had revealed to him (as well as to many other Frenchmen) Francis Bacon's prophetic views. Let me quote the first paragraph of this very remarkable preface:

Un des spectacles les plus dignes d'intéresser un œil philosophique, est sans contredit celui de développement de l'esprit humain, & des différentes branches de ses connoissances. Le fameux Chancelier Bâcon le remarquoit, il y a plus d'un siecle; & c'est raison qui lui faisoit comparer l'histoire, telle qu'on l'avoit écrite jusqu'alors, à un tronc mutilé de ses parties les plus nobles. Je ne sçais cependant par quelle fatalité cette branche de l'histoire a été de tout tems la plus négligée. Nos Bibliotheques sont surchargés de prolixes narrateurs de sieges, de batailles, de révolutions; combien de vies de Héros prétendus qui ne se sont illustrés que par les traces de sang qu'ils ont laissées sur leur passage? A peine trouve-t'on, comme Pline le remarque avec regret, quelques Ecrivains qui ayent entrepris de transmettre à la postérité les noms de ces bienfaicteurs du genre humain, qui ont travaillé, les uns à soulager ses besoins par leurs inventions utiles, les autres à étendre les facultés de son entendement par leurs méditations & leurs recherches. Encore moins en trouve-t'on qui aient songé à présenter le progrès de ces inventions, ou à suivre l'esprit humain dans sa marche & dans son développement. Un pareil tableau seroit-il moins intéressant, que celui des horreurs & des scenes sanglantes que produisent l'ambition & la méchanceté des hommes?" 33

33 ["One of the spectacles most worth interesting a philosophical eye is without

213

Much else of this preface would deserve quotation, for it is an admirable plea for our studies, which is as fresh and relevant to-day as it was two centuries ago. In fact Montucla's contemporaries, because of the influence of the *Encyclopédie* and of the *"philosophes,"* were in some ways better prepared to appreciate the history of science than the people of our own disillusioned times.

20. Outside of Bacon, Montucla names three other men who influenced his thought and determined him to undertake this great work, the awful magnitude of which he did not fully realize until he was too deeply involved in it to back out: James Bernoulli (1654–1705), the physicist Jean Jacques de Mairan (1678–1771), and the mathematician Pierre Rémond de Montmort (1678–1719). It would seem that the latter had actually begun to compose a history of geometry, a project which was cut short by his untimely death. Montucla inquired about his manuscripts but these been dispersed and lost by his heirs.

21. The *Histoire des mathématiques* is arranged in chronological order with the exceptions quoted below. Sometimes the history of a special question is dealt with as completely as possible in a single chapter, e.g., the duplication of the cube or the center of oscillation. Montucla claimed, and rightly so, that much of his work was pioneer work, and to prove it he gives an account of his forerunners beginning with Theophrastos (p. xvi–xxv). He apologizes for the form of his own work (p. xiv) which is not as elegant as one might wish and sometimes repellent to all but historically minded mathematicians caring for the facts and nothing else. The preface ends with a classification of mathematics which is interesting enough to be summarized.

---

dispute that of the development of the human spirit and the different branches of its knowledge. The famous Lord Chancellor Bacon noted it, more than a century ago, and that is the reason which made him compare history such as had been written up to then, to a shaft with its noblest parts mutilated. I do not know, however, by what fatality this branch of history has been the most neglected in all times. Our libraries are overburdened with verbose narratives of sieges, battles, revolutions. How many of the lives of pretended heroes are not renowned except for the trail of blood that they have left along the way? Hardly may one find, as Pliny regretfully noted, any writers who have undertaken to transmit to posterity the names of the benefactors of the human race, some who have worked to meet their needs by useful inventions, others to extend their faculties of understanding by their meditations and their researches. Still less may one find that they have thought to present the progress of these inventions, or to follow the human spirit in its path and in its development. Would such a picture be less interesting than that of the horrors and the bloody scenes which the ambition and the wickedness of men have brought about?"]

Pure mathematics

I. Arithmetic.
II. Geometry (ordinary; transcendental: finite, infinitesimal).
III. Algebra (finite, infinitesimal).

Mixed mathematics

I. Mechanics (statics, dynamics).
II. Astronomy (spherical, theoretical).
III. Optics (optics, catoptrics, dioptrics, perspective).
IV. Acoustics (acoustics, music).
V. Pneumatology.

22. The whole work is divided into four parts:

I. History of mathematics from the beginnings to the end of the Byzantine empire (vol. 1, 1–336). II. History of mathematics in the East: Arabs, Persians, Chinese, Hindus (vol. 1, 337–404). III. History of mathematics among the Latin and the Western peoples down to the beginning of the seventeenth century (vol. 1, 405–638). IV. The seventeenth century (the whole of vol. 2, 653 p.) Errata and addenda in vol. 1, xxxi–xxxvi, and vol. 2, 654–656. Index in vol. 2, 657–680.

The semi-chronological order of the first volume, i.e., the separate consideration of three separate streams of thought: Greek, Oriental, Latin, is one which I have often criticized, but which was more excusable two centuries ago than now. I believe it would be justifiable only if those three streams had been independent which they were not. A great part of the materials of vol. 1 are obsolete, and Montucla's method of reconstructing the distant past would not be tolerated to-day . . .

23. The second volume is far more important, and students of the seventeenth century would find it worthwhile to consult it; in fact it is one of the books which should be at their elbow. The explanations are sometimes much lengthened because Montucla explains not only the history but the mathematical and scientific facts themselves; [34] this is not necessarily a drawback for the modern reader, for it helps him to consider these questions from a point of view which may be less correct or less general than his own but is historically nearer, and to see them so-to-say in their contemporary perspective.

This volume II is divided into nine books:

[34] "Je me suis soigneusement attaché à présenter une idée distincte, & les véritables principes de toutes les théories de quelque considération, dont le système des Mathématiques est composé" (p. x).

Note that only three of these chapters out of nine are devoted to pure mathematics; optics, mechanics, and astronomy being dealt with each in two chapters. Out of 653 pages, 228 deal with pure mathematics, 169 with astronomy, 148 with mechanics, and 108 with optics; or otherwise, 425 deal with physics and astronomy, that is, almost twice as much as are devoted to mathematics.

24. The arrangement of each chapter is far from satisfactory, and it is clear that in many cases Montucla did not dominate his subject. This was partly unavoidable, as he was sometimes too near the events. Contemporaries may have certain advantages with regard to minutiae but they necessarily lose in breadth and depth what they gain in detail. We must not forget this if we would judge him equitably.

Vol. II is completed with an index relative to both volumes, which proves that they were meant as a whole; indeed they were published together. However it is clear that Montucla was already contemplating a third volume for we find at least one reference to it in vol. 2 (p. 660).

For further discussion of this work see the note below devoted to the second edition of vols. I–II, 1799, and the continuation, 1802.

25. *Récréations mathématiques et physiques. Qui contiennent les problêmes etc* . . . Par feu M. Ozanam . . . Nouvelle édition, totalement refondue et considérablement augmentée par M. de C. G. F. 4 vols. Paris, Cl. Ant. Jombert, fils ainé, 1778 (fig. 10).

Tome I. Arithmétique et géométrie. xx + 464 p., 16 folding plates.
Tome II. Mécanique, optique, acoustique et musique. 432 p., 16 folding plates.
Tome III. Astronomie, géographie, calendrier, navigation, architecture et pyrotechnie. 463 p., 35 folding plates.
Tome IV. Physique, et en particulier les phénomènes de magnétisme, de l'électricité et de la chimie, avec deux suppléments l'un sur les phosphores, l'autre sur les lampes perpétuelles. 523 p., 8 folding plates.

Every volume bears the same date, 1778. I do not know what the initials M. de C. G. F. were supposed to represent, but the new editor was undoubtedly Montucla, later editions bear his own initial, and the English translations his full name. One of the reasons why he may have had to hide himself so completely was the fact that when the royal privilege was applied for by the publisher, Jombert, fils ainé, in 1775, Montucla himself was royal censor! His approbation of his own work reads:

J'ai lu, par ordre de Monseigneur le Garde des Sceaux, les *Récréations Mathématiques et Physiques* de feu M. Ozanam, corrigées et considérablement augmentées: il m'a paru que cet Ouvrage, fort imparfait dans ses éditions antérieures, a acquis dans celle-ci un degré d'amélioration considérable, qui peut lui mériter place parmi les bons livres sur ces matières. Fait à Paris le 5 août 1775.
MONTUCLA *Censeur Royal.*[35]

The Privilège du Roi was dated August 30, and registered on Sep-

[35] ["By order of the Lord Keeper of the Seals, I have read the *Récréations Mathématiques et Physiques* of the late M. Ozanam, corrected and considerably enlarged; it appears to me that this Work, markedly imperfect in its previous editions, has acquired in this one a considerable degree of improvement which earns it a place among the good books on these subjects. Done at Paris 5 August 1775.
Montucla, Royal Censor."]

tember 4 of the same year; it was valid for six years, half of which were already spent when the book appeared.

26. To appreciate Montucla's edition, we must first consider Ozanam's original work. Jacques Ozanam was born in 1640 at Bouligneux in the principality of Dombes (near Villars en Bresse, Ain), a younger son of a well to do and honorable family of Jewish origin, which had been Christianized since a long time.[36] He was largely self-taught, and became a teacher of mathematics in Lyon, later in Paris. In peace time he would instruct foreign gentlemen, and in war time, when his students vanished, he would compose mathematical textbooks. The number and size of his books testify to his industry and the frequency of war years. His most important publications are a mathematical dictionary (1691), a complete mathematical course in five volumes (1693), and his mathematical recreations (1694) which put earlier books of the kind entirely in the shade. His religious attitude is illustrated by this saying of his: "il appartient aux docteurs de Sorbonne de disputer, au Pape de prononcer, et au mathématicien d'aller en paradis en ligne perpendiculaire." [37] He died in Paris in 1717.

The *Récréations mathématiques et physiques* were first published in 1694 (2 vols., 19 × 12 cm., xxx + 400 p., 44 pl., xiv + 304 p., pls. 45–64, Paris, Jean Jombert, 1694). The royal privilege was dated January 11, 1692. Vol. 1 deals with arithmetics, geometry, optics, gnomonics, cosmography; vol. 2, with mechanics, pyrotechnics, and physics and is followed by a *Traité des horloges élémentaires, ou de la manière de faire des horloges avec l'eau, la terre, l'air et le feu* (vi + 164 p., 18 pl.). The printing of this first edition was completed on the last day of April 1694. In the preface Ozanam quotes his foremost predecessor: Claude Gaspard Bachet de Méziriac (1581–1638), whose *Problèmes plaisans et délectables que se font par les nombres . . .* were first published in 1612, but not the Jesuit Jean Leurechon (1591–1670) whose mediocre *Récréations mathématiques*, first published in 1624, were immensely popular.[38]

27. Ozanam's book was also very successful. It was republished twice in 1696 (in Paris, and in Amsterdam). After Ozanam's death a revised edition was prepared by one Grandin [39] and published in 4 vols. in 1725, and

[36] My source for Ozanam's biography is Fontenelle's éloge (*Œuvres*, Nouv. éd., vol. 6, 506–515, 1790). This is summarized in the NBG (vol. 38, 1017, 1862), plus bibliography.

[37] Fontenelle, 514; ["it pertains to the doctors of the Sorbonne to dispute, to the Pope to pronounce, and to the mathematician to go to paradise in a perpendicular line"].

[38] Thirty-four editions before 1700, says D. E. Smith, *History of mathematics* (vol. 2, 535, 1925).

[39] Known to me only by the mention of his name in NBG (38, 1017). Perhaps

many times afterwards: 1735?, 1741, 1749–50, 1770. I have examined only the edition of 1725, *Récréations mathématiques et physiques* . . . par feu M. Ozanam. Nouvelle édition, revue, corrigée et augmentée (4 vols., Paris, Claude Jombert, 1725). The new editor is not named, and the dedication to the Chevalier d'Harcourt is signed by the publisher. The preface is substantially the same as the combined prefaces to the two volumes of 1694. The "approbation" signed by Varignon is dated April 28, 1720 (see end of vol. 3); a second approbation is printed at the beginning of the fourth volume, signed Andry, dated May 16, 1722.

These four volumes are divided as follows:

Tome I. Arithmétique, géométrie, musique, optique. Tome II. Gnomonique, cosmographie, mécanique. Tome III. Pyrotechnie, physique. Traité des horloges élémentaires. Tome IV. Phosphores naturels et artificiels, lampes perpétuelles, Tours de gibecière [leger-de-main, card tricks, etc.]

28. We now come to the third series of editions which was initiated by Montucla. The reedition prepared by him was first published in 1778, then again in 1790. In his anonymous preface Montucla recalls the earlier book of Bachet de Méziriac and the "pitoyable rapsodie" of E. van Etten (i.e., the Jesuit Leucheron above-mentioned) and also the original Ozanam collection, for his own edition was very different — by addition, subtraction, and correction — from the earlier ones. Indeed Montucla had taken great pains to renew this book as much as possible and to increase its attractiveness and usefulness. His analysis deserves to be quoted almost completely in spite of its length; it is curious that he is almost always comparing his book with Ozanam's, and criticizing the latter as if the intermediate editions had not occurred . . .

Montucla concludes that his book is not unworthy of consideration even by the most learned mathematicians and physicists, his favorable opinion of his own book being fortified by that of the Censor (that is, himself!!). It was really, within its scope, an encyclopaedic treatise of great interest not only to the contemporary readers but also to the historian of science who would know the state of knowledge on a multiplicity of subjects in the third quarter of the eighteenth century. It was very superior to the previous editions not only because of the valuable novelties which were included but almost as much because of the systematic omission of futilities. After having been brought down, presumably for the sake of popularity, to a low level, Ozanam's book was now raised to a new level which was somewhat higher than the original one.

29. Ozanam's collection was as well received in England as on the

---

identical with Martin Grandin, who lectured at the Académie des sciences in 1738 on the nature of fire and its propagation?

continent. In spite of the fact that many Englishmen were able to read it in French it was promptly translated. The original edition was Englished as early as 1708.

Recreations mathematical and physical . . . by Monsieur Ozanam. Done into English and illustrated with very many Cuts . . . (xxxvi + 530 p., 19 × 12 cm., London, R. Bonwick, etc. 1708).
The translator is not named on the title page and his preface is anonymous. An abridgment seems to have been made of this edition. At any rate the British Museum Catalogue contains the following title under Ozanam: *Recreations for gentlemen and ladies*, translated from the French (4th ed., 226 p., Dublin, 1790).
Montucla's revision was Englished by the mathematician and physicist Charles Hutton (1737–1823).[40] "*Recreations in mathematics and natural philosophy* . . . first composed by M. Ozanam, lately recomposed and greatly enlarged by the celebrated M. Montucla. And now translated into English and improved with many additions and observations by Charles Hutton. With near 100 quarto plates (4 vols., London, Kearsley, 1803). This was reprinted at least once, in 1814. A revision of this translation was prepared by Edward Riddle (1788–1854) mathematician and astronomer, and first published in 1840, then again in 1854.
Recreations in mathematics and natural philosophy. Translated from Montucla's edition of Ozanam by Charles Hutton. A new and revised edition, with numerous additions . . . by Edward Riddle [41] (1 vol., 21.5 × 14 cm., xiv + 826 p., more than 400 woodcuts, London, Thomas Tegg, 1840).

30. *Voyage dans les parties intérieures de l'Amérique septentrionale, pendant les années* 1766, 1767 & 1768 *par* Jonathan Carver. Ouvrage traduit sur la troisième édition anglaise par M. de C.[42] avec des remarques et quelques additions du Traducteur (24 + xxviii + 451 p., 19 × 12.5 cm., 1 carte, Paris, Pissot, 1784). Approved by the royal censor Le Tourneur, on March 11, 1783. Privilege dated April 15, 1783.

Jonathan Carver was born in Weymouth, Massachusetts in 1710; [43] he took part in the war against the French in Canada and was wounded at the siege of Fort William Henry in 1757. The war being ended by the

[40] About whom see DNB (28, 351–353, 1891).
[41] About whom see DNB (48, 273, 1896).
[42] Stands for M. de Chanla, Montucla's pseudonym.
[43] My biographical information is derived from William Browning, The early history of J. Carver (*Wisconsin magazine of history 3*, 291–305, 1920), and from Louise Phelps Kellogg in *Dictionary of American biography* (vol. 3, 552, 1929). Some of the data given by J. Westby-Gibson in *Dictionary of national biography* (9, 237–238, 1887) are very different. E.g., according to DNB, following J. C. Lettsom, Carver was born in Stillwater, Connecticut in 1732. It is now certain that Carver was born in 1710.

Peace of Paris, 1763, he resigned his commission, and began to think of exploring the western countries and maybe of finding a passage to the Pacific Ocean. He set out on his travels in 1766, starting from Boston in June. "He went west by the route of the Great Lakes, crossed to the Mississippi by the Green Bay–Fox–Wisconsin route, ascended the great river and entered the St. Peter's (now the Minnesota). He reached Lake Superior by the Chippewa and St. Croix rivers, and finally returned in the autumn of 1767 to Mackinac, whence in the next spring he made his way back to Boston" (DAB).

31. The first edition of his *Travels through the interior parts of North America* appeared in London 1778. The second part of this work dealing with "The origin, manners, customs, religion and language of the Indians" is largely a compilation from other books which he failed to mention (Charlevoix, La Hontan).[44]

The second London edition appeared in 1779, as well as a Dublin edition. Carver died in London in 1780 a poor and broken man. The third London edition appeared in 1781. The text is exactly the same in those three London editions, except that the third contains a biography and portrait of the author, and an index, added by the Quaker physician John Coakley Lettsom (1744–1815). The first American edition appeared only in 1784, in Philadelphia.[45] Carver's travels were translated into German (Hamburg, 1780), into French, by Montucla (Paris, 1784), into Dutch by J. D. Pasteur (Leyden, 1796). In short before the end of the century Carver enjoyed an international reputation, and his work was one of the most famous eighteenth-century works of American origin. It inspired a great many people, including Schiller and Chateaubriand.

32. We may now return to Montucla's translation. It was based on the third English edition (the third London edition, 1781, is meant), and contains an adaptation of Lettsom's biography. Montucla has

[44] The printed text differs materially from Carver's MS. preserved in the British Museum. Elaborate study of his sources by Edward Gaylord Bourne, The Travels of Jonathan Carver (*American historical review*; vol. 11, 287–302, 1906). This proves that some of Carver's borrowings amounted to plagiarism. However Bourne's destructive criticism is not final. For Carver's defense, read Louise Phelps Kellogg, The mission of Jonathan Carver (*Wisconsin magazine of history 12*, 127–145, 1928.)

[45] For later English and American editions, too many to be quoted here, see Joseph Sabin, *Bibliotheca americana* (vol. 3, 382–384, 1870).

added a number of notes, e.g., on natural history, each of which is clearly credited to himself ("Note du traducteur"), a short preface (7 p.) explaining the interest of Carver's book and apologizing for the shortcomings of his own translation caused by his lack of time,[46] and supplements relative to other expeditions in search of a North West passage to the Pacific taken from the writings of Le Page du Pratz (d. 1775), Arthur Dobbs (1689–1765), and baron de La Hontan (c. 1666 – c. 1715). Some of Montucla's notes throw a curious light on the colonial ideas of France in those days. For example, he remarks that the acquisition of Canada was for England "a very poor bargain!"[47]

A French translation of Carver's *Travels* was published in Yverdon 1784, and also in the "Bibliothèque des écoles chrétiennes" of the Librairie Mame of Tours in 1845 (reprinted at least seven times). All these editions are presumably derived from Montucla's.

33. *Histoire des Mathématiques* . . . Nouvelle édition considérablement augmentée et prolongée jusque vers l'époque actuelle. (4 vols., 25.5 × 20 cm. Paris, Henri Agasse, an vii – an x (1799–mai 1802). An VII = 1798/9, but vols. 1 and 2 actually appeared on August 7, 1799. The original price of the four volumes was sixty francs.

Tome premier (History of mathematics before the seventeenth century), an VII (viii + 739 p., 12 folding plates), Montucla's portrait.
This volume is a revision of volume 1 of the first edition. The general plan is the same and a large number of paragraphs have been transcribed either verbatim or with only minor corrections. However the additions, in the form of new paragraphs inserted between the old ones, or placed at the end of a book, or in the form of supplements, are so numerous, that an enumeration of them is out of the question. In spite of some omissions the total increase is considerable (739 p. against 638 less closely printed). For example, the book dealing with oriental mathematics is almost twice as long (130 p. against 68). The new preface was composed in the same way as the whole book: it is a mixture of old fragments, some unchanged, others modified, and of entirely new ones. Montucla indicates two new sources which had become available to him since the publication of the first edition: Jean

[46] "Ceux qui nous connoissent sçavent que, livrés par état à des occupations très impérieuses, nous n'avons pu donner ni à la revision de notre manuscrit ni à celles des épreuves, qu'un temps très limité" (p. 11). See similar excuse in his *Histoire de la quadrature* (p. xxx) and in his *Histoire des mathématiques* (2nd ed., vol. 1, p. viii, also p. iv). Such excuses have but little validity and they are too frequent in Montucla's books.
[47] "De bons esprits, même chez elle, avoient prévu que le Canada seroit pour les Anglois une acquisition funeste. En France, M. Turgot l'avoit dit à nombre de personnes" (p. xiii).

Sylvain Bailly's [48] treatises on the history of astronomy (5 vols., 1775–1787) and Joseph Priestley's history of optics (London, 1772). He praises the German translation of that work by Georg Simon Klügel (1739–1812), including valuable additions and corrections (1775–76). He did not use Priestley's history of electricity, although it had appeared as early as 1767, because, strangely enough, electricity was not within the scope of his survey, but he refers to his treatise on perspective (London, 1770).[49]

34. *Tome second. Quatrième partie, qui comprend l'Histoire de ces Sciences pendant le dix-septième siècle.* An VII (718 p., 14 folding plates).

The same remarks apply to vol. 2, which is substantially the same in both editions, though the second contains many corrections and additions, and the order of the nine chapters is different. However the modifications are on the whole less numerous and less important than in the first volume, which is not surprising, as the subject of the first volume is considerably larger (the whole of the past down to the seventeenth century!) than that of the second, and full of obscurities. This second volume is followed by an index relative to volume I and II which appeared together in the same year VII, in fact on the same day, August 7, 1799.

35. *Tome troisième.* Achevé et publié par Jérôme De La Lande. Paris, chez Henri Agasse, an X (mai 1802) (viii + 832 p., 17 folding plates), portrait of La Lande.

Tome quatrième. Achevé et publié par Jérôme De La Lande. Paris, chez Henri Agasse, an X (mai 1802) (688 p., 2 folding plates).

These two volumes published together in May 1802, with a single index, are really like a single volume divided into two parts. They are devoted to a single subject forming the fifth part of the whole of Montucla's history (vol. 1: parts 1 to 3; vol. 2: part 4; vols. 3–4, part 5), that is, the history of mathematical sciences in the eighteenth century . . .

In other words, out of the 1528 p. of these two volumes, only 454 (less than one third) deal with pure mathematics, 381 with astronomy, 227 with mechanics, 209 with navigation, 179 with optics, etc.

36. As I explained above when discussing the first edition of Montucla's history, he was already thinking of devoting a third volume to the eighteenth century before the printing of vols. 1 and 2 was completed, but administrative duties and other tasks prevented him from doing much work in that chosen field until the Revolution robbed him of his job. He then devoted the best part of his unwelcome leisure to

[48] About whom, see Fernand Laurent, *J. S. Bailly, premier maire de Paris* (Paris 1927; *Isis 11,* 393–395).

[49] Nothing more, see vol. 1, 712, vol. 3, 605. The History of electricity is also mentioned on p. 605.

the continuation of his history, but he soon realized that the task was far more difficult than he had anticipated and he expressed his discouragement to Lalande on August 7, 1799 (vol. III, p. vii):

Plus j'y réfléchis, plus je vois par les difficultés que j'éprouve, que j'ai été un téméraire d'entreprendre un pareil ouvrage. Je suis réduit à dire que je m'en tirerai comme je pourrai.[50]

We must bear in mind that at that time Montucla was 74 years old and that long years of administrative routine (not to speak of his Guiana adventure) had somewhat unfitted him for as ambitious an undertaking and one as full of difficulties and pitfalls. It would have required a far better mathematician and scientist than Montucla ever was to appreciate correctly and with any finality the achievements and the trends of that golden age.

37. As was often the case in the past, the printing of vol. III was begun when the manuscript was still far from complete. When Montucla died on December 19, 1799, twenty-one sheets (p. 1 to 336) had been proofread and printed, but the rest of the MS. was not entirely ready and the necessary revision was undertaken, presumably at the publisher's request, by Jérôme De La Lande, who called himself (vol. 3, 336) "one of Montucla's oldest friends."

Lalande [51] (1732–1807) was primarily an astronomer, and when he realized the imperfection of the manuscript he appealed to other scientists for advice concerning the subjects with which he was not sufficiently familiar. For example, the chapter on the integration of partial differential equations (vol. 3, 342–352) was revised by Lacroix. The optical book was partly edited (vol. 3, p. 427–495) by citizen de Fortia, i.e., the ci-devant marquis de Fortia d'Urban (1756–1843),[52] then, because of the latter's forced absence (see p. 483), the rest of that book was edited by Lalande, p. 496–537 being entirely written by him. For the mechanical book he tried vainly to obtain the coopera-

[50] [The more I think about it, the more I see by the difficulties that I experience that I have been foolhardy in undertaking such a work. I am compelled to say that I will pull out of it as I can.]
[51] The name is written de la Lande, or De La Lande, or La Lande, or Lalande, its own bearer using different forms at different times (e.g., vol. 3 of the *Histoire des mathématiques*, title page, p. 336; vol. 4, title page, p. 681). Many French names appeared in different forms before, during, and after the Revolution.
[52] About whom see NBG (18, 217–21, 1857).

tion of one Dillon whom I failed to identify, and had finally to do the work himself. While he was endeavoring to shift the responsibility of the optical and mechanical parts upon other shoulders, he carried the history of astronomy [53] so far that it was possible to print volume IV before completing the printing of volume III.

38. These two new volumes are distinctly inferior to vol. II. In many cases the author devotes much space to the explanation of scientific matters which one would expect to find in a treatise on natural philosophy or astronomy but which are out of place in a history of mathematical sciences. Sometimes on the contrary the account degenerates into an unreadable bibliography (e.g., III, 825–832). In any case the information thus offered to us is very precious, even if we have to check every item of it. To be sure much of it could be obtained otherwise, but some glimpses of contemporary feeling are truly invaluable. A good example is the criticism of Marat's optical theories, (p. 594–597) — Marat being the "ferocious beast" mentioned in the preface (vol. III, p. v): "la bête féroce dont mademoiselle de Corday d'Armont, jeune et belle héroïne, purgea la terre le 14 juillet 1793, en sacrifiant sa vie avec un courage dont aucune femme ne lui avoit donné l'exemple dans l'histoire." [54] By the way it is strange enough that Newtonian optics should have been attacked at about the same time by two personalities as different in almost every other respect as Marat and Goethe! [55]

---

[53] Lalande was well acquainted with the recent history of astronomy, witness his *Bibliographie astronomique avec l'histoire de l'astronomie depuis 1781 jusqu'à 1802* (924 p., Paris an XI = 1803). However, he remarks that his own account in this vol. IV was subordinated to Montucla's, which suggests that Montucla's history was almost complete at the time of his death: "Je ne me suis pas regardé comme obligé de faire une histoire de l'Astronomie, mais de publier celle qu'avait fait Montucla, en réparant les omissions qui l'auroient rendue défectueuse" (vol. III, p. vi).

[54] [The ferocious beast of whom Mlle. de Corday d'Armont, a young and beautiful heroine, purged the earth 14 July 1793, sacrificing her life with a courage which no other woman in history has exemplified.]

[55] Jean Paul Marat, *Découvertes sur le feu, l'électricité et la lumière* (42 p., Paris 1779); *Découvertes sur la lumière* (141 p. Londres et Paris, 1780); *Notions élémentaires d'optique* (48 p., Paris 1784); Traduction de l'Optique de Newton (2 vols., Paris 1787).

Goethe, *Beyträge zur Optik* (2 parts, Weimar 1791–92); *Zur Farbenlehre* (2 vols. xlviii + 654 p., 16 pl., xxviii + 758 p., Tübingen, 1810). Charles Lock Eastlake, *Goethe's Theory of colours* translated from the German (xlviii + 423 p., London 1840). This is a translation of Goethe's first volume only. Goethe's second

38*bis*. According to Miss Bertha Frick, who has examined various sets of this work, there are differences between them. The portrait of Montucla appears in the first volume, or in the third, or in the fourth; the portrait of Lalande appears in the third volume or in the fourth. There may be other differences. The copy I have used contains Montucla's portrait in the first volume, and Lalande's in the third. Obviously the portraits were interpolations which may have been added at any time to the several volumes to improve their sale. There may possibly be copies without portraits, either because these volumes were issued before the portraits were added, or because the portraits were eventually subtracted by print collectors.

39. *Final appreciation of Montucla's work.*

Montucla's history of the quadrature is still valuable, but the original edition has been superseded by the second one edited by Lacroix in 1831.

His treatise on variolation may almost be discarded, and the same may be said of his translation of Carver's *Travels*.

Though his edition of Ozanam's *Récréations* was far superior to the earlier ones, the mathematical part of that collection is now superseded by more recent and scientific ones, notably those of Edouard Lucas, *Récréations mathématiques* (4 vols., Paris 1882–1894) and Wilhelm Ahrens, *Mathematische Unterhaltungen und Spiele* (Leipzig 1901, second edition, 2 vols., 1910–1918).

Montucla's fame rests in the last analysis on his *Histoire des mathématiques* (2 vols. 1758), more especially upon the second edition (4 vols., 1799–1802), which is still a very valuable book, though only for the wary "connoisseur"; novices will do well to leave it alone. And I wish to repeat once more (as this is so often forgotten) that it is not only a history of mathematics, but also of mathematical sciences; it might even be called a history of science though it be a very incomplete one.

No man was better able to appreciate Montucla's achievement than Moritz Cantor (1829–1920) who renewed it on a magnificent scale a century later. It is clear that Cantor made full use of his predecessor's investigations, witness the abundant references to them throughout his *Vorlesungen*. Indeed these references are so numerous that at least as far as the history of mathematics is concerned, the modern scholar

---

volume deals entirely with the history of optics from the "Urzeit" to his own time. Marat's views are indulgently criticized on p. 601–606. These views had been translated into German by Christian Ehrenfried Weigel (Leipzig, 1783).

is hardly in danger of forgetting Montucla, for sooner or later Cantor will send the reader back to him. We may say that Cantor had lived in Montucla's spiritual intimacy for at least thirty years, hence he must have been thoroughly acquainted with his every quality or weakness. His final judgment is favorable to Montucla, and he found the gentlest and the most modest way of expressing his praise, saying that he would be fortunate indeed if later historians would consider the progress made from Montucla to himself half as important as the progress made from Vossius to Montucla.[56]

The student of the history of mathematics may generally neglect the histories anterior to Montucla, but he would be wise to refer to the latter, especially with reference to the seventeenth and eighteenth centuries. The statement of this simple fact is the greatest tribute we can pay to his memory. Montucla needs no tombstone, or monument, other than his *Histoire des mathématiques* which will remain an eternal witness to his learning and devotion, and the admirable continuity of his endeavor, as well as an impressive landmark in the evolution of mathematical thought.

40. *Bibliography.*

Auguste Savinien Le Blond, Notice historique sur la vie et les ouvrages de Montucla . . . de la Société libre d'agriculture de Seine-et-Oise, présentée a ladite Société . . . en sa séance du 25 nivôse an 8 [Jan 15, 1800]. 24 p. octavo, Paris, an VIII.

Auguste Savinien Le Blond, Sur la vie et les ouvrages de Montucla. Extrait de la Notice historique lue à la Société de Versailles, le 15 janvier 1800. Avec des additions par Jérôme De Lalande. In Montucla's *Histoire des mathématiques* (vol. 4, 662–672, 1802).

This is the only source for Montucla's biography, and I have made full use of it, correcting silently various inaccuracies and adding facts derived from the manuscripts and books quoted in this paper. I have seen only the second edition, the first being named after the catalogue of the Bibliothèque nationale, Paris.

Auguste Savinien Leblond, mathematician and naturalist, was born in Paris in 1760, and died in the same city in 1811. He was employed in the print cabinet of the Imperial Library. He was a great-nephew of Guillaume Le Blond (1704–1781) — whom Montucla used to meet in Jombert's shop, — mathematical instructor of the royal pages and princes. Was he also related to Jean Baptiste LeBlond [57] (1747–1815), physician and

[56] M. Cantor, *Vorlesungen zur Geschichte der Mathematik* (vol. 3, 2nd. ed., 1901, 500–502).

[57] Jean Baptiste Leblond, Description de la Guyane française, 2e éd. augmentée d'une notice sur M. Leblond par le Dr. Leblond son neveu (xvi + 91 p., Paris

naturalist, who travelled in the West Indies and South America from 1767 to 1802 and explored Guiana for the sake of cinchona? I have no means of knowing.

Thomas Carlyle, Montucla. One of the notices contributed by him between 1820 and 1823 to the *Edinburgh Encyclopaedia*, reprinted in his *Montaigne and other essays* (London, 1897, 293–7). Quoted for the sake of curiosity, derived from Le Blond and otherwise insignificant.

E. Evieux, Un mathématicien lyonnais, Montucla (*Le Salut public*, Lyon, 15 avril 1926).

Niels Nielsen, *Géomètres français sous la Révolution* (Copenhague, 1929, 190–192, *Isis 16*, 502). Contains nothing new; see notice on Lalande in same book (152–155).

The notices in NBG and other dictionaries, which I have consulted, are derived from Le Blond . . .

[1936]

1824). Not available to me; have seen only the first edition without the biography (91 p., Paris 1814).

Quetelet

(1796-1874)

Among the many centenaries to be celebrated in 1935 none appeals to my imagination more strongly than that of the publication of Quetelet's work entitled *Sur l'homme et le développement de ses facultés, ou Essai de physique sociale,*[1] one of the greatest books of the nineteenth century. The world would be better today if more politicians and administrators were trained to understand Quetelet's message, but the intellectual inertia of the so-called leaders as well as the stupidity of their flocks brings into greater prominence the genius of such men as himself and Galton. Quetelet's book on man and the development of his faculties with the bold subtitle SOCIAL PHYSICS was the first attempt to apply mathematical analysis to the study of man — not only of his body but of his behaviour and morality, his mind and soul. The book made a considerable stir in Europe, the original Paris edition being soon followed by a pirated one (Brussels, 1836), by German and English translations (Stuttgart, 1838, Edinburgh, 1842), and by abundant and acrimonious controversies. A small minority recognized its prophetic value, but for the mass of the educated people it was rather a cause of scandal and grief. How could anyone carry scientific indiscretion and impiety further than by attempting, as Quetelet did, to analyse man's transgressions as if they were physical accidents, to consider the passions of his soul as if they were abnormalities of the weather, and his very morality as a kind of climate? Quetelet's "average man" was ridiculed and tabooed.

Yet Quetelet had proved his case as completely as it was possible to prove it in his own time and with the means at his disposal. If the

[1] 2 Vols., 21 × 13 cm., xii + 327 p., 2 tables, viii + 327 p., 6 tables (Paris, 1835).

average number of crimes, suicides, births out of wedlock, etc. are constant in a given community, one cannot escape the conclusion that they must needs reveal realities comparable to physical realities, and that the most secret behaviour of men is submitted to social laws of the same kind as the laws of physics. Whichever might be the idiosyncrasies and the freedom of individuals, their average morality and behaviour could be foretold as well as their average physical features and longevity. Moreover, he showed that inasmuch as it is hopeless to study each and every individual, the only approach to social physics or sociology was the mathematical analysis or the statistical method to the explanation and illustration of which his book was devoted.

The statistical instrument is to the sociologist and statesman what the thermometer is to the physician; if one knows the data relative to a body politic presumably sound, the anomalous data relative to another body will reveal its illness. The physician observing an abnormal temperature knows that something is wrong; his next tasks are to locate the cause of the illness and find a remedy. So does the statistician who observes excessive rates of murder or suicide or sexual delinquency in a given community. He knows that there is something wrong, and such knowledge is the first condition of redress. Again, if he should observe that the inequalities of wealth and opportunity are excessive — that the rich are too rich and too few and the poor too poor and too many — he knows that the body politic of that particular community is not well. However, the majority of men are conscious or unconscious hypocrites; they are far more afraid of the publication of evil than of evil itself; and if they enjoy privileges which would not bear scrutiny they prefer darkness to light. Such people are very apt to mistake their own selfish interests for those of the community, to resent the diagnosis of a disease on which they have managed to thrive, and to browbeat the physician who exposes the evil and attempts to cure it.

Far from being a sacrilege, the search and revelation of truth is a duty, — it is not simply a scientific duty in a narrow sense, it is also a philanthropic duty and a religious one. The religious — or if you please the mystical — aspect of statistical inquiries was strongly evidenced in one of the earliest treatises on the subject, the one published almost two centuries ago by Johann Peter Süssmilch (1707–67), entitled

Die göttliche Ordnung in den Veränderungen des menschlichen Geschlechts (2 vols., Berlin, 1741).[2] It was beautifully expressed by that great woman, Florence Nightingale (1820–1910), "The Lady of the Lamp." According to Pearson's account: [3]

> Her statistics were more than a study, they were indeed her religion. For her, Quetelet was the hero as scientist, and the presentation copy of his *Physique sociale* is annotated by her on every page.[4] Florence Nightingale believed — and in all the actions of her life acted upon that belief — that the administrator could only be successful if he were guided by statistical knowledge. The legislator — to say nothing of the politician — too often failed for want of this knowledge. Nay, she went further: she held that the universe — including human communities — was evolving in accordance with a divine plan; that it was man's business to endeavour to understand this plan and guide his actions in sympathy with it. But to understand God's thoughts, she held we must study statistics, for these are the measure of his purpose. Thus the study of statistics was for her a religious duty.

Quetelet's book of 1835 had been prepared by statistical studies initiated ten years earlier. His golden age was probably the decade beginning in 1828. In that year he published his *Instructions populaires sur le calcul des probabilités* — one of the earliest popularizations of a subject of which relatively few people realized the fundamental importance in those days, and he read his memoir *"Recherches statistiques sur le Royaume des Pays-Bas,"* [5] in the preface of which he clearly expresses the value of comparative statistics for the diagnosis and understanding of social conditions. In 1835 — the golden year — appeared his *Social physics*, wherein his conviction was reiterated and bolstered up with a great variety of examples. A couple of years later the first king of the Belgians, Leopold I, invited him to give some lessons to two princes of his family — Ernest and Albert of Saxe-Coburg — during their stay in Brussels. These letters were eventually published under the title, *Lettres sur la Théorie des probabilités ap-*

[2] I have seen only a later edition (3 vols., Berlin, 1761–1776). Vols. 1–2 (1761–1762) are a second edition; vol. 3 (1776) an additional volume by Christian Jacob Baumann.
[3] Karl Pearson, *The life, letters and labours of Francis Galton* (vol. 2, 414, Cambridge, 1924; *Isis 8*, 186). See also our appendix.
[4] Presented to the Galton Laboratory by Miss Nightingale's niece, Mrs. Vaughan Nash, and now placed beside Darwin's gift of the *Origin of species* to Galton and Tyndall's gift of his Belfast address to Herbert Spencer. (K. P.)
[5] Read before the Royal Academy of Brussels on Dec. 6, 1828. *Nouveaux mémoires de l'Académie royale* (tome 5, 28–57, 12 tables, Bruxelles, 1829).

pliquées aux sciences morales et politiques (454 p., 26 × 17 cm., Bruxelles, 1846). Galton, who studied them in the English translation (London, 1849), considered them "the most suitable [treatise on the subject] to the non-mathematical reader." [6] When Euler wrote his famous letters for the niece of Frederick the Great, the Princess of Anhalt-Dessau (Petersburg, 1768) he did not speak of the calculus of probabilities though it was already fairly advanced in his day. It is much to the credit of Quetelet and of his royal patron that that calculus and its applications to the social sciences were now considered a fit subject for a ruling prince. Indeed could one imagine one more fit to give the latter some idea of his responsibilities? And yet I wonder how many of the remaining princes of our own days realize this as deeply as they should?

Galton [7] was not entirely fair to Quetelet when he said that the latter had not fulfilled the high promise contained in his work of 1835. It is true the second edition of the *Social physics* was not materially different from the first, though it appeared thirty-four years later,[8] but this was partly due to the fact that his genius had already reached its highest potential in 1835. The rest of his life was devoted not to any attempt to soar higher, or to undertake new explorations in the unknown, but rather to the consolidation of his initial effort. He was the leading spirit not only of the Observatory and the Academy of Belgium, but of almost every scientific endeavour in the new kingdom, and in addition to that he was the prime organizer of every international agency for meteorological and statistical investigations. He was one of the founders of the London (Royal) Statistical Society in 1834 [9] and when the American Statistical Association was founded five years later, he was its first foreign member. He was the creator of the international congress of statistics, and his unchallenged supremacy is proved by the circumstance that out of the nine congresses [10] he

[6] Needless to say that book is now obsolete if only because there is no mention in it of the theory of correlation, first published by Galton in 1888. Pearson, *Life of Galton* (vol. 2, 335, 1924; vol. 3, 50, 1930; *Isis* 22, 235–255).

[7] Pearson (vol. 2, 420; *Isis 8*, 186).

[8] *Physique sociale* was now the main title. "*Physique sociale, ou Essai sur le développement des facultés de l'homme* (2 vols., Bruxelles, 1869).

[9] The centenary of which was celebrated this year. See *Nature* (133, 560, 1934).

[10] The congresses were replaced in 1885 by a permanent organization, the

presided over seven! He was president of the first congress in Brussels 1853, of the third, Vienna, 1857, of the fourth, London, 1860,[11] of the fifth, Berlin, 1863, of the sixth, Florence, 1867, of the seventh, The Hague, 1869, of the eighth, Petersburg, 1872 (I do not believe there is another example in the history of international scientific congresses of such a persistent leadership). He failed to preside over the second congress (Paris, 1855) because he had an apoplectic stroke in July of that year, and over the ninth (Budapest, 1876), because of his death.[12] He was truly the father — or we might say the patriarch — of statistics.

At this point I beg leave to open a parenthesis for the sake of refuting a common error. It is often said, and not only by Germans, that the father of statistics was Achenwall. This is not simply erroneous but highly misleading. Far from being the father of statistics, Gottfried Achenwall (1719–1772) did not even know what statistics is. He may have been the first to speak of statistics, but he really spoke of something very different from what we understand by that word. I have examined his *Abriss der neuesten Staatswissenschaft der vornehmsten Europäischen Reiche und Republicken* (x+324 p., Göttingen, 1749). This is simply a brief description of the countries of Europe with special reference to their constitution, products, character and qualities of the inhabitants, laws, commerce, etc. The purpose is comparative, but no special chapter is devoted to a comparative survey of each of the elements dealt with in the other chapters. Numbers are seldom in evidence, and there are neither numerical tables nor graphs of any kind! As far as I could make out the statistical contents of this book are not essentially different from those which may be found in many other publications which began to appear two centuries earlier, such as Sebastian Münster's *Cosmographia* (1536, 1544), Giovanni Botero's *Relazioni universali* (1596), etc. Indeed statistics in that early sense

International Statistical Institute. John Koren, *The history of statistics* (New York, 1918; *Isis 4*, 387–389).

[11] The congress of 1860 was presided [over] by the Prince Consort. [Marginal correction by the author.]

[12] He was born in Ghent on February 22, 1796, and died in Brussels on February 17, 1874. Good biography by Emile Waxweiler in *Biographie nationale de Belgique* (18, 477–494, 1905).

is as old as almost any form of organized society, for has not every intelligent ruler (whether he be the king *gratia Dei* of a very elaborate commonwealth or the chieftain of a barbarian tribe) the wish to know as exactly as possible the amount of his resources in men and goods, and to know equally well the resources of his possible allies and enemies? Any systematic attempt to satisfy such curiosity was "statistics" in the old sense.[13]

Achenwall begins his *Abriss* [abstract] with the following words: "Der Begriff der sogenannten Statistic {sic}, das ist, der Staatswissenschaft einzelner Reiche wird sehr verschiedentlich angegeben, und man trifft unter der grossen Menge Schriften davon nicht leicht eine einzige an, welche in der Zahl und Ordnung ihrer Theile mit der andern überein kommen sollte." [14] This shows that by the middle of the eighteenth century the exact contents of the new science called "statistics" was not yet clearly understood in spite of its popularity; however it might be broadly defined as "a comparative study of states." It is often said that Achenwall was the first to use the word statistics,[15] but I am not sure even of that for if he had coined the term would he say "die sogenannte Statistic"?

The roots of Quetelet's thought must be sought outside of that "so-called statistical" literature. There are two main roots. First, the "political arithmetic" which developed in England in the second half of the seventeenth century; second, the calculus of probabilities which originated about the beginning of the same period (1654) in a correspondence between Pascal and Fermat, and reached a magnificent climax in Laplace's *Théorie analytique des probabilités* (Paris, 1812). Laplace lived until 1827. Quetelet was deeply influenced by him, and was introduced to him in Paris, in 1823.[16] I shall not insist on the

[13] To illustrate, consider Egypt. For what might be called the statistical organization of the old Empire (c. 3400 to c. 2475), see Adolf Erman and Hermann Ranke, *Aegypten* (Tübingen, 1923, 107). For the general census under the XVIIIth dynasty (1580–1350), see Serge Dairaines, *Un socialisme d'état quinze siècles avant J. C.* (Paris, 1934, 75). Consider also Israel : read Chs. 1 to 4 of the *Book of Numbers*.

[14] [The concept of so-called statistics {sic} that is, of the political science about individual states is variously stated, and one does not easily find in the great mass of writing a single one which in the number and order of its parts agrees with any other.]

[15] E.g., Littré's *Dictionnaire* s.v. statistique. The earliest English example given in Murray's *NED* is Zimmermann, 1787.

[16] Quetelet had a good mathematical training and began his scientific career

history of the theory of probability for that is too beautiful a story to be told in a hurry [17] but I may say a few more words of the political arithmeticians who illustrated so remarkably in this regard the English genius for concrete explanations.

These were Captain John Graunt (1620–1674) and Sir William Petty (1623–1687). The first prepared the *Natural and political observations upon the bills of mortality* (London, 1662), then Petty published a series of tracts on "political arithmetic" and "political anatomy" — and finally his famous treatise entitled *Political Arithmetick*, which he wrote as early as 1676–77. This was published surreptitiously in 1683, but the first duly licensed edition appeared only in 1690 after the author's death.[18] A third great forerunner was Edmund Halley (1656–1742), whose endless curiosity and brilliant mind were once more exemplified in a paper of his containing the earliest mortality table: "An estimate of the degrees of the mortality of mankind, drawn from curious tables of the births and funerals at the city of Breslaw, with an attempt to ascertain the price of annuities upon lives" (*Philosophical Transactions* for January 169⅔, vol. 17, No. 196, p. 596–610). Halley's interest in statistics went back at least to 1681.[19] Süssmilch, mentioned above, continued the English political arithmetic in a more mystical vein. It now became the mathematicians' business to keep this

as a teacher of mathematics. He and Jean Guillaume Garnier started in 1825 the publication of a journal entitled *Correspondance mathématique et physique* (11 vols., Ghent 1825–1839) which was of great importance for the mathematical education of Belgium. After its discontinuance in 1839, there was no mathematical journal in that country until 1874 when Eugène Catalan and Paul Mansion started the *Nouvelle correspondance mathématique*. From 1876 to 1880 Catalan was the only leader and raised the mathematical standard of his journal very high, perhaps too high for the rank and file. In 1881, it was replaced by *Mathesis*, the aim of which was more modest; *Mathesis* was originally edited by P. Mansion and J. Neuberg; it is still going strong today.

To return to Garnier and Quetelet's journal, it is significant that in spite of its elementary character (that is, the purpose was rather the diffusion of knowledge than original research) it included many statistical notes; it thus helped to popularize the statistical point of view.

[17] Read Isaac Todhunter, *History of the mathematical theory of probability from the time of Pascal to that of Laplace* (640 p., Cambridge, 1865). Helen M. Walker, *Studies in the history of statistical method* (338 p., Baltimore, 1929; *Isis* 13, 382–383).

[18] Lord Edmond Fitzmaurice (*DNB*, 45, 113–119, 1896). The only perfect copy of the unauthorized edition of 1683 is in the Bodleian Library.

[19] See his letter to Hooke, May 19/29, 1681, and also his letter to Caspar Neumann of Breslau, 1693, quoted in Eugene Fairfield MacPike, *Correspondence and papers of Edmond Halley* (Oxford, 1932, 52, 89; *Isis* 20, 470–472).

movement on the right track. The main difficulty as always was to fight off the theologians and philosophers who had no patience for austere investigations and were more anxious to know or to prattle as if they knew, than to study. Quetelet quoted approvingly Joseph Fourier's saying, "Les sciences statistiques ne feront de véritables progrès que lorsqu'elles seront confiées à ceux qui ont approfondi les théories mathématiques"[20] (*Correspondance mathématique*, 2, 177, Gand, 1826). Fourier's warning is still necessary to-day.

The victory of the political arithmeticians and even more so that of the theorists of probability was so overwhelming that the meaning of the word statistics changed radically, almost without anybody being aware of how, when, and why. The emphasis had been gradually transferred from the subject to the method. Statistics was no longer restricted to the description of states; it was applied to the study of any collection of facts which could be summarized in the form of tables, curves and graphs. It is now defined: "The science of the collection and classification of facts on the basis of relative number or occurrence as a ground for induction; systematic compilation of instances for the inference of general truths; the doctrine of frequency distributions."[21] Statistical training is focused upon the theory of probability and its applications to any problem which life or science may suggest. It concerns itself with such questions as the definition of averages, the appreciation of the homogeneity of collections, the best means of sampling them, the interpretation of the data with a minimum of distortion or error. Achenwall had neither knowledge nor conception of these matters. On the contrary, Quetelet was keenly aware of them, and realized their complexity, difficulty, and fundamental importance.

Another great injustice is made when Comte is called the founder of sociology, for Quetelet has better claims to this title than he, or at least they should be mentioned together. Auguste Comte (1798–1857) was probably the first to speak of social physics (as early as 1822) and

[20] ["The statistical sciences will not make real progress until they are intrusted to those who have mastered the mathematical theories."]
[21] Definition of the word statistics (construed as singular) in Webster's *New International Dictionary* (2d. ed., 1934).

of sociology (1839).[22] In 1824, he wrote to a friend, "Je crois que je parviendrai à faire sentir, par le fait même, qu'il y a des lois aussi déterminées pour le développement de l'espèce humaine que pour la chute d'une pierre." [23] Comte wrote on these matters as on many others with unbearable prolixity and conceit. In the meanwhile Quetelet was not only saying what to do, but was actually doing it, and doing it much better than Comte could imagine, for the real difficulties and the crucial points only appear when one is tackling concrete problems and tackling them in large numbers humbly and patiently; they remain almost always hidden from the superficial and supercilious minds of philosophers. Comte talked, strutted and soared, and apparently ignored the terre-à-terre activity of his fellow worker in "social physics," [24] but that activity was far more creative than his own. Comte was building proud castles on sand, Quetelet, humbler constructions on bedrock. Moreover Comte had no appreciation of the importance of the theory of probability, nor of statistics, nor of the statistical approach to biology and sociology.[25] I do not propose to discuss the question "who was the founder of sociology?" — but if the alternatives are Comte or Quetelet, — surely it was not Comte, but Quetelet.

From 1834 on, Quetelet was perpetual secretary of the Belgian academy, a post which his encyclopaedic tendencies and his universal curiosity made highly suitable for him. He was able to stimulate not only the scientific activities of his countrymen in almost every direction, but also, though to a lesser extent, their literary and artistic efforts. He soon realized that one of the best means of originating or encouraging new endeavours was to tell the history of the earlier ones and this

[22] *Cours de philosophie positive* (Tome 4, 252, 1839).

[23] In a very long letter dated Sept. 8, 1824. *Lettres d'Auguste Comte à M. Valat* (Paris, 1870, p. 139). ["I believe that I shall succeed in having it recognized through the fact itself that there are laws as well-defined for the development of the human species as for the fall of a stone."]

[24] I do not remember any reference to Quetelet in Comte's works, but have read them only in parts and at different times. The Comtian literature is very extensive and unindexed. At any rate Quetelet is not mentioned at the very places where one would expect at least a mention of his name.

[25] See his silly remarks in the *Cours de philosophie positive* (vol. 3, 410 ff., 418).

was probably what induced him to devote a part of his precious time to historical investigations.

There are a number of historical notes in the *Correspondance mathé-matique,* [26] but his first historical paper outside of his own journal appeared in 1835 (the very birthyear of *Sur l'homme*), in the form of a report submitted at the Dublin meeting of the British Association for the Advancement of Science: "Aperçu sur l'état actuel des sciences mathématiques chez les Belges" (*Report of the fifth meeting B.A.A.S.,* 35–59, 1836). The purpose of this paper was not only to spur on his countrymen, but to show the world what the new Belgium (then barely five years old) had already accomplished. After 1835, his statistical investigations engrossed his thoughts so deeply that he had no time for historical writing, except a few obituaries, and a note on the ancient academy of Brussels,[27] until almost thirty years later.

In 1864 and 1866 he published two large volumes: *Histoire des sciences mathématiques et physiques chez les Belges* (480 p., Bruxelles, 1864) and *Sciences mathématiques et physiques chez les Belges au commencement du XIXe siècle* (IV+754 p., Bruxelles, 1866).

The first of these volumes is a history of science in Belgium, with the general history of that country and the history of art as a background.

It is divided into four books: I. From the beginning (Roman times) to the birth of Charles the Fifth in 1500 (56 p.); II. To the end of the governorship of Albert and Isabella, 1633 (118 p.); III. To the foundation of the Academy of Brussels, 1773 (93 p.); IV. To the independence of Belgium, 1830 (92 p.). This is followed by two irrelevant appendices, explaining the purpose and functions of the Royal Observatory of Brussels, and a project of a Belgian Pantheon to be established in the Park of that city.

It is clear that Quetelet's historical efforts were largely inspired by his ardent love of the country whose rebirth in freedom it had been his privilege to witness. Moreover he was himself one of the leading artisans and promoters of the new kingdom, his own share in that leadership being especially glorious, as the scientific revival was largely due to him.

[26] For example, the first volume (1825) contains notes (by himself) on Huygens' MSS., Gregory St. Vincent, Gemma Frisius.
[27] Sur les travaux de l'ancienne Académie (*Bulletin de l'Académie de Belgique,* vol. 5, 14 p., 1858).

The second volume is, as the title suggests, a continuation of the first, but a very irregular one. It would perhaps be more correct to call it a collection of materials for the use of later historians. It is divided into four books: I. Organization of scientific research in Belgium, and international organization of science (a field of which Quetelet was one of the pioneers); II. Biographies of fourteen contemporary Belgian scientists; III. Biographies of Belgian men of letters and artists; IV. Biographies of twelve foreign scientists.[28]

These two historical works of 1864 and 1866 are somewhat heavy and repetitious; the author's patriotism and his zeal to illustrate the scientific achievements of his people were greater than his historical experience. These books are not distinguished except as the historical contributions of a very distinguished scientist. However it may still be useful to refer to them, especially to the second which is partly in the nature of memoirs, and as such really valuable in spite of careless writing. They contain the reactions of a candid witness to many scientific personalities and to important events of his time, —*quorum pars magna fuit.*

Quetelet lacked historical training and had no conception of historical difficulties. In this he was perhaps less excusable than other scientists because his long experience in another — his own chosen — field should have taught him that things are not always as simple as they look. History is just as easy, or as difficult, as statistics: it is just as easy to write poor history as to compile poor statistics; it is just as difficult to do good historical work as to do good statistical work. Keenly aware as he was of the many statistical pitfalls, he seemed unconscious of the historical ones, and as a result he made himself ridiculous in one remarkable instance. He published two letters purported to have been written by his "illustrious countryman" [29] the Holy Roman Emperor Charles V to François Rabelais in 1542. Charles wrote to Maistre Rabelais (in French) that he had promised a thousand

[28] Arago, Humboldt, Alexis Bouvard, H. C. Schumacher, Gauss, Goethe, Gioberti, F. X. J. Droz, Malthus, A. R. Falck, D. J. van Ewijck, baron de Keveberg de Kessel. These notices are interesting because they include personal recollections. With regard to Quetelet's contacts with Goethe, see Auguste Collard, *Goethe et Quetelet* (*Isis 20*, 426–435, 1934).

[29] Charles-Quint was born in Ghent in 1500; he died in 1558. Rabelais was born c. 1490 and died in 1553. The letters were published in the *Bulletin de l'Académie de Belgique* (vol. 22, 204–207, 1866). Controversy with Gachard and facsimiles (*ibidem*, 343–346, 478–479, 544–555).

écus to whomever would solve the quadrature of the circle, but in vain. Would not Rabelais try? The archivist Louis Prosper Gachard proved that these two letters were apocryphal. Their text had been communicated to Quetelet by the French geometer and historian Michel Chasles (1793–1880). It was not yet known then that poor Chasles had been for years the chosen victim of a clever and unscrupulous forger, otherwise Quetelet's discomfiture would have been even worse.[30]

Two other historical papers deserve mention. "Tables de mortalité et leur développement" (*Bulletin de la Commission centrale de statistique de Belgique*, tome 13, 40 p., Bruxelles, 1872). The first part of this paper (p. 4–17) is historical. It contains a very interesting comparison (tabular and otherwise) between nineteen mortality tables, beginning with Halley's famous Breslau table of 1693. The second paper was the "Premier siècle de l'Académie royale de Belgique," which Quetelet contributed as its perpetual secretary to the memorial volumes celebrating its first centenary, *Académie royale de Belgique. Centième anniversaire de fondation*, 1772–1872 (2 vols., Bruxelles, 1872). Quetelet's paper covers p. 117 to 174 of the first volume. He was admirably qualified for the writing of his general survey, for he had been the academy's moving spirit for almost forty years, that is, for a substantial part of its whole existence, the period of maximal activity up to that time.

We gather from the preface to his book of 1866 that he was planning to write in cooperation with his son, the astronomer Ernest Adolphe François Quetelet (1825–1878) three more volumes on the history of science in Belgium, dealing respectively with astronomy, meteorology, and terrestrial physics, but on account of the father's death and the son's inefficiency, that project failed to materialize.

Quetelet's historical studies suggest another comparison with Comte.

[30] See P. Tannery's notice on Chasles in the *Grande Encyclopédie* or in his *Mémoires* (vol. 6, 517–521). "Son goût pour les recherches historiques lui attira une mésaventure célèbre. Un faussaire, du nom de Vrain-Lucas, lui vendit successivement, par pièces détachées, une immense collection d'autographes dont Chasles se servit notamment pour revendiquer en faveur de Pascal un certain nombre de découvertes qui font la gloire de Newton. Faugère en France, Brewster en Angleterre, démontrèrent la fausseté des pièces invoquées par Chasles et finalement celui-ci, en 1869, reconnut cette fausseté et fit poursuivre Vrain-Lucas qui lui avait extorqué près de 200,000 francs."

The latter was one of the pioneers of the history of science movement,[31] but as usual he preached by precept rather than by example. On the contrary, Quetelet's interest was concrete, and its application immediate. He undertook to write the history of science in his own country, and accumulated a considerable amount of materials for later historians. Unfortunately if he was a born statistician he remained until the end an indifferent historian.

I like to think of the constant presence in any sound Republic of two guardian angels: the Statistician and the Historian of Science. The former keeps his finger on the pulse of Humanity, and gives the necessary warning when things are not as they should be. The Historian of Science — or let us say simply the Historian (for in the future every historian will have enough scientific training to appreciate the importance of science) will not allow Humanity to forget its noblest traditions or to be ungrateful to its greatest benefactors. If the Statistician is like a physician, the Historian is like a priest, — the guardian of man's most precious heritage, of the one treasure which, whatever may happen, can never be taken away from him — for the past is irrevocable. Humanity must be protected by the watchful Statistician, and it must be sustained in its newer and bolder efforts by the consciousness of every antecedent effort, to which it owes its culture, its dignity and its excellence.

Quetelet realized these two needs ahead of the great mass of the people, even of the best educated, and such prophetic vision of the intellectual necessities of the future, if that is not genius, what else is it and what else is genius?

Cambridge, Massachusetts.
[1935]

APPENDIX

. . . As explained in the text, the *Physique sociale* of 1869 was not essentially different from the first edition published in 1835 under the title *Sur l'homme.* Thanks to the courtesy of the Department of applied

---

[31] G. Sarton, L'histoire de la science (*Isis 1*, 9, 1912).

statistics of University College, London, and of Mr. Egon Sharpe Pearson, we are able to reproduce [omitted here] the title pages of the copy presented to Florence Nightingale, bearing Quetelet's dedication in his own hand and Miss Nightingale's remarks in her own hand. As these inscriptions may be [are] partly lost in the reproduction (the ends of some words have already been cut off in the binding), I give the full text here.

Quetelet's dedication: *Mademoiselle Florence Nightingale. Hommage de respect et d'affection. L'auteur. Quetelet.*

F.N.'s remarks on the half-title page: *Organic periods = positive creed.*

Critical periods = no convictions but that the old ones are false.
Xtianity   = organic period.
Reformation   = critical   "
Will last until a new organic period has been inaugurated by the triumph of a yet more advanced creed (? the New Moral World resulting from Law).

On the main title page:
the sense of infinite power
the assurances of solid certainty
the endless vista of improvement

from the principles of PHYSIQUE SOCIALE if only found possible to apply on occasions when it is so much wanted. Nov. 1, 70 [the date being cut by the binder is uncertain; it might be read Nov. 17 without indication of year].

These remarks together with the passage which I quoted above from Pearson's biography of Galton, are highly significant and throw a new light on her personality . . .

Aimé Bonpland

(1773-1858)

A CENTURY AGO Alexander von Humboldt was by far the most famous man of science in the world.[1] Such popular fame as he enjoyed is due to a natural ebullience of feelings which are generally well founded. It is the result of an unconscious plebiscite which would have no chance of succeeding, if it were not based on a sufficient number of individual convictions, scattered, unrelated, spontaneous, yet well documented and enthusiastic. Indeed, the achievements of this new Alexander were far more admirable than those of his eponym, the two-horned devil who tried to conquer the world. The exaggerations of popular glory are generally followed by a critical reaction which may be unduly severe, as if people regretted having admired a man too much and were suddenly jealous of him; then after a while historians reexamine the evidence and reestablish the man's fame on a less exalted level but on a more durable foundation.

This has been the case for Alexander von Humboldt as for every great man. After having been submitted to various evaluations and devaluations, his renown is now as secure as any, for we can measure his achievements and see them all around as it were in their proper surroundings. Not only do we know the seeds he has sown and the trees he has planted, but we have tasted their fruits and licked our lips.

Alexander the Great was not born in Macedonia, 356 B.C., but in Berlin, 1769. The early one, whom many generations of idiots, unable to admire anything as much as brutal power, have called "great," might have become a great man had he been capable of understanding

[1] A good criterion is the very frequent use of his name for eponymic purposes in many countries.

Aristotle's lessons, instead of which he degenerated into a dictator, a reckless driver of men, being gradually overwhelmed by his genius which was genuine enough but wholly evil.

It is a joy to watch a plant grow and in due time bear gracious flowers and luscious fruits; it is a greater joy to see the bird develop out of a fledgling or the domestic tiger out of a playful kitten. It is sheer happiness to attend the gradual blossoming out of a child into a good man or woman. We can give ourselves that happiness over and over again in a vicarious and of course imperfect manner by reading biographies. It is possible in the same way to observe from a safe distance the creation of evil as well as the creation of good. Strangely enough, many people, though not evil-minded themselves, have a fascination for the evil of other people, especially when it was done on a monumental scale. They admire and almost worship such demons as Alexander or Napoleon, Francia or the second Lopez, not to mention living ones; I suppose they have not yet completely emerged from slavery. They need not read these pages, for I am writing now for free men, men who love virtue and beauty and above all the truth, as much as is available to us, men who are gentle and meditative. To such as them, yourselves, my readers, there can be no greater pleasure than to contemplate in a frail body the unfoldment of a beneficent genius, that is, a genius which tends to increase the goodness, not the evilness, of mankind. To return for a moment to the old Alexander, Alexander the Less, and cast a final glance at him, when we say that he conquered the world, that seems honorable and glamorous, but it really means that he scattered destruction, famine, and pestilence over the face of the earth and caused millions of men, women, and children, most of them better than himself, to suffer infinite misery. Now let us refresh ourselves and contemplate the achievements of Alexander von Humboldt, the spontaneous yet steady growth of his good genius.

The outstanding event in his life as well as in Bonpland's was their voyage to the equinoctial regions of the New Continent from 1799 to 1804.[2] They travelled together with no companions but Indians and

[2] Humboldt seemed predestined to become a new Columbus, the scientific discoverer of America. His mother was born Maria Elisabeth von Colomb, belonging to one of the families expelled from France by the Revocation of the Edict of Nantes (1685). Thus he might have called himself Humboldt-Colomb. The name

the simplest equipment (except for a few scientific instruments which were the best of their kind), and they covered some nine thousand miles, many of them in wild and unexplored country. Their fortitude and heroism were on the same level, Bonpland deserving perhaps a little more credit, because he was more liable to fevers and was sometimes incapacitated by them. Humboldt was a few years older (they were, respectively, thirty and twenty-six at the beginning of their journey) and not by any means immune; one of his arms remained lame as a result of exposure in the Orinoco forests. He was the initiator and the guiding spirit. The encyclopaedic purpose dominating the journey was an idea of his youth. The scientific training to which he had submitted himself in Göttingen, Freiberg, and other places was so diversified yet so thorough that it could hardly have been improved upon if he had then already tried to prepare himself for the expedition which he undertook many years later. He was preparing himself, as all men of genius do, for the task of his life before he knew clearly what that task would be. In a letter to the friend of his youth, Willdenow,[3] written just before sailing from Coruña for the great adventure (June 5, 1799), he exclaimed, "*Man must ever strive after the good and great!* All the rest depends on fate." [4] That is a generous "cri du coeur," a bit vague. At the same moment he was writing more specifically to the Austrian mineralogist, K. E. von Moll (1760–1838), "I shall make collections of plants and fossils, and I hope to make some astronomical observations with the excellent instruments I have with me. I intend to institute a chemical analysis of the atmosphere. But all this does not form the main object of my journey. My attention will ever be directed to observing the harmony among the forces of nature, to remarking the influence exerted by inanimate creation upon the animal and vegetable kingdoms." [5] That is already the "cosmic" view which sets him going.

Colomb (and variants) was not uncommon in Western Europe; it was probably derived from columba (dove). Many early women saints, Irish, Spanish, Cornish, Burgundian were called Columba, and there is an Irish saint Columbanus. The name Colomb had been illustrated in France by Michel Colomb (1431–1512), "prince of French sculptors."

[3] Karl Ludwig Willdenow (1765–1812) was Humboldt's main botanical tutor and but for his premature death would have been the botanical editor of the expedition instead of Karl Sigismund Kunth (1788–1850).

[4] Written in German. French translation in Hamy (1905, 19).

[5] In German. English translation in Bruhns-Lassell (vol. 1, 247).

Seven years of scientific training, five years of exploration, then thirty years of research ad hoc and publication of the results (33 volumes). In the meanwhile, another stream of his thought — the synthetic view — was steadily developing. Of course, we get many glimpses of it in his letters beginning with the one just quoted. The first systematic account is given in the *Ansichten der Natur* (1808) often reprinted and translated into several languages, then in the Berlin lectures (1827–28), finally in the *Cosmos* of which the first two volumes, of special meaning in this respect, appeared in 1845–47, and the fifth (and last) in 1862, three years after his death at ninety. Seventy years of almost uninterrupted development; that is a fine stretch.

So continuous and intense were his encyclopaedic interests, so monumental their ostensible results that, after his contemporaries had overcome the first spell of admiration and stupefaction, some of them began to insinuate that he was not a real man of science but a theorist indulging grandiose conceptions without experimental responsibility. We now know full well that they were wrong. Looking across the interval of a century, we realize that a number of scientific discoveries or inceptions must be definitely ascribed to him.[6] Let me just mention a few. He was the first to determine the amount of carbonic acid in the atmosphere (1791); he recognized the magnetic action of serpentine rocks in Heidberg (1798), this being the first observation of its kind, which he had occasion to repeat later in Tenerife and Cumana; just before his departure (1799) he invented respiratory masks for miners and proposed the use of oxygen in badly ventilated mines; he observed in Cumana on Nov. 12, 1799 the first shower of Leonids (i.e., the first meteoric radiant, in Leo) and thus opened a new branch of astronomy; in the following year he observed the astonishing communication between the Orinoco and Amazon basins;[7] in 1803 he observed the *Gegenschein* or counterglow. After his return from America he made a series of eudiometric investigations with Gay-

[6] In L. Darmstaedter's *Handbuch* (2nd ed., 1908) there are 24 items bearing his name from 1791 to 1845, in spite of the fact that such a narrow chronological list will always tend to favor the analytical investigator against the synthetist. However, some of these items refer to synthetic achievements.

[7] It has been shown later by Hermann von Ihering and others that that strange phenomenon is the rule rather than the exception in S. America (*Isis 28*, 137).

Lussac (1805), studying the composition of the atmosphere at various altitudes; in 1807 (1815) he established the geography of plants on a sounder basis; in 1808 he improved the scientific description of mountains; in 1816 he founded comparative meteorology and introduced the idea of isothermic line; in the following year he published the first isothermic map (*Mém. Société d'Arcueil*, III, 462), this being the first example of isogram. Humboldt was one of the first to apply graphical methods to meteorological investigations. In 1820, he discussed the meaning of various isograms relative to snow. In the meanwhile, he was gradually revealing his genius as one of the first organizers of international observations. By 1829, he had succeeded in establishing a network of magnetic stations all over the world. He deeply realized the need of continuous and regular meteorological observations in as many places as possible. His main interest was terrestrial magnetism for the study of which he enjoyed Gauss' cooperation, but he saw the importance of other meteorological data and together with Quételet organized their collection on a large scale.[8] With regard to barometric observations he showed their complexity, the necessity of noting the time at which maxima and minima occur in each locality, of repeating the observation at least every hour, etc. He had had opportunities of noticing in Brazil barometric variations so regular that one could almost consult a barometer instead of a watch to know the time! In 1845, he showed that the curious tapering off of continents southward (noted by Buffon in 1749) was repeated in the majority of peninsulas. At the end of the biographical notes, "Mes confessions," which he put down in 1805 for his friend Pictet,[9] Humboldt remarked (Hamy, 1905, p. 244):

Je n'ai parlé que de mes ouvrages, mais il y a beaucoup de mémoires de moi dans le journal de Lamétherie, les Annales de Chimie de Paris, celles de Crelle, le Journal allemand de Freyberg, le journal astronomique de Zach, le Magasin historique de Biester, le journal espagnol de Cavanilles. Ce sont toujours des expériences ou des observations, bonnes ou mauvaises, mais jamais des théories dont je ne suis pas prodigue.[10]

[8] See Ad. Quételet's own account of this in this *Sciences mathématiques et physiques chez les Belges* (p. 592–607, Bruxelles, 1866).

[9] Marc Auguste Pictet (1752–1825), Genevese physicist.

[10] ["I have spoken only of my own works, but there are many of my reports in the journal of Lamétherie, the Annales de Chimie of Paris, those of Crelle, the German Journal of Freyberg, the astronomical journal of Zach, the historical Magasin of Biester, the Spanish journal of Cavanilles. These are always experi-

This shows that he was sensitive to the criticisms to which he was already subjected, but his defense made no impression on those who wished to denigrate him. It is always the same story. Many of his technical papers which would have made the reputation of smaller men were forgotten in the glamor of the "Aspects of nature" and eclipsed by the immense popularity (much of which was unavoidably of a poor kind) which greeted the *Cosmos*.

It is foolish to try to dismiss the scientific organization of science as if it were simply a matter of generalization and administration. Of course, it entails administrative problems — every organization does in proportion to its size, — but the scientific organization proper is far removed from idle generalizations, for its success depends largely on the careful determination of every instrumental and experimental detail. Humboldt and Quételet excelled in this field because their encyclopaedic purpose was combined with a thorough understanding of those details. They organized meteorological and magnetic observations all over the world. Humboldt may be called one of the founders of terrestrial physics, meteoric astronomy, scientific orography, and geography of plants. His views on those subjects were never vague and irresponsible generalizations, but detailed programs of research, specific instructions being given with regard to the instruments to be used, the methods of observation and registration to be followed. In fact, Humboldt and Quételet may be said to have created the prototypes of international scientific research which were gradually imitated in every field of science and made geographical syntheses of every kind possible. After their time it began to be felt necessary to discuss every phenomenon from a cosmic angle; our knowledge was considered incomplete short of that.

Even as Humboldt's concrete observations have been somewhat neglected because the general public knew little else than his *Cosmos*, even so many people have forgotten that he was not alone on his equinoctial journey, but that a young Frenchman shared his exaltation and his efforts, his fatigue and his dangers, and should share his glory. Let us now turn our attention to that companion, snatch him out of the obscurity wherein he has sunk, and put him back in the center of

ments or observations, good or bad, but never theories which I am not lavish with."]

the stage with Humboldt. This is the more necessary because, while the latter may always be quoted as one of the most fortunate men of science that ever lived, Bonpland is a good example of infortune. He needs our admiration and our love more than Humboldt does, and as he deserves them, too, he should have them abundantly.

Aimé Bonpland was born in the parish of St. Bartholomew of La Rochelle on August 28, 1773. He belonged to an old Rochellian family called Goujaud; his father was the first member of it who added Bon-plant (or Bonpland) to its name, probably to distinguish his branch from others.[11] This father, called Simon Jacques (alias Jean) Goujaud-Bonpland, was a physician of some distinction, for he became chief surgeon in the hospital of La Charité in La Rochelle; he had married in 1769 Marguerite-Olive, daughter of a sea-captain, François Aimé de la Coste. They had five children, the first and last of whom died in infancy. The three others were: (1) Michel Simon (b. 1770), military doctor, physician in the hospital Saint Louis, Paris: (2) Elizabeth Olive (b. 1771) who married the lawyer Gallocheau; and (3) Aimé (b. 1773). This last named received a medical education in Paris, Xavier Bichat being one of his masters, and became a surgeon in the French navy. Thus were the medical strain on his father's side and the naval one on his mother's harmonized in him. However, under the influence of Lamarck, Antoine-Laurent de Jussieu, and Louiche Desfontaines, he had developed a deep interest in natural history, chiefly botany, which needed only a little encouragement to flare out marvelously.[12]

Having completed his naval service in 1795, Aimé Bonpland returned to Paris to continue his medical studies; he followed various courses,

[11] This habit has already been discussed by me apropos of Anquetil-Duperron (*Osiris 3*, 197). The final name Duperron (or Bonpland) is the equivalent of an American middle name; sometimes it became the main name as happened for Aimé (Goujaud-) Bonpland.

[12] Bonpland had herborized in and around La Rochelle, either before going to Paris or during vacations. Indeed, when Pyramus de Candolle (1778–1841) undertook in 1802 his thorough revision of Lamarck's *Flore française* he made use of many regional herbals including Bonpland's herbal of La Rochelle. See *Mémoires et souvenirs d'A. P. de Candolle* (Genève, 1862, p. 139). That extremely valuable biography contains other notes on Bonpland (p. 152, 159, 218); it is a rich mine of information on botany in the period 1798–1840, but unfortunately there is no index.

attended clinics, and herborized with his brother Michel. It so happened that he and Humboldt were dwelling in the same apartment house and met occasionally in the concierge's lodge when they took or returned their keys. Humboldt noticed that the younger man was carrying a vasculum and that was enough to arouse his curiosity and his sympathy. They got acquainted and soon agreed to try their luck together. The history of their early projects and false starts has often been told apropos of Humboldt and need not be repeated. Neither shall I attempt to describe their expedition. It will suffice to make a few remarks concerning Bonpland. Though Humboldt was an experienced botanist, as he recognized his companion's superiority in that branch of science, he abandoned the collection and determination of plants largely to him. This was the more natural because Bonpland's botanical interest was somewhat exclusive, while Humboldt was obliged to give much of his time to the general direction of the undertaking as well as to astronomical, physical, and meteorological observations. It is probable that in his search for plants in dismal places Bonpland exposed himself more than his friend; in any case he fell ill more often and more deeply. One such illness, occurring at Santo Tomas d'Angostura (Guiana), was particularly severe. Humboldt took him to the house of a friendly planter in a cool valley four miles from the Orinoco, and thus gave him a good chance for recuperation. A vivid account of that incident, which might have become tragic, is given in a letter to Humboldt's brother Wilhelm.[13] In spite of these difficulties and many tribulations, they managed to collect some 60,000 plant specimens, most of them garnered by Bonpland, and four fifths of them described by him.[14] It is clear that Bonpland was very active in the field, courageous and cheerful, a good fellow and a first-rate collector willing to bear with any risk or any amount of fatigue in order to secure a coveted specimen, — but nonchalant and lazy otherwise. Both men being thrown together in complete isolation for long periods must have been equally gentle and unselfish to emerge from

[13] Dated Cumana, Oct. 17, 1800 (Hamy, 1905, 86–90). Accounts of Bonpland's other illnesses (Hamy, 1905, 126, 142).

[14] The Bonpland's type specimens are in the Muséum, Paris. There are important sets of duplicates in the Botanisches Museum, Dahlem; Istituto botanico, Firenze; New York Botanical Garden; and Field Museum, Chicago. Information kindly given by Dr. Frans Verdoorn (4206.07).

their ordeal in the equatorial swamps and forests warmer friends than they were at the start.

After their triumphal return to Paris, Humboldt employed himself to insure a position for his friend. He obtained for him from the French government a pension of three thousand francs and later (1808) his appointment as botanist to the empress Joséphine. This illustrates Humboldt's generosity which it is well to insist upon, for it has been doubted.[15] The doubting was apparently justified by the fact that Humboldt became a regular courtier of the king of Prussia; not only was he a courtier but in spite of occasional grumblings he seems to have liked it; that was his form of servitude; other scientists have to accept other forms of servitude, such as teaching or administration, and if they be wise they make the best of it. It is better to like our chores than to dislike them. Humboldt's main task was to keep company, when required, with the king of Prussia. At the court of Berlin he learned to be smooth-spoken and his critics concluded that he was insincere and selfish. That is not my impression. Humboldt never ceased to show generosity to Bonpland in spite of the fact that the latter disappointed him; he gave him full credit for what he had done and spoke always very highly of him; he defended him through thick and thin. The explanation of this is simply that Humboldt was a great man who could not become small even when he was a courtier; he might and did become somewhat pompous and smooth-spoken but he remained essentially generous.[16]

To return to Bonpland and the empress Joséphine,[17] to call him her botanist is perhaps a little misleading. He was really her chief gardener, and later her intendant, but to be her gardener was somewhat like being the scientific head of a botanical garden. She was deeply interested in flowers and was an ambitious horticulturist;

[15] Ugly suggestions in Henri Cordier (1914, p. 8).

[16] A good example is his continued kindness to the great but unfortunate mathematician Gotthold Eisenstein (Bruhns-Lassell, 2, 295–305).

[17] To refresh the reader's memory, — Joséphine Tascher de la Pagerie, born at the Martinique, 1763, accompanied her father to France in 1799 and married there the viscount Alexandre de Beauharnais; he was beheaded in July 1794. In 1796, she married general Bonaparte and was crowned with him on Dec. 2, 1804. Napoleon divorced her in 1809 (*invitus invitam dimisit*). However, she was richly endowed and able to keep a royal establishment at the Malmaison near Paris. She died there in 1814. She had bought the Malmaison in 1799 during Bonaparte's absence in Egypt.

thanks to her zeal the garden of the Malmaison became famous. Bon-pland's predecessor as her "botanist," Etienne Pierre Ventenat (1757–1808), had devoted to it two magnificent volumes illustrated by the Liégeois artist, Pierre Joseph Redouté (1759–1840), who was the most illustrious painter of flowers of the romantic age. Another book illustrated by the same artist was written by Bonpland himself.[18]

Bonpland was in charge not only of the Malmaison but also of the domain of Navarre near Evreux (in eastern Normandie), where he had assembled among other things a collection of some 130 kinds of heather. The empress took a personal interest in the plants, knew their names, studied catalogues, suggested new acquisitions or sent her botanist to inspect other gardens in France or abroad with the view of improving her own. The six or seven years which Bonpland spent at the Malmaison seem to have been happy ones. Next to herbo-rizing there was nothing he loved more than horticulture. It was not enough for him to find plants, determine and collect them; he must see them grow and if possible breed them. Moreover, practical occupations suited him better than purely intellectual or bookish ones from which he instinctively shrank. Hence he could not bring himself to write the botanical account of his journey, worked at it fitfully at longer and longer intervals, to Humboldt's distress. His duties to the unfortunate empress gave him the best of alibis. In order to enrich the Malmaison, he visited most botanical establishments of Europe, except those of England, which he did not see until after Joséphine's death. The Malmaison must have been to him a little Eden, complete down to the Serpent. The latter embroiled him in a love affair with a young creole woman who was one of Joséphine's childhood friends; [19] her name is unknown but when Bonpland met her at the Malmaison in 1810, she was a widow with a small daughter called Emma; he married her about 1813 and spent the rest of his life regretting it.

After the empress' death in 1814, Bonpland did not fancy continu-

---

[18] E. P. Ventenat, *Le Jardin de la Malmaison* (2 vols. folio, 120 plates, Paris, 1803–04). A. Bonpland, *Description des plantes rares cultivées à Malmaison et à Navarre* (folio, pl. in colors, Paris 1813). Colored plates of magnolias and peonies in this volume are counted among Redouté's masterpieces. According to William T. Stearn (*Journal Arnold Arboretum*, vol. 23, 110–111, 1942), Ventenat's book was published in four parts, 1803–1805, and Bonpland's in eleven parts, 1812–1817.

[19] It is possible that Joséphine brought them deliberately together, for she was always plotting marriages among her friends and the members of her household.

ing in the service of her son, the prince Eugène de Beauharnais (1781–1824), and dreamed of returning to the New World. For a time he thought of joining Bolívar el Libertador, who had made tempting offers to him.[20] He finally accepted another proposition made to him by Bernardino Rivadavia (1780–1845) in the name of the Argentine Republic. He left the Havre in Nov. 1816 with his wife, stepdaughter, a maid, and two assistants, taking with them an enormous baggage including the whole of his American herbal and the notes relative to it. That was hardly fair to Humboldt, for on account of Bonpland's own dilatoriness the American plants were still largely unpublished. Kunth came all the way from Paris to claim the plants in Humboldt's name, but he only got the MSS, the plants went to America and were not returned until much later.

Bonpland spent four years (1816–1820) in Buenos Aires, practising medicine, collecting, teaching a little at the University, but on the whole failing to obtain the success — professional or financial — which he had fondly expected; he experienced, if not poverty, at least money difficulties,[21] and his married life became more and more unpleasant. His wife and daughter finally abandoned him and he then decided to start a new venture, a plantation on the Paraná River. He established it in one of the ruined Jesuit missions, at Santa Ana, near the river but SE of it.[22] There he found himself in his own element. He was able to undertake agricultural experiments on a large scale, notably on the *curupay*, tree rich in *angico* gum used in tanning, the *caa-obi*, a kind of *indigo*, and the *yerba mate* which had been cultivated so successfully by the Jesuits. He had herborized in many natural yerbales trying

[20] Bolívar was a member of the Humboldt group in Paris. He, Humboldt, and Gay-Lussac had climbed Vesuvius together in 1805. However, Bolívar's main appeal for men of science was made only after the constitution of the Colombian union at Angostura, 1819. It was then that his agent, the naturalist Francisco Antonio Zea (1770–1822), enlisted among others Jean Baptiste Boussingault, one of the founders of agricultural chemistry, but that is another story (*Isis 10*, 190).

[21] My impression is that he was one of those men who are never completely in business or out of it, and create incessant trouble to themselves and to others by semi-commercial transactions lightly assumed and carelessly pursued.

[22] This detail is important. Being SE of the Paraná, Santa Ana was not in Paraguay but in the Argentine province of Corrientes. The famous "Jesuit missions of Paraguay" were most of them out of Paraguay. Out of thirty, only eight were in that country, the others in what are now Brazil or the Argentine provinces of Entre Rios, Corrientes, and Misiones. R. B. Cunninghame Graham, *A vanished Arcadia, being some account of the Jesuits in Paraguay 1607 to 1767* (New York, 1901, p. 174).

to find the best varieties, and within a year or two had formed a collection of some 850 species of plants growing south of the Paraná, not to speak of insects, shells, and other specimens.

Alas! his renewed happiness was not allowed to last very long. On Dec. 8, 1821, Bonpland's flourishing plantation was suddenly attacked and sacked by four hundred Paraguayos, who had been ordered to do so by the dictator, Dr. Francia. Bonpland's Indian laborers were killed or wounded, and himself made prisoner, loaded with chains, and taken across the river to Santa Maria de Fé, in Paraguayan territory. The dictator had feared that Bonpland's success in cultivating *mate* would interfere with his own attempt to monopolize that business.[23] This is not the place to discuss Paraguayan politics of a century ago. It will suffice to remark that if I had written this essay some ten years earlier, I would not have hesitated to call Francia and his grandnephew, the second López, the most ferocious and unscrupulous tyrants of modern times.

Bonpland was kept prisoner in Paraguay for more than seven years. He was permitted to settle down in el Cerrito between Santa Maria and Santa Rosa but was forbidden to leave the adjoining territory; during those many years he left it but once at the risk of death in order to prospect a mercury mine which was in Mercedes, that is, not very far off, between Santa Maria and the river Tibicuary. The ending of his detention was as brutal as its beginning. Thanks to the solicitude of Humboldt and other friends, diplomatic efforts had been made for years by France and England in order to obtain Bonpland's release. Dr. Francia long refused to listen but being suddenly annoyed he ordered him on May 12, 1829 to leave the country within five days. This meant that the new business which Bonpland had succeeded in creating for himself as an agriculturist, doctor, and apothecary had to be jettisoned and sacrificed. For the second time he was ruined by the same tyrant, and in the meanwhile the French pension had been stopped because he had been unable during the years of his captivity to prove his continued existence to the satisfaction of the French treasury.

He sailed down the Paraná to Buenos Aires with the idea of return-

---

[23] Robertson (vol. 3, 1839), chiefly letter XXI (p. 275–290). *Yerba mate* (*Ilex paraguayensis*) or "Paraguay tea" is used extensively in S. America instead of tea.

ing to France, but when he reached the city he realized that he had become so completely acclimatized to the New World, especially to the unsophisticated country, that he had lost the wish and the strength of leaving it. It is not clear to me how quickly he reached Buenos Aires, or, if he sailed straight to it, what he did next. It is possible that having become intolerant of city manners he did not stay very long but began to roam in search of a new plantation, and incidentally of more plants. According to his own testimony (Hamy, 1906, p. 81) he lived an errant life from May 12, 1829 to February 2, 1831, i.e., twenty months and twenty days. In 1832, he spent eight months in Buenos Aires and during that period forwarded twenty-five boxes of specimens (minerals, plants, animals) to the Paris Muséum. That shipment included bones of *Megatherium* and *Glyptodon* which must have been among the earliest examples of the Pleistocene fauna of the pampas to reach Europe.[24]

"It is worthy of remark," wrote Robertson (vol. 3, 279), "that M. Bonpland always spoke in very moderate terms of all that had befallen him through the orders of Francia." The same remark applies to his letters. If we had no information but Bonpland's sayings and writings we would never suspect the dictator's cruelty. This shows that he had become similar to the inhabitants of that unfortunate country whose fear of Dr. Francia and his spies was so intense that their mouths were sealed. Indeed, the people had been so thoroughly frightened that even after Francia had been dead for many years, they did not yet mention him by name, lest the incarnate devil be evoked, but called him "il difúnto."

In 1831, Bonpland had organized a new estáncia in San Borja [25] on the eastern shore of the Uruguay River; about 1838, he established

---

[24] Having applied to my Harvard colleague, Alfred S. Romer (who is preparing a bibliography of vertebrate palaeontology) for information, he kindly wrote to me (June 2, 1942): "Bonpland's material of *Megatherium* was definitely not the first known from the Argentine, for there had been a complete skeleton of this form in Madrid half a century or more before. *Glyptodon* appears to have been discovered a bit earlier, for there is a mention of a carapace in Father Thomas Falkner's *Description of Patagonia* (p. 55, Hereford, 1774; *Isis* 27, 137) and material for this form collected by Fr. Sellow was described in the Prussian Academy Memoirs for 1827 (1830, 217–293) by Christian Samual Weiss. All this material comes from the pampas deposits of the La Plata basin."
[25] Now in the Rio Grande do Sul, Brazil, and the present name is of course Portuguese, São Borja or São Francisco de Borja.

still another one in Santa Ana,[26] where the province of Corrientes had given him five square leagues of land in emphyteutic lease; he later received full title to it. The San Borja plantation became very prosperous in a short time. He cultivated citrus fruits, peaches, manioc, batatas, corn, melons, peanuts, etc. He was producing alcohol and liquors, and had a carpentry shop and a smithy. Apparently he never ceased to practise medicine. Apropos of this we may observe that in spite of many calamities he was never unhappy. He had the good fortune to be a well-trained physician with the prestige of a Paris diploma at a time and in places where medical assistance was rare. Thus he could always maintain himself, body and soul, as a doctor, until new opportunities enabled him to satisfy his heart's desire and be a planter. There is no point in following the activities of the final period of his life (more than twenty-five years) which were largely agricultural, financial, political. The last named could not be discussed without analyzing the multiple conflicts which were then agitating that lovely country, often with terrible violence and incredible savagery. San Borja was in what is now Brazilian territory, Argentine was across the river, Paraguay not very far to the North and Uruguay not very far to the South. His existence was thus strangely mixed with the development of four South American countries[27] (not to speak of course of his early life with Humboldt in many others). His scientific work had come practically to an end. He was still collecting plants, for he could not help that, and he sent packages from time to time to Professor Mirbel[28] of the Paris Muséum; he created a provincial museum in the city of Corrientes; he continued to make horticultural experiments, especially with regard to *mate* and citrus fruits.

The large plantation established by him in San Borja in 1831 had to be abandoned from 1838 to 1842 because of civil wars; he reoccupied it from 1843 to 1851. During that second occupation he created a new family[29] with a native woman by whom he had three children,

[26] Santa Ana on the west shore of the Uruguay R. a little below Restauración (= Paso de los Libres). Not to be confused with the other Santa Ana, SE of the Paraná, where Bonpland had his first plantation, destroyed by Francia.
[27] With Uruguay less than with the three others. He visited Montevideo and stayed there probably more than once but did not travel in the Banda Oriental.
[28] Charles François Brisseau de Mirbel (1776–1854), Botanist.
[29] Perhaps we should say his first family, for his wife had given him endless troubles but no children, no home. His stepdaughter, Emma, was taken as a

a daughter, Carmen (b. 1843), and two sons, Amadito (b. 1845) and Anastasio (b. 1847), to whom he was exceedingly devoted. The elder son bearing his father's name (Amado, Amadito) had himself four children, Sofía, Benjamín, Georgina, and Pompeyo. The last named was a student in the medical school of Buenos Aires in 1905 and revealed a good many MSS which had belonged to his illustrious grandfather (Cordier, 1914).

The war had impoverished the country around San Borja, and Bonpland returned for good to his estate of Santa Ana in Corrientes. Though he was now well advanced in years, he was still very active and managed to gather in that immense plantation large herds of sheep and abundant cultures of many kinds. In 1857, Francia having been dead since 1840, Bonpland ventured to travel to Asunción and see the heart of Paraguay which had been so long forbidden to him. He was then 84 years old but judging from a letter of his to Humboldt, he was still capable of reviving the kind of enthusiasm which they had shared together in their youth, more than half a century earlier. He wrote the letter on his way back, while he was stopping in Corrientes, where he had founded his museum of natural history (Hamy, 1906, 212–216): "I am not afraid of saying that in the course of your immortal voyage we have not discovered a single place offering us as beautiful a flora, a site as varied and enchanting, as the neighborhood of Asunción . . . For years it has been exceptional for me to find plants which I had not yet studied, yet in Asunción more than half were unknown to me. I am all afire with the desire to return to Paraguay." The old man was really planning to explore the country with the permission of the dictator Lopez.[30]

In the meanwhile, thanks to his Indian wife and children, he had reverted to native standards. Used to camp-life, his needs had always been the simplest; they were now rudimentary. We have a vivid picture of him drawn by the German traveller, Avé-Lallemant,[31] who

companion (demoiselle de compagnie) by the princess of Nassau, and while there in 1829 married a dentist called Edouard Buchey (Hamy, 1906, p. xxxvii).

[30] That was Carlos Lopez, Francia's nephew and successor who ruled Paraguay until 1862, and was relatively gentle. His son and successor, Francisco Lopez, who ruled the country from 1862 to 1870, and ruined it, degenerated into a monster of cruelty.

[31] Robert Avé-Lallement (1812–84) of Lübeck, wrote various books on Brazil and tropical botany, and a part of Humboldt's biography.

visited him on April 18, 1858. Avé-Lallemant had first been to San Borja, where he talked with the curate Gay, who had been one of Bonpland's intimates.[32] Rumors of Bonpland's death had been circulating for weeks. Avé-Lallemant was very anxious to see the illustrious exile in order to be able to give a report of him to Humboldt. He sailed down the river to Uruguayana, crossed it to Restauración, and rode to Santa Ana. Bonpland was then visibly on the decline, though he could still speak a little, — a man of 85 with a foot in the grave, and hence Avé's pathetic account of him should be discounted. The man whom he actually saw was but a shadow of the good giant whom he had come to see. Less than a month later, on May 11, 1858, Bonpland died in Restauración, where his children had taken him to obtain medical help. The news of his death reached Humboldt in August, and he communicated it at once to Elie de Beaumont, who was perpetual secretary of the Académie des sciences (Hamy, 1906, 242–243). Humboldt himself, who was four years older than his companion, died almost exactly a year later, on May 6, 1859.

Long before his death, Bonpland had become a legendary figure. Of course, he was well known to every botanist because of the monumental publications of the Humboldt-Bonpland expedition, but he had been lost sight of as a living being during his long detention in Paraguay,[33] and by the time he emerged into the free world again he had himself lost interest in European matters and "civilization" and had become a planter wholly immersed in his own agricultural and economic problems and in the political and military difficulties of his adopted country. When we speak of his adopted country we should think of the Argentine province of Corrientes,[34] the land limited West

[32] This curate, called Jean Pierre Gay, was a Frenchman. He organized a masonic lodge in his parish in 1853 and asked Bonpland to be one of the charter members. Bonpland accepted with alacrity and thus became a Freemason at the age of 80. His letter of acceptance addressed to the curate on Sept. 5, 1853 is very remarkable. It begins, "A Monsieur le Vicaire Jean Pierre Gay, mon très estimable compatriote et ami . . ." (Cordier, 1914, p. 13).

[33] As mentioned above, the officers of the French treasury refused for a long while to pay the arrears of his pension because they lacked administrative proofs of his being still alive.

[34] His first Santa Ana estate was, it is true, in Misiones, but not far from the Corrientes border; San Borja was in Brazilian territory but just across the river from Corrientes. Two places are now called Bonpland in the Argentine, one near each Santa Ana estate, one in Misiones, the other in Corrientes.

and North by the Paraná, East by the Uruguay, and south by the parallel 30° S. Though he had cut himself off from Europe, Europe rediscovered him gradually. He had received a few honors in his youth. As early as 1800 his name had been given to the American genus *Bonplandia* [35] by Antonio José Canavilles (Hamy, 1905, 153). In 1817, he had been elected a correspondent of the Académie des sciences, but that meant chiefly that the Parisian botanists expected to receive from him many specimens (*Isis 29*, 439). In 1830, he was elected a correspondent of the Muséum, — same meaning. Then the curtain falls. It is true Guizot obtained for him a cross of the Legion of honor in 1833, but even that was strangely forgotten, for the same cross was awarded to him again in 1849! It was only when he approached his eightieth anniversary, and his scientific work was long done, that real honors began to come to him. The Académie des sciences wrote him a letter of congratulation on April 7, 1852, and his eulogy was ready before the Société de géographie (of Paris) on August 22, 1853. More substantial honors came to him from Germany, largely because of Humboldt's defense of him. A review named after him "Bonplandia" began to appear in Hannover, Jan. 1, 1853, and from then on it became impossible for botanists not to know his name. He was decorated by the king of Prussia in 1854, received a doctor's degree from the University of Greifswald in 1856, became a member of the Academia Caesaro-Leopoldina in Halle in 1857, and died the following year in very old age.

Those honors in extremis were richly deserved. In fact, the botanical work done during his journey with Humboldt would have been more than sufficient to deserve them. He collected thousands of specimens of new plants and diagnosed them with the utmost care. Being a physician he had a special interest in plants which might have medicinal virtues and he sent many of them to the Muséum for chemical analysis. He was also deeply concerned with their economic value. Unfortunately, the results of his agricultural experiments remained largely unrecorded. He was the first to investigate the culture of *mate* and to try to improve it in a scientific manner.[36] Finally, he was one

[35] Close to *Hoitzia* and *Phlox* but different from both. Family of *Polemionaceae*.

[36] John Miers, History of the maté plant and the different species of *Ilex* employed in the preparation of the "yerba de mate" or Paraguay tea (*Annals and magazine of natural history*, vol. 8, 219–228, 398–401, London, 1861). This in-

of the first botanists to observe one of the marvels of the floral world, the giant water lily or *Victoria*.[37]

All considered, the best and main part of his work was done in his early years in cooperation with Humboldt and perhaps would never have been done without the latter's initiative and heroic driving power. It is instructive to compare these two men who were so different in many ways, yet helped each other so well. Humboldt was primarily an encyclopaedist. His *Cosmos* (vols. I–II) is one of the finest syntheses ever attempted, one which will remain forever a source of inspiration to the humanized scientist. Alas! Most of our scientists today are unable to appreciate it; if they read it at all they concentrate their attention on the shortcomings, some of which were unavoidable a century ago, and can see nothing else. Well, that is *their* shortcoming, their own blindness, and it condemns them. Humboldt had learned the skilled and patient use of many instruments, but his main tool was the pen. Bonpland, on the contrary, is the best example of a collector, whose energy is inexhaustible in the field, but who dislikes book work and to whom the writing of reports is so distasteful that he would rather risk his life in a new expedition than have to sit too long at his desk. These characteristics of his appeared very early and grew worse as the years rolled by. He was forever taking notes, filling whole books with them, beginning many times new redactions and completing none. In 1810, Humboldt complained already that Bonpland could not write as much in eight months as another botanist would produce in a fortnight (Bruhns-Lassell, 2, 11–14). This was very trying and became unendurable. Bonpland's work had finally to be intrusted to another man, Karl Sigismund Kunth, who completed it. You see the opposition of both men; with less generosity on either side they would have easily become enemies. It is very much to Hum-

---

cludes a curious defense of Doctor Francia, represented as a benefactor of his country. Eight specimens of six species of Ilex had been sent to Miers by Bonpland from Corrientes, 17 June 1857.

[37] The very first was the Bohemian, Thaddaeus Hanke, who saw it in 1801 and fell on his knees in worship! Bonpland observed it in 1819 and jumped into the water to approach it; A. D. d'Orbigny saw it in 1827, etc. The name *Victoria* was given to it by John Lindley in 1837. See note in *Bonplandia* (vol. 2, 7, 1854). I am indebted to my Harvard colleague, Dr. E. D. Merrill, for much information on the history of *Victoria*, much more than could be published in this footnote, if it is to remain a footnote.

boldt's credit that he not only forgave Bonpland's abandonment of their great design, but understood it and continued to help him in every way. Humboldt did not care for collections of material objects, for he was primarily interested in ideas; the objects were means to an end, — not their preservation but the writing of reports and the enrichment of science; when they had been properly investigated, and the results had been duly published, these perishable objects were in his way; he did not want them any more. For Bonpland, on the contrary, his collections were everything and his jealousy concerning them is natural enough, if we bear in mind that he had often jeopardized his life in order to obtain coveted specimens. Literary people who might pooh-pooh his inarticulate efforts are often themselves collectors, collectors of books, as proud and jealous of their treasures as it is possible to be, though they have done nothing more heroic to get them than read catalogues and sign checks. The true collector satisfies himself with his collections; they become his aim instead of being a means; they provide him with an easy catharsis and give him an illusion of knowledge and noble life. If the collecting is done with sufficient intelligence and continuity, we should not complain, for sooner or later somebody will use the materials thus assembled and do the real work. On the other hand, we should make an effort to understand Humboldt's subtler and nobler reactions and give him at least as much sympathy as we are ready to give mere collectors. Humboldt realized as well as anybody else the necessity of collections (they constitute the first step in almost every study), but he instinctively avoided their ownership. He did not want to be deflected from his high purpose by such impedimenta; the more precious collections are (in money or otherwise), the more cumbersome, the greater the danger of being sacrificed to them. Such heavy ballast keeps the spirit down. Good collectors become necessarily more and more earthbound; they begin by owning treasures and they end by being owned by them. Humboldt wanted to remain free from material possessions and in spite of being a courtier and a man of the world, he preserved that freedom remarkably well and almost succeeded in dying poor.

It is worth while to compare these two men, but there is no point in saying that the one was better than the other, for they were essentially different and there is no common measure. They accomplished together a great purpose. On the basis of Humboldt's often repeated testimony, the American journey would not have been the success it was without Bonpland's good fellowship and his single-minded devotion to plants. It is true Bonpland failed Humboldt in the redaction of his notes, but that could be and was done by others.

These two heroes shared adventures and dangers for many years in order to give us a better knowledge of the equinoctial parts of the New World. They lived and suffered together for the same purpose and should remain united in our gratitude. One can hardly teach the history of science in the nineteenth century without devoting a lecture to Alexander von Humboldt, and one should never speak of the latter without paying tribute to his unfortunate companion, one of the most illustrious sons of La Rochelle, Aimé Bonpland.[38]

Cambridge, Mass.
June 2, 1942

APPENDICES

I. 'Bonplandia'

The botanical review entitled *Bonplandia* began to appear on January 1, 1853. It was devoted to 'applied' botany, was edited by Berthold Seemann (1825–1871) and published by Carl Rümpler in Hannover . . .

After graduating in Göttingen, Seemann went to Kew in order to fit himself for travel as a botanical collector. In 1846, he was appointed as naturalist to the Pacific exploration of H.M.S. Herald, and was with her from 1847 to 1851.[39] After his return he was elected a member of 'Imperial L. C. Academy Naturae Curiosorum' (that is the way he put it on the title-page of his *Narrative*) and assumed the cognomen Bonpland.[40] Soon afterwards he began the publication of *Bonplandia*; there is obviously a relation between these two facts. The title indi-

[38] I can think only of two other Rochelois who deserve our grateful remembrance, Réaumur (1683–1757), about whom see Torlais' book (1936; *Isis* 28, 112–115), and Eugène Fromentin (1820–1876), distinguished as a painter but even more so as a writer and critic.

[39] ADB (33, 581–584, 1891). DNB (51, 194–195, 1897). B. Seemann, *Narrative of the voyage of H.M.S. Herald 1845–51* (2 vols. London, 1853); German transl. 1858.

[40] This was an old academic tradition which continued in the Leopoldina until 1870 (*Isis* 16, 144).

cated in an indirect way Seemann's editorship of it. As far as I know members of the Academy never chose as cognomen the name of a living person. Did Seemann believe in Jan. 1853 that Bonpland was dead, or almost as good as dead? [41] No references to Bonpland were made in the whole of vol. 1; a few appeared in vol. 2, 1854; his biography was published in vol. 3, 1855; his portrait in vol. 4, 1856. In 1857 Bonpland was himself elected a member of the Leopoldina and Humboldt selected for him the cognomen Desfontaines, after his botanical teacher Réne Louiche Desfontaines (1750–1833).[42] It is probable that during their long Orinocian nights Bonpland had often spoken of his teacher, or had bolstered up his arguments with references to the latter's opinions.

At the time when a journal bearing his own name as title was being published, Bonpland was so far away that he did not hear of it, and perhaps would never have heard of it but for Humboldt's solicitude. Judging from the letter which he addressed to the editors from Montevideo, Jan. 26, 1856 (printed in vol. 4, 131, 1856), he had received the news from Humboldt in 1854 but had not seen the actual copies of vols. 1 and 2 until later. Moreover, he could not read German and hence had little use for the journal, beyond the pleasure which such international recognition must have given him. Think of it, the official organ of one of the oldest academies of Europe, bearing his own name for a title! It must have tickled the old man to exhibit that journal to his fellow estancieros in Corrientes.

On every number B. Seemann is named as the editor, but on the title-page of each volume two editors are named, Berthold and his brother Wilhelm; the latter was also a member of the Leopoldina with the cognomen Loudon.[43] Beginning with vol. 4, 1856, both brothers were named as editors in each number.

[41] The news of his death in Corrientes 1846 had been announced in the *Berliner Nachrichten* no. 140 and copied in the *Botanische Zeitung* (4, 504, July 17, 1846). However, it was denied in the following year (*Bot. Z.* 5, 336, 1847; again 5, 799, 1847; 9, 429, 1851) and Bonpland received German decorations in 1851 (*Bot. Z.* 9, 743, 1851) and 1854 (*Bot. Z.* 12, 296, 1854). Courtesy of Frans Verdoorn.

[42] Desfontaines was very kind to young botanists such as Bonpland and A. P. de Candolle; see the latter's *Mémoires et Souvenirs* (Genève, 1862, p. 62 and passim).

[43] After John Claudius Loudon (1783–1843), landscape gardener and horticultural writer.

The link existing from the beginning between that botanical review and the Leopoldina was tightened in the second number when the celebration of its second centenary [44] gave the editor occasion to declare that the Academy recognized *Bonplandia* as its official organ.[45] This continued to be a fact until the end of 1859. At the beginning of vol. 8, 1860, it was stated that the Academy would henceforth publish its own organ, to be entitled *Leopoldina*, in Jena. However, *Bonplandia* continued to publish academic news. It existed two more years and ended as quietly as it had begun. In the last number (Hannover, 31 Dec. 1862, no. 25 of vol. 10, only 4 p.), the editor announced the end of *Bonplandia* without much explanation or expression of regret, and the beginning in 1863 of a new monthly journal, *The Journal of Botany, British and foreign*, which is still going strong to-day. I suppose that the main reason for replacing *Bonplandia* by the *Journal of Botany* was that Seemann, established in England, lost too much time in publishing his journal in Germany, and he was so Anglicized that it was tiresome for him to edit it in German rather than in English. It was a delicate matter to explain to his German readers, and the best was to announce the change as he did it with as little fuss as possible.

I have examined the whole collection of *Bonplandia*, especially for facts concerning Bonpland, but reading other articles as well. It was a very interesting journal, containing a large amount of information. The articles being generally short, there was considerable variety in the news. The ten volumes contain 3568 pages printed in two columns, with many illustrations, some of them in color. In the last number, Seemann announced the preparation of a general index; unfortunately, that index whether it was prepared or not, was never published.

It gratified me to write this note on *Bonplandia* not simply for the sake of Bonpland but also for the sake of the Leopoldina of which it was the organ. That academy was the first foreign academy to admit me to its membership (in 1925) and the first election of that kind is generally the most welcome. Moreover, the Leopoldina has shown in recent years more independence and more dignity than the other academies of Germany.

[44] The 200th anniversary of the Leopoldina was celebrated in Wiesbaden in 1852, the 250th anniversary, in Halle in 1937, after a more correct determination of the birthdate.

[45] The motto of the academy "Nunquam otiosus" was printed on every number.

AIMÉ BONPLAND

II. Books bearing Bonpland's name on the title-page
The great folio edition of the American expedition bears the general title:
Voyage aux régions équinoxiales du Nouveau Continent fait en 1799, 1800, 1801, 1802, 1803, et 1804 par Alexandre de Humboldt et Aimé Bonpland, rédigé par A. de Humboldt (Paris, 1807 etc.).
Bonpland's name reappears on a special title-page of each botanical volume, some of which were composed by him, others by others. Each volume was published under a serial title and also under an independent title. . . .
Aimé Bonpland, *Description des plantes rares cultivées à Malmaison et à Navarre* (1 vol. folio, 56 x 41 cm., 160 p., 64 col. pl., Paris, 1813). Admirable illustrations by Pierre Joseph Redouté. For a description of this book and other publications of that famous artist see Gordon Dunthorne, *Flower and fruit prints* (folio, Washington, 1938, p. 228–234; *Isis 33*, 154). The title-page of Bonpland's book is misleading as to date; the book was published in parts from 1812 to 1817. See footnote no. 18.
Archives inédites de Aimé Bonpland.
Tome 1. *Lettres inédites de Alexandre de Humboldt* [à Bonpland]. With a Spanish preface by Juan A. Domínguez and a French one by Henri Cordier. Humboldt's letters are reproduced in facsimile, without transcription. They are easy to read for anyone having a fluent knowledge of the French language, but almost unreadable to others. Some of them contain brief notes in Bonpland's hand, stating, e.g., when and where he received the letter and when and where he answered it. The plates containing the facsimiles are unnumbered and unlisted, I counted 64. This is probably the largest collection of Humboldt MSS available to the public. Its edition is very much to be desired.
Tomo 2. *Journal de botanique.* Prólogo in Spanish by Juan A. Domínguez. Followed by Bonpland's botanical journal in complete facsimile, without transcription or notes. The edition of this text is also very desirable; it could be done only by a competent botanist with a good knowledge of Latin and French.
These two precious collections of original documents were published in the *Trabajos del Instituto de botánica y farmacología*, Facultad de ciencias médicas de Buenos Aires, and constitute nos. 31 and 42 of those *Trabajos*, 2 vols. folio (37.5 x 29 cm., 37 x 27 cm.) (Jacobo Peuser, Buenos Aires, 1914–1924). The initiative of that publication was apparently taken by the Genevese botanist Eugène Autran (1855–1912), who died in Buenos Aires before it could appear. It would seem that Autran transcribed the letters, or some of them at least, but if so I did not see his transcription. The publication was carried out in this sumptuous form by Juan A. Domínguez, director of the Instituto de botánica.

III. Publications on Bonpland
1. Amans Alexis Monteil, Traité et matériaux manuscrits de divers genres d'histoire (p. 359–361, extracted from an unknown journal, or catalogue, Paris, imprimerie E. Duverger, 1836). Running title reads "de la géographie

et des géographes." Extract bound in the Arnold Arboretum volume mentioned below in no. 6. It contains the description of two MSS "Portefeuille contenant des manuscrits autographes du naturaliste voyageur Bonpland. 30 fr." "Journal de voyage en Espagne fait en 1798 par M. Bonpland. 50 fr."

2. John Parish Robertson and William Parish Robertson, *Francia's reign of terror, being the continuation of Letters on Paraguay* (in 3 vols., vol. 3, London, Murray, 1839).

3. *Bonplandia* edited by Berthold Seemann (vols. 2 to 5, 1854–1857; vol. 8, 1860).

4. Petro de Angelis, Noticia biográfica de M. Bonpland (*Revista del Plata*, Nov. 1854, Buenos Aires). Reprinted in pamphlet form, Buenos Aires, 1855.

5. Robert Avé-Lallemant, *Reise durch Süd-Brasilien* (2 vols., Leipzig, Brockhaus, 1859; vol. 1, 305–374).

The author's account of his visit to Bonpland is reproduced in Bruhns (1872), translated into English in Bruhns-Lassell (1873) and into French in Hamy (1906).

6. Adolphe Brunel (1810–1871), *Biographie d'A. Bonpland* (40 p., portr., Paris, 1859); second ed. (75 p., Toulon, 1864); third ed. (185 p., Paris, 1871).

I have seen only the third edition published in Paris, London, and Montevideo, 1871, soon after the author's death. It contains Bonpland's portrait and bibliography, a catalogue of his MSS in the library of the Paris Muséum, and a note on his collections preserved in the same Muséum. The specimens of minerals and fossils are 154 in number, and the catalogue written in Bonpland's own hand is entitled "Catalogue pour servir à la géologie des côtes de l'Uruguay, du Parana, de la Plata, d'une partie du Paraguay, de toutes les Missions, de la province de Corrientes et d'une grande partie de la province d'Entre-Rios (Buenos Ayres, décembre 1836)." Dr. Adolphe Brunel was born in Hyères (Var) in 1810; entered the medical service of the French navy, becoming eventually surgeon-major; he resigned in 1842 and settled down in Montevideo. He signed the preface of his third edition in Paris, August 1871, and died on Sunday, Oct. 29, 1871, in the Louvre museum, where he was conducting his family . . .

7. Karl Bruhns (and others), *Alexander von Humboldt* (3 vols., Leipzig, Brockhaus, 1872).

Still the standard biography though much additional information has come to light since 1872.

8. Karl Bruhns (and others), *Life of Alexander von Humboldt*, translated by Jane and Caroline Lassell (2 vols., London, Longmans Green, 1873).

The Humboldt bibliography of vol. 2 and the whole of vol. 3 (special technical studies) were left untranslated. Hence this English translation cannot replace the original for scholars, but it has the great advantage of being indexed.

9. Eduardo L. Homberg, Correspondencia inédita de Humboldt y Bonpland. Un hallazgo interesante (*Caras y caretas*, vol. 8, no. 365, Buenos Ayres, 30 Sept. 1905). Two quarto pages containing 12 illustrations,

AIMÉ BONPLAND

portraits of all the Bonpland descendants, views of his tomb in Paso de los Libres, etc.

10. Ernest Théodore Hamy (1842–1909), *Lettres américaines d'A. de Humboldt*, 1798–1807 (xi+309 p., Paris, Guilmoto, 1905).

11. E. T. Hamy, *Aimé Bonpland, médecin et naturaliste, explorateur de l'Amérique du Sud. Sa vie, son oeuvre, sa correspondance* (cxviii+300 p., Paris, Guilmoto, 1906).

The two Hamy books are very painstaking and valuable studies, unfortunately unindexed. Hamy has corrected many errors made by Brunel.

12. Henri Cordier, *Papiers inédits d'A. Bonpland* conservés à Buenos Aires (24 p., *Trabajos del Instituto de botánica*, Faculdad de ciencias médicas, no. 30, Buenos Aires, 1914).

[*IV. Iconography* and *Thanks* are omitted.]

Moseley

[1887-1915]

The Numbering of the Elements

It HAS OFTEN been observed that exceptional talent or genius, if it exists at all, is generally revealed early in life, say, before the thirtieth year. This does not mean of course that a man of genius is likely to be famous at that early age, for his discoveries or new points of view being truly original may seem arbitrary and superfluous, they may be too far out of the beaten track to be appreciated and receive the consecration of public praise. It may happen also (and this is very common) that though his new ideas are sufficiently clear in his own mind to dominate and shape the whole course of his life, yet considerable labor will be needed during a large number of years, even unto death, to materialize them, to complete his discoveries, to build up the monument he is dreaming of. Not only detached spectators, but even his friends, can not see his genius, or be sure enough of it, before he has had time to explain himself and fulfil his promise. And the more daring the promise, the longer it may take to fulfil it and the least credit he can reasonably expect to receive even from those who wish him well and love him best. But mind you; genius was there all the time; it was not less real for being intangible. The goal had not yet been reached but the man was on his way, bent upon a mysterious errand which outsiders could neither understand nor even imagine. For all the world he might be a fool, and if he stumbled and died on the road, he would be spoken of as a fool.

It must necessarily occur that men of genius die before having been able to justify themselves and to give out the treasures that were in them, and these are perhaps of all events the most tragic. Just think of the loss which mankind is thus suffering, for in the last analysis everything great and really worthwhile is due to the genius of individuals, — and think also of the pity of having been called to the human stage to play an exceptional part and being swept off before having begun. The tragedy is not so much to die young, but to die before having done what one was prepared to do. Thus it breaks our hearts to see children die, or young lovers, or men who might have enriched humanity by their creations.

Moseley's untimely death, before he was twenty-eight, is tragic enough. It is vain to speculate as to what he might have achieved if he had been permitted to live longer. But our grief is assuaged by the thought that his fame was already established on such a secure foundation, that his memory will be green for ever. He is one of the immortals of science, and though he would have made many other additions to our knowledge if his life had been spared, the contributions already credited to him were of such fundamental significance, that the probability of his surpassing himself was extremely small. It is very probable that however long his life, he would have been chiefly remembered because of the "Moseley's law" which he published at the age of twenty-six. Thus he died not without having fulfilled his promise, not without having shown who he was. He died in beauty. The sudden termination of this noble life on the battlefield was an additional glory. It bestowed on his personality a touch of romance and mystery, which completed its consecration.

Henry Gwyn Jeffreys Moseley was born on November 23, 1887. He belonged to a scientific family; his father and his two grandfathers were Fellows of the Royal Society.

The grandfather Henry Moseley (1801–1872), generally called Canon Moseley (he was Canon of Bristol and Rector of Olvaston near the Severn), was a mathematician and physicist, for a time professor of natural philosophy and astronomy at King's College, London, later one of Her Majesty's inspectors of schools. He was elected F. R. S. in 1839. He wrote a number of textbooks on astronomy, mathematics and engineering.

The father, Henry Nottidge Moseley, was born in 1844. He was educated at Harrow [1] "where he chiefly occupied himself in birds'-nesting and 'bug-hunting' in conjunction with a small band of kindred spirits. He was essentially a sportsman, knew every kind of game and how to pursue it. He thoroughly disliked the ordinary routine of school work, such as it was in those days, and it was not until he had entered at Exeter College (Oxford) and come under the teaching of the late professor Rolleston, that his really keen and remarkable intellectual powers began to show themselves. He had somehow developed in early youth the most deep-rooted scepticism which I ever came across among men of my own age; hence it was the *reality* of the work which he did in the dissecting-room at the Museum which delighted him and gave confidence that there was 'something in it' worthy of his intellectual effort. With unfeigned astonishment he would say, on dissecting out the nervous system of a mollusk or some such structure, 'It is like the picture, after all!' He had a profound disbelief in the statements made in books unless he could verify them for himself, and it was this habit of mind, perceived and encouraged by Rolleston, which made him in after life so admirable an observer and so successful as a discoverer of new facts. Rolleston used to say that you had only to put down Moseley on a hill-side with a piece of string and an old nail, and in an hour or two he would have discovered some natural object of surpassing interest." A close friend of Ray Lankester they visited the Channel Islands together, graduated in 1868 and in the following year spent six weeks in the Auvergne and South Eastern France. Their companionship continued during their postgraduate studies in Vienna and Leipzig. In 1871, Moseley went to Ceylon as member of the Government Eclipse Expedition led by Norman Lockyer, made spectroscopic observations at Trincomali and brought home a large booty of land planarians. He was one of the naturalists attached to the Challenger (1872–1876). Though primarily a zoologist he undertook the collecting of plants whenever the ship touched land and he made an anthropological investigation of the Admiralty Islanders. While at the Cape, he took special pains to obtain specimens of Peri-

[1] My information on H. N. Moseley is almost exclusively derived from the obituary by E. Ray Lankester in *Nature*, vol. 45, p. 79–80, 1891; the quotation marks refer to that obituary.

patus, then very imperfectly known, and described them elaborately. He also devoted much attention to the study of living corals. When he returned home in 1876, his father and mother having died during his absence, he was elected to a fellowship in his old college, Exeter. He became a F. R. S. in 1877. Soon after, he visited Oregon and published an account of it.[2]

In 1881 he married Amabel, daughter of John Gwyn Jeffreys (1809–1885) of Ware Priory, Harts. This Jeffreys was a distinguished conchologist and oceanographer (F. R. S., 1840). In the same year Moseley succeeded his friend and teacher George Rolleston (1829–1881) in the Linacre professorship of human and comparative anatomy at Oxford. While continuing his own research he was obliged to do an enormous amount of work to prepare his teaching (of which he had no experience), organize laboratory exercises and guide special students, but unfortunately that generous activity was suddenly interrupted in 1887 by a severe illness. He died at Clevedon, in Somersetshire, on November 10, 1891. To complete this sketch of his manifold endeavors I must still add that he was one of the promoters of the Plymouth Laboratory of Marine Biology and that he was largely instrumental in obtaining for his university the Pitt-Rivers collection of anthropological objects. He was the recipient of one of the Royal Medals in 1887. I have already indicated the originality of his mind, the diversity of his interests; he was also extremely energetic. Says Ray Lankester, "The amount and variety of work in which he engaged, in addition to the remarkable and extraordinarily minute course of lectures and laboratory work provided by him for his pupils, were certainly more than was wise for him to undertake. But it was a strange and to him a disastrous fact that he never felt tired. He was an exceedingly strong man, and I never saw him fatigued either by physical or mental exertion." We shall notice presently similar qualities in his son. However it is worth while to observe that with all his strength, the father did not live to be old. He was forty-seven when he died, but his scientific activity had come practically to an end when he was only forty-three.[3]

[2] *Oregon; its resources, climate, people and productions.* 125 p. London, 1878.
[3] A letter kindly written to me by Sir Edwin Ray Lankester on July 25, 1926, when this article was already written, enables me to complete it in some important respects. Moseley's father "suffered from cerebral sclerosis during the last four

To return to the subject of this biography, Sir Edwin Ray Lankester who had been, as I showed above, an intimate friend of Moseley, the zoologist, knew the latter's son chiefly as a boy: little Harry. He recalls [4] that Harry "was a keen and observant naturalist and knew every bird and bird's nest in the neighbourhood of his home. In this and in the collection of flint implements he was enthusiastically aided by his sister." Thus the boy seemed to have inherited his father's interest in natural history, but these biological proclivities were happily mixed with a strong mathematical and physical bent, which may have come to him from his grandfather, Canon Moseley. It should be noted that his father was relatively well acquainted with chemical and physical questions; I have already alluded to the spectroscopic observations made by him at Trincomali. However the scientific influence of his family was purely a matter of heredity, not of environment, for the child never knew his grandfathers and his father's activity was already ended at the time of his birth. Harry was only four years old when his father died; his mother was the only guide of his early education.

He entered Eton at the age of thirteen with a King's scholarship and seems to have been a better student than his father had been at Harrow, for he achieved distinction both in classics and mathematics.[5] At eighteen he entered Trinity College, Oxford, and obtained his degree with honors in natural science in 1910. By that time his career was already determined, for he had conferred with Ernest Rutherford in Manchester and arranged a program of research in radioactivity. Soon after his graduation he was appointed lecturer in the Physics Department of the University of Manchester. But as his work grew upon him he needed more and more time for investigation; after

---

years of his life. The disease began with violent headache and fits of an epileptiform character and rendered him mentally imbecile. It showed itself quite suddenly and for four years he was cheerful and without pain but his mind, was, so to speak, gone. The origin of this condition was not ascertained." Sir Edwin was his successor in the Linacre professorship. Moseley's mother became the wife of William Johnson Sollas, professor of geology in Oxford, and is still living. Moseley had two sisters; the elder died soon after her father, the younger (Mrs. Hewell, still living) studied biology at Oxford and showed great ability. She has written valuable papers especially on a rudimentary gill of the crayfish (Astacus), — new to science."

[4] *Philosophical Magazine*, vol. 31, p. 174, 1916.

[5] Biographical details are largely derived from Rutherford's notice in the *Proc. R. S.*, A, vol. 93, 1916.

a couple of years he resigned his lectureship and was awarded the John Harling Fellowship. Later he returned to Oxford to live with his mother. Most of his work was done in Manchester: it was under Rutherford's guidance that he found himself and developed his wonderful abilities; yet the most important of the few papers which he had time to write, the classical memoir on the high-frequency spectra of the elements, was completed in the Electrical Laboratory of Oxford directed by Professor J. S. Townsend.

His father and mother were great travellers, they had visited together some parts of Canada, the United States, and Mexico, not to speak of more accessible countries. The Australia meeting of the B. A. A. S. gave Mrs. Moseley an opportunity to renew her acquaintanceship with America, for she accompanied her son, who went to Australia via Canada and the Pacific. This was in the summer of 1914. Their arrival in Australia coincided with the beginning of the war and as soon as the meeting was over, young Moseley hastened back to England to offer his services. Sir E. Ray Lankester assures us that Moseley was offered work suited to his scientific capacity at home, but that he preferred to share with others the dangers of active service. For such a noble youth, this was natural enough and it would be impossible to complain of his sacrifice though the whole world would be poorer because of it. "He was granted a commission in the Royal Engineers, and later was made signalling officer in the 38th Brigade of the First Army, leaving for the Dardanelles on June 13 (1915). He took part in the severe fighting at the Suvla Bay landing on August 6 and 8, and was instantaneously killed on the tenth, by a bullet in the head, when in the act of telephoning an order to his division, at the moment when the Turks were attacking on the flank only 200 yards away."

The list of Moseley's writings appended to this essay includes a summary of each and thus it is not necessary here to enter into many technical details, which would be of little interest except to a very few readers. It will suffice to lay stress upon the more general aspects of his activity.[6]

[6] I refer to Moseley's papers by quoting their ordinal number in the list below, followed by their date.

When Moseley came to Manchester in 1910, a large amount of work was being done in the physical laboratories under Rutherford's stimulating direction. This great leader had already detected Moseley's extraordinary aptitudes and wanted to give him an opportunity to complete his technical development. A task was found which would enable him to gain experience in accurate measurements, — the determination of the number of β-particles emitted in the disintegration of radium (no. 2, 1912). It involved measuring the charge carried by β-rays in a high vacuum. After having mastered that very delicate technique, Moseley asked himself whether there was any limit to the potential which an insulated body containing radium would reach in such vacuum (no. 4, 1913). He was thus able to obtain a steady difference of potential of 150,000 volts. I do not insist upon other incidental researches which he carried through with the assistance of K. Fajans (no. 1, 1911), W. Makower (no. 3, 1912), and later with that of H. Robinson (no. 7, 1914).

While he was engaged in these difficult investigations, startling developments in other directions arrested his curiosity. I quote the main events in chronological order to explain the genesis of Moseley's new thoughts. In 1911, the large-angle scattering of α-particles in passing through matter had led Rutherford to propound his nuclear theory of the atom. According to that theory the main mass of the atom is concentrated in a positively charged nucleus, surrounded — like a sun by its planets — by a number of negative electrons sufficient to neutralize its own charge. The main properties of the atom must depend upon that nuclear charge which controls the number and arrangement of the planetary electrons. Moreover various experiments had suggested that that charge was proportional to the atomic weight.[7] In the following year (1912) Max von Laue discovered that X-rays could be refracted and made to interfere by means of crystalline plates, the experimental proof of this momentous discovery being completed by W. Friedrich and P. Knipping (*Isis* 5, 526). This was promptly followed up in many laboratories, chiefly in Leeds, where

[7] E. Rutherford. The scattering of α- and β-particles by matter and the structure of the atom. *Philosophical Magazine*, vol. 21, p. 669–688, 1911. See p. 687 : "The general data available indicate that the value of this central charge for different atoms is approximately proportional to their atomic weights, at any rate for atoms heavier than aluminum."

W. H. Bragg and W. L. Bragg (father and son) proved the presence of bright lines in the X-ray spectrum of platinum (1913). In the meanwhile Moseley, working in Manchester with the help of C. G. Darwin (a grandson of Darwin, now professor at the University of Edinburgh) was able not only to confirm Bragg's result, but to map out for the first time the bright lines in the spectra of the softer radiation [8] emitted by a platinum target (no. 5, 1913). These remarkable experiments carried out in Leeds and Manchester marked the beginning of a new method of investigation — X-ray spectroscopy — which has been justified by abundant fruits. I shall show a few of these presently, but to give the reader at once some idea of the significance of the method, the following simple remark may be useful. The wave lengths of X-rays are about of the same order of magnitude as the atomic distances; thus their use enabled us to objectify these distances; it is as if the keenness of our vision had been magnified ten thousand times.

Rutherford's suggestion above mentioned [9] was confirmed by various other experiments and the notion gradually crystallized that the nuclear charge of the atom (or the number of outer electrons) was probably equal to the atomic number (the ordinal number of the atoms in the Periodic System).[10] This notion was incorporated by Niels Bohr in his quantum theory explaining the constitution of the atoms and of their spectra (1913) (*Isis 6*, 185). According to the new conception the essential characteristic of each atom was no longer its atomic weight but its atomic number. At the beginning of 1913, these views were plausible yet highly speculative, because no atomic property could be definitely represented by the atomic number. Sir Ernest Rutherford records a discussion with Moseley wherein the latter proposed to test that theory by examining the X-ray spectra of a whole series of elements. This was the subject of Moseley's last investigations, those which will immortalize his name. They involved great experi-

[8] When a beam of X-rays falls upon a plate of some chosen element, the plate emits secondary X-radiations, some of which are characteristic of that element. C. G. Barkla showed (1913) that each element possesses two types of characteristic radiation differing greatly in hardness; he called these the K and L radiations, the K being the harder. The hardness of both kinds of radiations increases with the atomic number.

[9] I refer to the sentence quoted in footnote 7.

[10] This is a provisional and approximate definition; its inexactitude is pointed out in footnote 12. The atomic number is exactly defined below.

mental difficulties, because it was necessary to test a continuous series of elements and many of them were hardly suitable to be used as targets in X-ray tubes; moreover the radiations were often extremely absorbable. Yet Moseley developed an ingenious method of photographing X-ray spectra and working with his habitual energy at a tremendous speed he managed in less than half a year to measure the wave-lengths of the main lines in the high-frequency spectra of a large number (38) of elements [11] (no. 6, 1913–14). This enabled him to discover the fundamental law which bears his name: The frequency of any line in the X-ray spectrum of an element is proportional to $(N - b)^2$, wherein N is the atomic number and b a constant. In other words he established a very simple relation between the atomic numbers and the corresponding X-ray spectra; he gave thus an easy means of locating missing elements and predicting their high-frequency spectra with certainty. The real significance of Moseley's discovery lies in that it established conclusively that the atomic number does truly represent the number of outer electrons of each atom. Moseley's expectations were thus more than fulfilled. Surely he deserved to make a great discovery, his genius and zeal justified almost any reward, yet it must be admitted that he himself would hardly have dreamed of hitting such a simple law as this! If one recalls how intricate the ordinary spectra are and how long it has taken to explain their structure and to connect it with the structure of atoms, the relatively simple constitution of high-frequency spectra and their very simple relations with atomic numbers was startling indeed. While the Braggs were using the X-rays to explore the intricacies of crystalline structure, Moseley used them to detect the fundamental modes of vibration of the atoms. His discovery completed admirably the new atomic theories.

Moseley's views were soon confirmed by brilliant applications. In the first place the chemical behavior of nickel and cobalt was inconsistent with their mutual positions in the Periodic Table. Their high-frequency spectra proved that cobalt ought to precede nickel instead of following it; this proved once more the superior taxonomic value

---

[11] Up to silver (N = 47) he measured the K radiation; for heavier elements it was more expedient to measure the L radiation, which he did.

of atomic numbers as compared with atomic weights.[12] In the second place, as I have already indicated, Moseley was able to say how many elements were missing, to state their exact position, and to foretell the very spectra which would lead to their discovery. Each element is characterized by a definite number of planetary electrons. From hydrogen which retains one electron to gold which retains 79, there are 79 elements (H and Au included) and there can not be more. Of these Moseley knew all but three,[13] and he could indicate their place and essential characteristics with far greater certainty and accuracy than the Periodic System would allow.

The power of the new method was admirably illustrated when Georges Urbain, who had been devoting a life-time to the study of the rare earths, came to Oxford for the very purpose of submitting some preparations to Moseley. The latter was able to determine in a few days the elements which were present in them, to estimate their relative proportion, and to say that 61 was not one of them. Moseley spoke of this at the Sydney meeting but had no time to complete and publish this his last investigation. Urbain gave him full credit in a very handsome statement addressed to Sir Ernest Rutherford.[14] "Ainsi la loi de Moseley, pour la fin du groupe des terres rares comme pour

[12] The case of cobalt and nickel is not unique. It is necessary to invert the order of two other couples in the Periodic Table. Here are the facts:

Elements:	A	K	Co	Ni	Te	I
Atomic numbers:	18	19	27	28	52	53
Atomic weights:	39.88	39.10	58.97	58.68	127.5	126.92

[13] Numbers 43, 61, and 75. Element 72 was believed to be known but was not. Thus four elements were unknown, 43, 61, 72, and 75. They have since been isolated: 43, *Masurium,* by W. Noddack and Ida Tacke in 1925; 61, *Illinium,* by B. S. Hopkins in 1926; 72, *Hafnium,* by D. Coster and G. Hevesy in 1923, and 75, *Rhenium* (*Dwi Manganese, Bohemium*), by W. Noddack, I. Tacke, J. Heyrovsky, and V. Dolejšek in 1925 (?). The heaviest known element is uranium, 92; there may possibly be heavier ones, but up to and including uranium, there can be only 92 elements, all of which are known except 85 and 87 (and possibly 75 if its isolation is not confirmed).

[14] Letter dated Paris, Sept. 26, 1915, quoted by Sir Ernest Rutherford in *Proc. R. S.,* A, vol. 93, p. xxvii, 1916. ["Thus Moseley's law, for the end of the group of rare earths as for the beginning, in a few days sanctioned the results of my efforts during twenty years of patient labor. Moreover it was not just this that made me admire Moseley's work. His law substituted for Mendeléef's somewhat romantic classification a truly scientific precision. It brought to an end the period of hesitant research on the chemical elements. It concluded one of the most beautiful chapters in the history of science."]

le commencement, consacrait en quelques jours les conclusions de mes efforts de vingt ans de patient travail. Ce n'est d'ailleurs pas cela qui me faisait admirer le travail de Moseley. Sa loi substituait à la classification un peu romantique de Mendeléeff une précision toute scientifique. Elle mettait du definitif dans la période des recherches hésitantes sur les éléments chimiques. Elle terminait un des plus beaux chapitres de l'histoire des sciences."

The conception of the Periodic System in the final form given to it by Lothar Meyer (1864, 1870), and better still by Dmitri Ivanovich Mendeliev (1869, 1871) was rightly considered one of the greatest triumphs of natural philosophy. It was impossible not to be impressed by the fulfilment of Mendeliev's bold prophecies; there was in that something as great and awful as the discovery of Neptune which Leverrier and Adams had accomplished by purely mathematical means a quarter of a century before. And yet in spite of Mendeliev's claims (in his memoir of 1871) that the Periodic System was a natural system and that it was, at least in principle, free from every kind of arbitrariness, it failed to satisfy the mind entirely. Any professor having to teach that theory to a class of intelligent students must have realized its conventionalities and imperfections even if long habit had gradually blunted his own sense of them. Why did the periods exist and what did they really mean? Irregular as they were, how did it come to pass that the atomic weights were grouped as they were? Why were there not more of them, or less? Why were their arithmetical values so complex? One could not help asking oneself such questions. Leaving aside minor difficulties, of which there were not a few, the conclusion was forced upon us that the Periodic Law gave only a glimpse of reality. It was undeniably right as far as it went, but there must be something at the back of it. As late as 1906 (and 1909) Pattison Muir wrote: [15] "The future will decide whether the Periodic Law is the long looked for goal, or only a stage in the journey, a resting-place while material is gathered for the next advance." This future was then unexpectedly near. The long series of momentous discoveries were then already on their way, which would transform

[15] M. M. Pattison Muir, *History of chemical theories and laws.* London, 1909 (first pub. 1906), p. 375.

278

radically our atomic conceptions and give the Periodic Law a new significance. It was necessary first of all to transfer the emphasis from the atomic weight to the less obvious but deeper concept of atomic number. This revolutionary change was clinched by Moseley's discovery. Moseley's law was the cornerstone of the new edifice. Much was still to be done to complete its construction, and to remove other incongruities of the Periodic Law, for example to explain the fractions of the atomic weights, but that is another story. Would that Dmitri Ivanovich had been given to witness this purification of his grand synthesis! The classification which we have finally reached is at once simple and natural: the elements are arranged in order of increasing nuclear charge, the first having a charge of one electrostatic unit, the second a charge of two units, the third a charge of three units and so on without discontinuities. No arrangement could be simpler. In each "series" of the old Periodic Table, the number of planetary electrons increases one by one as we pass from one element to its neighbour; the elements which are placed in the same column (which belong to the same "group") have the same number of electrons in the outer shell and hence it is not surprising that their behavior, that their external reactions are somewhat similar. The obscurities, artificialities, and inconsistencies of the Periodic System have been cleared away.

Moseley's life work was done in four years. His career was like the meteor of a summer night. Thus he did not belong to any academy, because he was already gone before they knew of his existence or had time to consider his election.[16] His apprenticeship as an experimenter had lasted only a year and then he had plunged at once very deeply into original research. His success was due to the combination of rare intelligence, excellent mathematical training, experimental skill, and last not least (for there can be no genius without that) enormous endurance. "His powers of continuous work were extraordinary, and he showed a predilection for turning night into day. When his researches were at an interesting stage, it was not unusual for an early arrival at the laboratory to meet Moseley leaving after about

[16] Sir Ernest Rutherford's obituary appeared in the *Proceedings of the Royal Society* in pursuance of a special resolution of the Council. Moseley was not a Fellow.

fifteen hours of continuous and solitary work through the night. His originality and unusual powers as an investigator were soon recognised by his co-workers in the laboratory, while his cheerfulness and willingness to help endeared him to all his colleagues." [17]

One of his fellow workers, C. G. Darwin, remarked that "Moseley was without exception or exaggeration the most brilliant man whom he had ever come across." Immersed as he was in his studies, his mind was not lobsided. A good classical training had given him a great facility and felicity of expression; he could explain his views with force and clearness. Like his father he was a genial friend and could share and shine in any conversation. He used to spend his vacation with his mother in their cottage of the New Forest, he loved gardening and had kept from the days of his boyhood a keen interest in natural history. This stood him in good stead during his days of soldiering in the Near East. It was of course impossible to continue chemical or physical experiments while doing his military duty, but he had opportunities to observe the plants and birds around him.

"His last letters home from the East were full of observations on the plant-life, the birds, the beasts and the flint implements *of all ages* which he found in a day's ramble on the hills where he was encamped." [18]

Thus the last weeks of his life were not entirely overwhelmed by the horrors and brutality of war, they were brightened as much as they could be by his geniality and by his sympathy with nature, his keen understanding of the little world which continued its innocent and humble life in the midst of that human inferno. We can imagine him knowing, as the bravest did, moments of melancholy and despair, but being soothed by the contemplation of a passing bird or of a little flower: the bird sings a hymn of joy in the face of human folly; — the flowers put a touch of beauty at the edge of a shrapnell hole . . . Life goes on.

APPENDICES

I. — *Moseley's Writings.*

1. Radio-active products of short life (with K. Fajans). *Philosophical Magazine*, vol. 22, 629–638, 1911.

[17] *Proc. R. S.*, A, 93, p. xxviii, 1916.
[18] Sir E. Ray Lankester, *Philos. Mag.*, vol. 31, 174, 1916.

1. Actinium emanation is succeeded by a solid product which emits α-particles, and has a half-value period 0.0020 second.

2. Thorium emanation is succeeded by a similar product with half-value period 0.14 second.

3. The product obtained by recoil from actinium active deposit is pure Act D. The supposed complex nature of Act C is therefore not confirmed.

2. The number of β-particles emitted in the transformation of radium. *Proc. R. S.*, A. vol. 87, 230–255, 1912.

1. Each atom of radium B and of radium C emits on disintegrating probably one β-particle, although measurement gives in either case as the average number 1.10 β-particles. Each atom of radium E appears to emit less than one β-particle.

2. The absorption of the β-radiation from radium active deposit has been studied, measurements being made both of the number of β-particles penetrating the absorbing material and of the ionisation they produce. From these data the ionising power of a β-particle in air and its variation with the absorption coefficient of the radiation have been calculated, the number of ions produced per centimetre of path being found to vary from 82 when $\lambda = 15$ cm.$^{-1}$ aluminium to about 160 when $\lambda = 100$ cm.$^{-1}$.

3. With the help of data obtained by Geiger and Kovarik the numbers of β-particles emitted on disintegration by atoms of uranium X, thorium D, and actinium D have been estimated to be 1, 0.8 and 1.4 respectively.

4. The number of secondary β-particles emitted by material traversed by γ-rays has been measured. It has been deduced on certain assumptions that each atom of radium C emits on disintegrating two γ-rays.

5. Surfaces penetrated by β-rays emit a secondary radiation. This radiation is very similar to the δ-rays. It appears that the secondary radiation cannot leave the surface unless assisted by an electric field, and that of the δ-rays some are emitted with a small velocity corresponding to a difference of potential of the order of 2 volts.

3. γ-radiation from radium B (with W. Makower). *Philosophical Magazine*, vol. 23, 302–310, 1912.

1. γ-rays of absorption coefficient about 4 cm.$^{-1}$ for lead between the thicknesses 3 mm. and 5.94 mm. and about 6 cm.$^{-1}$ between 0.97 mm. and 1.72 mm. are emitted by radium B. These rays contribute about 12 per cent. to the total ionization produced by the active deposit measured through 3 mm. of lead and not more than 1 per cent. through 2.3 cm. of lead. Radium B appears, therefore, to give no hard γ-radiation.

2. Radium C$_2$, if it emits γ-rays at all, gives an amount too small to be detected by the method used.

4. The attainment of high potentials by the use of radium. *Proc. R. S.*, A., vol. 88, 471–476, 1913.

A radioactive substance made by the emission of β-radiation charge itself positively to a potential difference of more than 150,000 volts from its surroundings. This fact provides a striking direct proof of the large amount of energy involved in the expulsion of a β-particle. It also extends somewhat our knowledge of the insulating properties of a vacuum.

5. The reflexion of X-rays (with C. G. Darwin). *Philosophical Magazine,* vol. 26, 210–232, 1913.

1. X-rays "reflected" from crystals have the general properties of ordinary X-rays.

2. The radiation from an X-ray tube with platinum target is of two kinds, (A) radiation of indefinite wave-length, analogous to white light, (B) five types of monochromatic radiation, probably characteristic of the platinum.

3. The radiation (A) is reflected at all angles of incidence. The reflection has been studied at different angles, and the results have been interpreted.

4. Each of the radiations (B) is reflected only at special angles. These angles have been measured with three crystals, and the results are in good agreement with the simple theory deduced from the principle of interference.

5. The wave-lengths of these radiations have been calculated to be 1.642, 1.397, 1.375, 1.194, 1.157 $\times$ K $\times$ 10^{-8} cm. where K is probably either 1, ½, or ⅓.

6. Their homogeneity has been examined.

7. An attempt has been made to estimate the distribution of energy in the wave-lengths for the general X-rays.

6. The high-frequency spectra of the elements. *Philosophical Magazine,* vol. 26, 1024–1034, 1913. Part II *Ibidem,* 27, 703–713, 1914.

1. Every element from aluminium to gold is characterized by an integer N which determines its X-ray spectrum. Every detail in the spectrum of an element can therefore be predicted from the spectra of its neighbours.

2. This integer N, the atomic number of the element, is identified with the number of positive units of electricity contained in the atomic nucleus.

3. The atomic numbers for all elements from Al to Au have been tabulated on the assumption that N for Al is 13.

4. The order of the atomic numbers is the same as that of the atomic weights, except where the latter disagrees with the order of the chemical properties.

5. Known elements correspond with all the numbers between 13 and 79 except three. There are here three possible elements still undiscovered.

6. The frequency of any line in the X-ray spectrum is approximately proportional to $A(N - b)^2$, where A and b are constants.

7. The number of ions produced by the β- and γ-radiations from radium (with H. Robinson). *Philosophical Magazine,* vol. 28, 327–337, 1914.

8. Atomic models and X-ray spectra. *Nature,* vol. 92, 554, Jan. 15, 1914.

Answer to objections made by F. A. Lindemann, *ibidem,* p. 500, Jan. 1, 1914. Another reply was made by N. Bohr, *ibidem,* p. 553, Jan. 15, 1914. Rejoinder by Lindemann, *ibidem,* p. 631, Feb. 5, 1914.

Moseley was given an opportunity to explain his views at the Australia meeting of the British Association for the Advancement of Science. On August 25, 1914, he read in Sydney a paper on high-frequency spectra, quoted by title in the report of that meeting. On August 18, in Melbourne, he had taken part in a discussion on the structure of atoms and molecules led by Sir Ernest Rutherford.

"He explained the results of his classification of elements by their X-ray spectra. The frequency of the principal line in the X-ray spectrum is represented very closely by the formula $\gamma^{1/2} = K(N - B)$ where K and B are constants, and N an integer increasing by a unit as we pass from element to element up the Periodic Table. If we take this atomic number N as ordinate, and the square root of the principal frequency as abscissa, the different elements will therefore give points lying approximately on a straight line. The secondary frequencies will at the same time give points on other straight lines. The order of the elements determined by N is nearly that of increasing atomic weight; there are one or two exceptions, and in such cases the order given by N, and not the atomic weight is evidently the correct order corresponding to chemical properties. For example, the atomic weight gives the order Cl, K, A, whereas the X-ray frequency gives the order Cl, A, K. The latter is the order required by the Periodic Table. There are between aluminium and gold four missing elements, indicated by the double jump of N required to make the formula fit. These correspond generally to gaps indicated also by the Periodic Law." The report of the Australia meeting contains nothing but what I have quoted (pp. 299, 305).

II. — *Writings on Moseley.*

Sir Ernest Rutherford. Obituary. *Nature*, vol. 96, 33–34, Sept. 9, 1915; a longer one in *Proc. R.S.*, A., vol. 93, xxii-xxviii, 1916 (this second obituary includes everything which was contained in the first and thus supersedes it). Moseley's work on X-rays, *Nature*, vol. 116, 316–317, 1925 (apropos of the discovery of Moseley's portrait).

Sir E. Ray Lankester. Obituary in *Philosophical Magazine*, vol. 31, 173–176, 1916 (including a note by N. Bohr and W. Makower). Information on the technique of Moseley's experiments may be obtained for example in Manne Siegbahn, *The spectroscopy of X-rays*. Oxford University Press, 1925 (*Isis 8*, 614).

III. — *Moseley's Portrait.*

No good portrait of Moseley was known until the recent discovery of a snapshot taken (by N. Garrod Thomas) probably in the Balliol-Lincoln Laboratories at Oxford in the summer of 1910 about the time of his graduation. The portrait of Moseley which formed a part of this negative was enlarged by Mr. W. H. Hayles of the Cavendish Laboratory and a small reproduction appeared in *Nature*, vol. 116, 316, 1925. . . It is a beautiful portrait which will help us to think of Moseley, not only as a great scientist, but as a very lovable man.

Cambridge, Mass.
July, 1926

[English as an International Language]

A Letter to the Editor of the New York *Evening Post*, February 22, 1919

Sɪʀ: The publication of *Isis*, an international quarterly devoted to the history and philosophy of science, was brutally interrupted in 1914 by the German invasion of Belgium. In a letter which appeared in *Science*, February 14, I announced that this publication would be resumed before the end of the year. I also announced some changes which I propose to introduce in the new *Isis*.

One of these changes was used as a text for your editorial of February 17, entitled "International Relations in Science," but was so unfortunately misconstrued that I trust you will kindly insert the following explanation:

Before the war, *Isis* was published in four languages, French, German, English, and Italian. I propose to drop at once two of them, German and Italian, and, furthermore, to abandon the use of French, my own language, as soon as possible.

The writer of your editorial seems to have been under the impression that I had decided upon this change as a war measure, as a kind of reprisal against Germany, and he rather inconsiderately denounces it as an attempt to injure the internationalization of science.

As a matter of fact, if he had taken the trouble of investigating the question, he would have found that I am myself as international-minded as it is possible to be. I have been a staunch supporter of the League of Nations (of the genuine and generous kind) at a time when it was considered by many wise men as a good subject of jokes. Now that this "Utopia" is slowly becoming a reality, I see clearly that its fulfilment will open a period of such intense international relations in every field that to the people of the next century the pre-war period will seem to be, in comparison, utterly provincial. The war will probably play in the internationalization of the world the same part that your Civil War played in the unification of this country.

Whatever the feelings of the individual scientist may be, science as such must remain a sanctuary far above human hatred. Let us hope that proper agencies will be established to adjust all political wrongs and to punish the international crimes of this war and of the future; but it is not the province of science to judge and to punish crimes.

It is precisely to increase the international value of *Isis* that I decided to restrict its publication to one language instead of four. There are, of course, far more people able to read comfortably any one of these four languages than the four of them. I found out that the polyglottism of *Isis* was a serious and unnecessary obstacle to its circulation and consequently to the diffusion of the history of science and of the ideal of the New Humanism.

But why did I choose English, although this meant for me, a French writer, a great personal sacrifice, — not simply an additional burden, but also a sentimental sacrifice? I am rather glad to have an opportunity to declare the reasons of my choice.

English is the language which is spoken by far the greater number of civilized people. It is the language not of one single nation but of many great commonwealths. Indeed we may reasonably dream of the time when it will be the international language of the world.

From the beginning, *Isis* found some of its most faithful friends in Japan and India, and I much hope that the new *Isis* will have many more friends not simply in these countries but also in other Eastern countries and will become in its field a common interpreter between East and West. Now I cannot reasonably expect my Eastern readers to master four European languages for *Isis'* sake, and the language which is most popular in Asia, and bids fair to become its "lingua franca" is certainly English.

My chief reasons for choosing English rather than French, however, are my faith in the Anglo-Saxon conception of life, and also my love of and my hope in the younger civilizations of the world: first of all, this United States, then also Canada, Australia, South Africa, and New Zealand. It is a very happy circumstance indeed that all of these peoples speak English almost exclusively.

I believe that as far as the diffusion of common sense in politics and the spirit of fair play are concerned these young nations are the hope of the world. They are, on the whole, less trammeled by precedent and by prejudice, and more capable of working out radical ideas in a conservative way. I trust that the ideal of the New Humanism — that is, the reconciliation of science and art, truth and beauty — will find a more appreciative audience among them.

That is why in the middle of my life, I choose to speak English.

George Sarton.

Cambridge, Mass., February 20, [1919].

The Tower of Babel

DURING THE last decades, the number of languages employed for scientific purposes has considerably increased. Old dialects have been raised to the dignity of national languages; they are used for teaching not simply in the lower schools but in colleges and universities, and many of these universities feel it is their duty to publish scientific treatises, monographs, and even scientific journals, in the national language. In many cases, the undertaking is so new and artificial that the teachers have to learn the language in order to teach in it, or to use it for the writing of scientific papers, thus to justify the national ambitions.

There is something noble in that kind of cultural emulation, something far nobler than a competition which would be purely economic or military, yet I am afraid that it is doing harm as well as good, and perhaps more harm than good. If our distant aims be the unity and brotherhood of mankind, it is clear enough that that aim is defeated by the multiplicity of languages. Reread chapter XI(1–9) of Genesis. That is a very sad story and the more so, because, if we must believe it, it was the Lord himself who deliberately "confounded the language of all the earth." It is not my intention, however, to revive that old scandal, the very thought of which causes me insufferable pain. The controversy relative to the old Tower of Babel is closed and nothing is to be gained by reopening it.[1] I am more concerned with the new

---

[1] After writing this essay, I happened to read the treatise of Philo the Jew (I-1) "on the confusion of tongues" (Loeb edition of Philo's works, vol. 4, 1932), wherein he tries to justify the story told in Genesis. On the one hand, he claimed that "the possession of a common language does more harm than good"; on the other, that the confusion of languages should not be understood as a separation of them, but rather as a thorough confusion (not a mechanical mixture, *mixis*, but a chemical one, *krâsis*) and he concludes: "Thus it is a work well-befitting to God to bring into full harmony the consonance [*symphonia*] of the virtues, but to dissipate and destroy the consonance of vices. Yes, confusion is indeed a most proper name

Tower of Babel which is being built under our own eyes. Must the old story, the confusion of languages, be repeated, or should we rather do our best to avoid its repetition?

One world does not necessarily mean one language; it is not impossible nor even difficult for men to know more than one, but it is no less certain that if linguistic fragmentation and jealousy are carried too far, the world can never be united. We are trying to build a high tower; must it again be destroyed?

The argument will be much clarified if we point out, at the very outset, that we have no hostility against any language but only object to their misuse. A language is an instrument which answers many different needs; some of those needs are purely domestic, communal, tribal, religious, poetic; other needs are intertribal, international, inter-religious. We are concerned, as always, with the needs of the second group, but recognize that for most people the needs of the first group are the most urgent as well as the most important. People must be able to express their feelings, as is done when parents converse together or with their children; artisans must be able to discuss their craft; fellow citizens, their social problems; poets must give voice to the highest aspirations of their community. Social groups are amalgamated by the common language which each member has learned at his mother's knees. It has been said that the strongest bonds of any nation are its religion and its language. When these bonds are intertwined, their united strength is unconquerable.

As an old Flemish proverb put it, "De taal is gansch het volk." Language is the whole people. There is much truth in that, yet one might also say, Religion is the whole people. It would be vain to argue which of the two bonds is the stronger by itself, for that must vary for each individual. The influence of language on religion is so great that some mediaeval doctors feared that those who studied Hebrew too closely might become Jews.[2] As a matter of fact, a modern convert to Judaism testified that his conversion had been prospered by his

for vice, and a standing evidence of this is every fool, whose words and purposes and deeds alike are worthless and unstable." (Translation by F. H. Colson.) God meant to throw into helpless disorder not simply the tongues but the minds of sinful and arrogant men.

[2] D. B. Macdonald, *Aspects of Islam* (p. 231, New York, 1911).

288

Hebrew studies.[3] Many scholars have been gradually led to the altars of the Catholic or of the Orthodox church because of their love of Latin or Greek, and of their increasing joy in reading the Scriptures and breviaries in those languages. On the other hand, each religion established its own sacred language more strongly and more deeply than could have been done by any other agency.

One is tempted to exclaim: "No good man would ever wish to destroy or to harm the religion or the language of other men," but unfortunately that is not so. Some men were so convinced of the supreme and unique value of their religion or of their language that they considered it their duty to oblige other people to accept them and were ready to persecute the recalcitrant. The darkest pages in the history of mankind have been blackened by that delusion and by that criminal perversion of faith and love.

Languages, we should always remember, are the result of unconscious biological developments. Before the dawn of Greek culture nobody ever thought "We are going to speak a new language which will be governed by such and such rules" . . . In spite of their infinite complexity languages grew naturally, and their admirable paradigms were not "chosen" any more than the birds of a certain kind ever "chose" their exquisite feathers and "arranged" them in beautiful and whimsical patterns. Greek grammar existed from the beginning of the Greek speech, for grammar is really the skeleton of a language, yet it was not "discovered" or "realized" until after the masterpieces of Greek literature had been composed. There comes a time in the life of any language when some changes are consciously introduced, but that time is always late and the changes, superficial. The vocabulary of any language is continuously enriched by the development of new needs or by contacts with other languages, but the grammar remains essentially the same, and new words cannot be integrated into the language unless they be subordinated to its grammatical functions.

Language is the best mirror of the people using it; its own evolution follows their own; its life is their life. Some words go up or down because the ideas which they represent are appreciated or cheapened. Words may wear away like other things and are then thrown out of the language for a time or forever. Language is an instrument of such

[3] Aimé Pallière, *Le sanctuaire inconnu* (p. 62, Paris, 1926).

infinite complexity and richness that no man could make full use of it. Thus, every individual speaks to some extent a language of his own, and that special language is the best mirror of his own soul.

Living creatures must eventually die; living species may die. But, when the last dodo expired toward the end of the seventeenth century, its species vanished. The same may happen to languages. For example, it happened to Syriac and Coptic which almost ceased to be spoken in the sixteenth century (if not before) and are hardly used today except for liturgical purposes.[4] The last person to speak Cornish was an old woman, Dolly Pentreath, who died in 1777.[5] The last speaker of Dalmatian, Anthony Udina, was killed in a mine explosion in 1898.[6]

Every dead language which is sufficiently known by literary documents might be resurrected, but is it worthwhile to do so? Some languages which were hardly used for domestic purposes such as Hebrew have been revived; others which had been degraded to the status of dialects like Irish and Estonian have been restored to their ancient dignity. Nobody will quarrel with that as long as the rest of the world is not obliged to learn Gaelic or Estonian; that is, as long as the Irish and Estonians are not intolerant of other languages, but willing to recognize the spatial limitations of their own, and if they have messages to deliver to the world, ready to write them in a language which the world may be assumed to understand (it is their interest to do so).

The real natural language is spoken;[7] the writing of it introduces necessarily some artificiality, and in the course of time lexicographers and grammarians proceed to standardize it, trying, as it were, to embalm its latest stage for posterity. If the language has any vitality,

[4] *Introd.* (3, 358, 361).

[5] See article in *DNB* (29, 267) under her married name Dorothy Jeffery (1685–1777). The author of that article claims that she was not the very last Cornish speaker, but that hardly affects the argument. (Maybe the last dodo to be observed was not really the very last to exist). A monument was erected to her memory in 1860, near Penzance, by Prince Louis Lucien Bonaparte.

[6] Holger Pedersen, *Linguistic science in the nineteenth century* (p. 93, Harvard Press, 1931).

[7] Compare Plato's remarks about the spoken vs. the written word in *Phaedros,* end of p. 275 ff., and also Goeth's saying, "Schreiben ist ein Missbrauch der Sprache" (*Dichtung und Wahrheit*, 2. Teil, 10. Buch). Yet, Plato and Goethe were copious writers! On the value of oral traditions, see Solomon Gandz, The dawn of literature, (*Osiris* 7, 261–522, 1939), G. G. Coulton, *Medieval panorama* (p. 575, Cambridge, 1938).

they are bound to fail; its grammar will change a little and its vocabulary very much. From time to time new grammars and new dictionaries will be published.

The contrast between the spoken language and the written helps us to understand other differences within a single language between special forms devoted to different purposes. The two extreme forms are the poetic and the scientific. Genuine poetry comes closest to speech while the scientific language is furthest remote from it, being rational instead of intuitive, clear and univocal instead of dark and ambiguous.

Poetry is so close to the essence of language that it cannot be translated without considerable distortion; on the contrary, a good scientific text might be translated without any loss at all. No dictionary could define completely the words of any language unless it included innumerable examples, for each word is colored by its context and whenever it is used in a creative way by a great writer some of the new color clings to it forever. Thus, each word carries with it an infinity of undertones. Every time a poet uses such a word he takes advantage of some of those undertones and tries to add new ones. The poetic language thrives in verbal ambiguities, harmonies and dissonances. The poet tries to enlarge the atmosphere of every word, while the man of science does his best to restrict it as much as possible. Poetry is like music while scientific prose aims to be as precise as algebra.

It does not follow that such prose should be ugly; it is patient of great beauty. There is a deep distinction between poetic and scientific language, but there should be none between literary and scientific language. It is worthwhile to insist on that, because some of our men of science have been so badly educated that they have no sense of literary virtue; they write like barbarians and drag their scientific ideas in a kind of mud. They cannot even express themselves simply and clearly, at least not without the help of secretaries, editors, and "rewriters."

The scientific use of language is very different from the common use or from the poetical use. It has been beautifully defined by Lavoisier (under Condillac's influence) in the introductory discourse to his *Traité élémentaire de chimie* (first edition, 2 vols., Paris, 1789). Said Lavoisier, "One cannot improve the language without improving science, nor science without the language and however certain the facts be, however just the ideas which those facts evoked, they would transmit only false impressions if we lacked exact ways of expressing them." [8]

It is not necessary to insist on the qualities which we expect to find in good scientific language; they are implied in Lavoisier's statement. I have explained at greater length the qualities of common or poetic language, which may seem irrelevant to my subject, in order to show that I fully appreciate the value and the beauty of language, irrespective of its use.

Languages are the richest flowers of humanity. The humanities revolve around the arts, and especially the art of language . . . The language which we use for common life and poetry is local or national; it may be difficult for people of other nations to understand it or to appreciate it; they can hardly ever enjoy all its undertones. On the contrary, the language used to express scientific ideas may obtain an international currency. It is to the scientific language that the rest of this essay is devoted.

The following story will illustrate my point of view. When the Syrian Protestant College (later called American University) of Beirūt organized medical teaching in 1867 it was first thought that it would be best to teach in Arabic which was the natural language of the students of that region. That generous idea could be implemented because of the devotion of teachers such as Cornelius Van Dyck and George Edward Post, who translated a number of medical and other scientific books into Arabic.[9] These elementary textbooks were adequate at the time of their publication, but as the years passed, it was realized not only that more textbooks were needed but also that those available had to be revised.

[8] That quotation was used by Emile Picard at the beginning of his "Discours de réception" read at the French Academy on 11 Feb. 1926. He added "One could not better express the necessity of collaboration between the Académie française and the Académie des sciences." Yes and no. Both academies are interested in good language, but their literary purposes are not the same. Their emulation is nevertheless very stimulating.

[9] The scientific Arabic treatises of Cornelius Van Dyck (1818–1895) appeared in Beirūt between 1852 and 1878, those of George Post (1838–1909), between 1874 and 1884. A bibliography of their Arabic writings with many facsimiles of title pages appeared in Isis, being appended to their biographies by Lutfi M. Sa'di (Isis 27, 20–45, 1937; 28, 387–417, 1938).

All this was very difficult, if not impossible. In order to have text-books adequate to the expanding knowledge it would have been necessary to maintain a whole body of translators, to monopolize the services of a printing press, and to sacrifice the remainders of many editions in order to replace good books by better ones. Moreover, those text-books whether in the form of translations or adaptions would always be posterior and often inferior to their models; in some respects, they would already be behind the times at the moment of their publication. An Arabic physician, wishing to know medical news as soon as possible, would have to master one of the great languages of the world. If so, would it not be simpler to teach him medicine in that language to begin with?

After long discussions it was finally decided that the main teaching at the medical school of the American University would be in English, not in Arabic, and in spite of my love of the Arabic language, I think that was a wise decision.[10]

It is useful to publish elementary textbooks in Arabic or in other national languages for the benefit of primary and secondary schools or of the educated public, but the needs of university students and of advanced scholars can hardly be satisfied without the literary resources, immense to begin with and constantly renewed, which are available only in the international languages.

The new nations making heroic efforts to establish or reestablish a national language find it much more difficult to bow to that necessity than do some of the older small nations, which happen to be among the most civilized nations of Europe, the Scandinavian kingdoms and the Netherlands. A Dutch or Swedish scholar will readily admit that he could not continue his work without the use of the international languages; he is not a bit ashamed to make that admission because he has no inferiority complex. The Dane loves his native tongue as much

[10] For further details, see Stephen B. L. Penrose, Jr., *That they may have life. The story of the American University of Beirut 1866–1941* (p. 32–45, New York 1941; *Isis* 34, 40–41). It is interesting to note in retrospect, that the passage from Arabic to English was precipitated in 1882–83 by a dispute about the Darwinian theory of evolution. A professor, Edwin R. Lewis, defended that theory in the commencement address of 1882; the trustees accepted his resignation (that is, they forced him to resign) and other professors resigned in protest. "The controversy nearly ruined the medical school." It was necessary to appoint new professors who had no knowledge of Arabic and hence it was decided to make a new start in English.

293

as anybody else; you may hear him declare that it is the best of all languages but that its literature is hopelessly inadequate for his scientific needs. He might just as well declare that Denmark is a wonderful country, the best of all countries for a Dane, yet that it is frightfully small. There is no contradiction in that, and no confession of guilt.

Let us consider another example. A Belgian mathematician, Maurice Lecat, published in 1924 a bibliography of relativity. The following remarks are extracted from the review of it which appeared in *Isis* (*6*,567–568) in the same year. Lecat had listed no less than 3,775 items written by 1,175 authors.[11] The languages most frequently represented in his list are the following (in order of percentages as indicated): German 38, English 30.5, French 18.5, Italian 5.7, Dutch 3.4.[12] (The percentages would be very different now, for the Germany destroyed by Hitler would have to move many rows back, while Russia would come close to the front. In all probability, English would be first with a wide margin.) The main point is that a scholar knowing only the first two languages (we go back to the statistics of 1924) would have been able to read 68.5 percent of all the publications; knowing only three he could have read 87 percent, knowing only four he could have read 92.7 percent. It is true it would have been necessary to know 21 languages in order to read all the writings listed by Lecat. But who would be crazy enough to wish to read them all? Or who could even if he would? The statistics would be even more telling if it were possible to give a weight to each item. We must assume that the great majority are derivative and superfluous; they add nothing to our knowledge, but explain it more or less well to a new public. Every new idea must thus be explained on different levels of thought in order to satisfy different categories of readers. This takes us out of the field of scientific research into the field of education and general reading.

[11] One wonders how many one could list today, twenty-five years later? Lecat lists only 38 items in Russian (1 percent of the whole); today the Russian items would constitute a much higher percentage. The list of 1924 is quite sufficient for our argument, however; the list for 1948 would strengthen rather than weaken our conclusions.

[12] The relative abundance of Dutch items was probably due to the fact that Lecat, established in Louvain, in the Flemish part of Belgium, had better opportunities of knowing Dutch books and papers than those published in other non-international languages.

We may safely assume that the fundamental items on relativity were published in one of the international languages. If a Dane had made a new discovery or simply discovered a better way of integrating relativity into the general pattern of physics, he would have been anxious to find appreciative readers and his chances of doing so would have been enormously greater in the English reading world than in the Danish one.

It would be all right to explain the theory of relativity in Danish for the relatively large body of Danish readers whom the subject might interest; it would be very foolish to publish in Danish a new mathematical development of that theory, for the new theory would concern only a small number of readers scattered all over the civilized world.

We may now examine together a more general problem, the case of the Utopians. Since the time of Thomas More, their civilization has developed by leaps and bounds. They have not produced any great man of science, any great scholar, or any great artist, but the average level of their education is astonishingly high. Their popular magazines are far superior to the American ones, because they contain at least as many good things and do not mix them with a mess of frivolities and stupidities. It is true their editors have an easy time; they read the leading journals of many countries and they translate or adapt the best of each of them. They can do that without hindrance of any kind, for nobody reads their difficult language outside of their country, or cares to know what is published in Utopian . . .

The only trouble with the good Utopians is that they are a little too pleased with themselves. They are always boasting that they have never spent a cent for military defense and therefore have been able to devote the whole of their budget to public health, general education, and other such purposes; that is true enough and wholly admirable; their teachers explaining Utopian ideas to the children point out the stupidity of the European and American nations which are hardly through with one war but are already preparing another one, and thus mortgage for destruction the greatest part of their immense resources. After having painted that very black (and not incorrect) picture of foreign wickedness, they contrast it with their own virtue, thanks to which — so they say — they are able to enjoy perpetual peace and devote the whole of their small resources to the good life. Of course, their descriptions are right, yet their interpretations are very misleading. Their peace and happiness are not due, as they seem to believe, to a superior morality but are simply the result of their almost complete geographical isolation and of their relative poverty. Their island is so small that they can easily manage without means of quick communication; their husbandry and industries are so simple that they have but little need of the mechanical arts; they have no gas or oil, nor other resources which might excite the greed of other nations. I would be tempted to say — not as they do, that their peacefulness and virtue are the results of their superior morality — but rather that their superior morality was induced by the peaceful and simple conditions of their lives, conditions which they have not chosen in any way, but to which they have wisely submitted.

Much knowledge of their happy country has reached me through an old friend of mine who was sailing in the south seas and was abandoned by his companions on an islet near Utopia. He would almost certainly have perished had not good Utopians rescued him; they treated him very generously, and he became like one of them. In fact, he is now more Utopian than the very Utopians, and never ceases to dilate upon the wisdom and the virtues of his new friends who welcomed him, as well as upon the vices and the folly of the old people who cast him out. His gratitude to the former and his anger against the latter are natural enough. As I am a historian of science, he is always telling me that the Utopian view of history is very much the same as my own. The Utopian children are given some idea of the pathological development of mankind (as exemplified by the wars and revolutions of foreign people), but their attention is focused upon the history of art and science. My friend often sends to me long lists of articles on the history of science which appear in their journals and would like me to include them in the Critical Bibliographies of *Isis*. But why should I clutter my bibliographies with Utopian items, which our readers could not possibly obtain, or could not even read if they obtained them? As far as I can make out from a few observations and from the unguarded reflections of my friend, Utopian scholarship is almost entirely borrowed from European, American, and Australian models. They have never bothered to develop a scholarship of their

296

own, hence they have neither original scholars nor expert critics. Why should I list in *Isis* Utopian essays, say, on Stevin, Galileo, or Harvey, which are simply adaptations of, or abstracts from, books and papers available in our own libraries? What can be the value (to others than the Utopians themselves) of an elegant but undocumented article on Lavoisier cribbed from a standard French book on the subject? Why should any sensible man wish to study that tongue-splitting and brainracking language in order to read things which are already familiar to him or are easily obtainable in simpler and better form? My friend's enthusiasm is so contagious that I can not help admiring and loving the Utopians, but for all that it cannot be denied that their culture is derivative and mediocre. They dwell on a cultural mesa, high above the ocean, but very flat.

The Utopian case is extreme but not essentially different from many others which the editor of *Isis* is forced to consider almost every day. If he were to listen to some of his foreign friends, the Critical Bibliographies would be so full of titles in many small languages that the English titles or those written in other international languages would be lost among them. This is due to the fact that the small languages are so numerous . . .

The reader will ask, "What are the international languages?" "On what basis do you distinguish them from the other languages?" The internationality of a language is determined much less by the number of people speaking it naturally, than by the number of people knowing it in addition to their own native language; in other words, it is determined by its international currency rather than by its national one. The six international languages recognized by *Isis* from the beginning are English, French, German, Italian, Latin, and Spanish.[13] No explanation is needed for the first four. The value of Latin is largely retrospective; it concerns older publications rather than new ones; in a sense, no scientific language was ever more international than Latin was for at least seven centuries (say, from the twelfth century to the eighteenth); Latin is still an international language for the clergy, and to some extent for the laity, of the Catholic church; though the study

[13] Or more briefly "Efgils." It is curious that the alphabetic order of these languages is very close to their order of importance.

of it is neither as general nor as thorough as it used to be, the proportion of educated people of all countries having some knowledge of it is still considerable. The international value of Spanish is due to the fact that the people conversant with it belong not to a single nation but to many; Spanish is spoken not only in old Spain but in a large part of the Americas.

Russian, Greek, Chinese, and Arabic are not international in the same sense and to the same degree as the six languages quoted above. Though the number of people speaking and writing Russian or Chinese is truly immense, these languages are not much used by non-Russians or non-Chinese, outside of Russia or of China. Arabic was a true international language in the Middle Ages, say, from the tenth to the twelfth centuries, but it has long lost that importance because of the scientific decadence of Islamic lands. The fact that these four languages are written each in a script of its own (different from the script used for the Efgils) weakens their value for international purposes. Though it would not take any intelligent person more than a few days to master the Greek or Russian alphabet, that difference of script constitutes a psychological barrier which is sufficient to keep a large number of potential readers out.[14]

Not only have the six languages mentioned above a wide international currency, but the main publications in those languages can generally be found in the great libraries of the world . . .

The most civilized of the countries whose languages lack international currency, such as the Scandinavian countries, are already taking pains to have their most valuable works translated into one of the international languages. By so doing they facilitate the diffusion of those works in the whole Republic of Letters, and they obtain for them international criticism and international recognition. A good Danish book translated into English will make more friends for Danish culture in a shorter time than if one were to wait for a considerable number of foreigners to learn Danish for the purpose of reading it.

[14] It should be noted that a knowledge of the Russian language is insufficient to read the publications of the Soviet Union, which is a Babel in itself. In 1938, newspapers of the Soviet Union were published in 68 languages besides Russian. Books and pamphlets have been published since the Revolution in 115 (one hundred and fifteen) different languages. Henry E. Sigerist, *Medicine and health in the Soviet Union* (New York, 1947, p. 4).

298

On the other hand, if a historian of science were especially interested in an entire field of work done in a country whose language had only a national currency, it would be easier and quicker for him to master that language than to wait for translations. Moreover, the available translations would never cover the whole field, and a large amount of materials would remain out of his reach. Thus, a student of Linnaeus or Berzelius should learn the Swedish language, and that would not be difficult. The difficulty does not lie in any language needed for a definite undertaking, but in the multiplicity of languages which a scholar might have to study if he wanted to read everything that was written on a particular subject. As he cannot know more than a few languages, let him concentrate his efforts on the international languages, and perhaps, in addition to that, on one small national language which happens to be of special interest to him.[15]

No mention has been made of the artificial international languages such as Esperanto and Ido, because I do not believe in their value for scholars. The brave statements made by such great men as Descartes and Leibniz are very misleading. Take Leibniz's: "Si una lingua esset in mundo, accederet in effectu generi humano tertia pars vitae, quippe quae linguis impenditur." [16] If there were an international language (Leibniz means a single language known and used by everybody) people would save a third of their lives which they have to spend in order to learn other languages. Of course, they would, but such an ideal is absolutely unattainable. A new international language, to be as widely used as, let us say, Dutch or Polish, would have to succeed beyond the wildest hopes of its promoters. However successful it might prove to be, it would not drive the other languages out of the field; hence, the total result would be the establishment of one more language and perhaps the necessity of studying it in addition to the others. There would be no gain but a loss. The situation of the modern

[15] I hope there will always be a few adventurous and generous spirits ready to learn a small language and to learn it well, for the sake of understanding the peculiar people who speak it and of loving them better.

[16] Quoted together with a similar statement made in French by Descartes, in the form of epigraphs to the excellent *Histoire de la langue universelle* by Louis Couturat and Léopold Léau (Paris 1903); I used the "deuxième tirage" (608 p., Paris 1907). See also their supplementary volume, *Les nouvelles langues internationales* (120 p., Paris, no date, 1907).

Tower of Babel is bad enough; let us not make it worse. The practical problem of international scholarship is to diminish the number of necessary languages rather than to increase it.

A practical man might welcome a new language, driving all others out of existence (if it were conceivable that all the nations would sacrifice their own language, their most precious heritage, on the altar of cold internationality); this would not help the scholar who would still have to study the other languages in order to read the ancient publications.

Even if all the nations accepted the principle of an international language, superseding their own at least for international purposes, it is not easy to see how they could agree on any one language against all others. Couturat and Léau's History is very stimulating, because it gives one a new appreciation of human genius; it is also very depressing because it reveals chaos where order, and competition where unity, would be the first condition of success. In their first volume, they describe fifty-seven different attempts (from Descartes, in 1629, to 1902); in the second they discuss eighteen specimens dating from 1734 to 1907, many of them, it is true, already included in their main history.

The main objections to the choice of one natural language to be the only international language are sentimental and political. The language thus selected would confer a kind of spiritual hegemony on the country (or countries) where that language was naturally used. If English were chosen, let us say, the English-speaking people would have a definite advantage upon the non-English-speaking people. And yet that advantage would not be without drawback. The non-English peoples obliged to study English in addition to their own language would have a real superiority over those lazy English, who had remained monoglot. Indeed, the study of a second language is much more than a linguistic asset, the possession of a second tool; it represents an intellectual growth; the man who has learned a second language is better able to appreciate the full beauty of his own.

Efforts to obtain the official selection of one of the national languages, such as English or French, as the obligatory international language would probably fail because of national jealousies, but the same result may possibly be obtained without official decision, in the

300

course of time owing to the force of circumstances. The decimal system of numbers is used everywhere in spite of the fact that no effort was ever made by anybody to universalize it. It is conceivable that the currency of one language may gradually increase to such an extent that the competition of other languages (for international purposes) dwindles to nothing.

From that point of view, I think that the diffusion of Basic English may be extremely useful. Basic English has the great advantage over artificial languages that it is not artificial. Any person having mastered Basic English has a key to English and to the immense treasure of English literature. If he had mastered Esperanto or Ido, he would find himself in a blind alley leading to no literature whatsoever.

Every cause is spoiled by perfectionists who are satisfied with no solution unless it be extreme and exclusive. The great human problem as I see it does not consist in reducing to unity the multiplicity of languages, but rather in reducing that extravagant multiplicity to a fewness. I am not sure that any single international language would be as desirable as some enthusiasts seem to think.

The Tower of Babel is jeopardized by the co-existence, not of a few languages, but of a great many. If all the educated people of the earth would study in the primary school one of the six international languages (in addition to their own) and perhaps two in high school, a very large proportion of them would be able to understand one another.

In my *Introduction* I have taken pains to describe the translations which were produced to make certain treasures of knowledge available to new groups of people. Individual translations are interesting when one studies the tradition of a definite book, but it is even more interesting to consider, as I did repeatedly, the whole body of translations made within this or that century from this language into that, for this helps us to understand by which channels our cultural heritage came down to us. Books were translated from Greek into Arabic and from Arabic into Latin and not vice versa. At any time translations were made from the language which represented a superior culture into others which represented inferior ones — even as water flows from higher reservoirs into lower ones and not in the opposite direction.

In the polyglottic world of today the situation is very different. People using "small" languages (i.e., languages of very restricted circulation) may be and often are as civilized as the people using international languages. The "small" languages and the culture which it expresses is not necessarily inferior in any respect (except the number of users) to the "great" language. Thus, at present, translations have not always the symbolic meaning which they had in the past. Moreover, the number of books which one might have to translate from each great language into the smaller ones is so immense that the task has become hopeless.

The movement of translation has been very largely replaced by a movement of language study. It would be foolish to attempt to translate all the English books or a majority of them into Norwegian; it is much simpler for the educated Norwegian to study English and he does so. To be sure, some English books are still translated into Norwegian but that has no general significance. On the contrary, the translation of a Norwegian book into English is always significant, because it means that the chances of circulation and influence of that book are enormously increased. It is as if the spiritual potential of that book had been raised to a much higher level.

The idea of translation brings us back to the distinction made at the beginning of this essay between the poetic language and the scientific one. For purely literary purposes, translations are always insufficient; the insufficiency is extreme in the case of the poetry, but it exists in the whole field of *belles lettres*. A good translation is a re-creation, — the creation of something different from the original. The translation of a poem, if it be worth anything, is a new poem. It is true, one might go a step further and assert that each person reading a poem can not understand it without adapting it to his own mind, that is, without "translating" it, even if he be an Italian reading Dante or an Englishman reading Keats. Without going to such extremes we may conclude that as the translations are always insufficient, the small languages will always be necessary within their own, domestic and poetic field. The multiplicity of languages is not objectionable at all; on the contrary, it is a blessing, if it corresponds to a multiplicity of separate cultures, to a richness of autochthonous ideas, to an exuberance of literary creation and poetic verve.

It becomes highly objectionable in wider fields. We have been thinking mainly of scientists and scholars and their international needs which cannot be satisfied except by the means of international languages. Yet one might think also of administration and politics above the municipal or regional level. A wise nation like the Swiss can put up with three or four languages, but its national life would be simpler if all the citizens spoke only one. In this case, the weakness of polyglottism within a small area is compensated by an unusual amount of common sense. It is questionable whether many other nations could stand that test.

Consider the difficulties of the past. In 1577, when the Estates-General of the Netherlands wished to vindicate their rights against the Spanish governor Don Juan of Austria, they found it necessary to publish their defense in seven languages (the six international languages already named, plus Flemish).[17] As no translation is ever perfect, it is easy to imagine the opportunities which six translations of the same text opened to Don Juan's legal advisers, if they wished to quibble. In politics and diplomacy every translation is a new source of innocent or deliberate misunderstandings. . . .[18]

In the field of science the excessive multiplicity of languages is not only objectionable, but stupid and wicked. The scientific needs of mankind are served best by the monopoly or quasi-monopoly of a few languages. The unity of scientific thought is already favored by the use of abstract symbols and of identical terminology but that is not enough. The reading even of a mathematical treatise may be made unnecessarily difficult and uncertain by verbal explanations in a "small" language. Why should one jeopardize the universal appeal of equations by the concomitant use of parochial phrases?

The defense of the humanities begins with the defense of language. Let every nation enjoy its own language which is the best flower of its culture, the key to its soul. On the other hand, the nations whose

[17] John Lothrop Motley, *The rise of the Dutch Republic* (edition of New York 1864, vol. 3, p. 275).

[18] That peculiar danger is so well understood today that when treaties are published in many languages, it is generally specified that one text, say, the French or the English, is binding, its translations being offered only for the sake of convenience.

languages have no international currency should realize that limitation and encourage their own citizens to use international languages in preference to their own for international purposes. The growth of science is an international undertaking; the nations which inhibit that great endeavor by means of linguistic fetters will gain nothing and lose much. The publication of scientific or scholarly papers of limited appeal in small languages is an absurdity defeating its own end; it does not raise the level of those languages but jeopardizes the circulation of the new ideas. As long as the Utopians publish their criticism of the rest of the world in Utopian, they will convince nobody but themselves. If they wish to persuade the Republic of Letters, they must use a language which the citizens of that Republic are likely to understand.

Isis is deeply concerned with the unification of mankind, and therefore it will devote most of its attention to the writings published in the international languages . . . This policy is not inspired by the dislike of small countries and of small languages but by the love of science and the love of humanity.

October 1947

Notes on the Reviewing
of Learned Books

THERE are many sides to every question and as far as the reviewing of books is concerned there are at least five points of view which are obviously different: the points of view of the author, of the reader, of the editor, of the publisher, of the sponsor. All of these points of view are familiar to me, for I have read innumerable books, written quite a few, edited *Isis* for thirty-six years. I am still the publisher of *Osiris* as well as its editor and I have sponsored many books, either by contributing prefaces or in other ways.

Moreover, I realized very early the fundamental importance of good reviewing, because learning cannot progress without appreciation or criticism. Soon after beginning the editing of *Isis*, I published a little guide, *Recommandations aux collaborateurs d'Isis* (3 pp., dated Wondelgem, 19 décembre 1912), 2e édition, revue et augmentée (8 pp., Wondelgem, juin 1914).[1] The following notes are derived partly from those *Recommandations* and partly from the outline prepared by me when the matter of reviewing was discussed in my Seminar on the History of Science, in Harvard University on 30 March 1939. As I have been thinking of this subject for at least thirty-six years and have been obliged to consider it from every angle, it may be worth while to summarize the results of my experience.

Before asking oneself how to review a book, it is useful to ask a more fundamental question, "How should one read a book?" (The following remarks deal only with books of learning; books of imagination and

---

[1] This second edition is a bibliographic curiosity, because it was published in the form of an offprint from *Isis* (Extrait anticipé du tome II, fasc. 2), but Belgium was suddenly invaded by the Germans, so that that number did not appear until five years later at the end of 1919, and did *not* contain the *Recommandations*. That pamphlet is thus a "preprint" of an article which was never printed!

poetry should be read in a very different way and their criticism raises many difficulties which do not concern us.) How should one read a book in order to obtain and preserve information? How should one select the books to be read, and in each book the information which may be needed, and how should one record it for further use?

If it were possible to answer such questions completely, one of the main problems of scholarship would be solved. Unfortunately, it is not possible to answer them, except perhaps after long experience, and then only for one's own satisfaction. Even if it were possible to answer them fully, the answers would not be intelligible or profitable to the people standing in greatest need of them.

One might, of course, publish a book entitled "How to become a scholar," but the reading of such a book would be almost as useful to the non-scholar, as a book entitled "How to become a millionaire" to the hobo. By the way, it is significant that such books as the last-named are not written by rich men, but on the contrary by poor devils, the kind of hacks whose industry publishers like to exploit.

The few indications which I now venture to give are not meant to solve the problem but simply to help the few people who are already so well prepared by their own nature and nurture that they can make the most of any guidance which is offered to them.

How does one absorb knowledge and wisdom out of books? Consider two other cases. When one looks at paintings one sees them at a glance. Of course, longer contemplation of them would reveal details in outline or color, in design, rhythm or intensity which one could not notice immediately; yet, the fundamental knowledge is obtained at once, as it were in a single intuition. Now, if one listens to a symphony, he cannot absorb its message immediately in its wholeness, because he must wait until it is unfolded, and if it be long, it may not be possible to remember the whole of it at one hearing. Examining a work of art implies a kind of spiritual involution, listening to music an evolution. Reading a book is something between the two, for if the book has a good table of contents one can appreciate the wholeness of it even before reading.

In every case, looking at a painting, listening to music, reading a book, little can be accomplished if the looking, the listening or the

306

reading is not active, critical, creative. This requires experience and energy and without expenditure of the latter and availability of the former no emolument can be gained.

The art of reading implies the art of non-reading, and more energy is sometimes needed in order to skip rather than continue useless drifting. Many would-be scholars never learn anything not only because they cannot read, but also because they cannot stop reading: they are like asses turning round and round in a mill with blinkers on their eyes.

Before attempting to read a learned book one should find out whether it is worth reading, and if so one should prepare oneself to give it the kind of reading which it demands. The table of contents will tell us what the book contains and how it is built. The preface and introduction explain the author's purpose and methods. The bibliography lists the sources. The index enables one to do a bit of sampling. After having used those preliminary means of investigation, any intelligent scholar should be able to decide whether he should read some parts of the book, or the whole of it, or leave it alone. When the reading is begun, he should be prepared to interrupt it and to regulate its speed and intensity. Some of my friends have given me the evil reputation of being a very fast reader. It is true that I can read very fast when I am driven to it, but if a book holds my attention and is sufficiently difficult my progress may become very slow. If one should say of me that I am one of the fastest readers, it would be fair to add that I am also one of the slowest.

A young scholar must necessarily begin with random reading. As his goal becomes clearer, his reading will be more selective but a certain amount of randomness should never be abandoned. It is not enough to see one's own goal in as good a focus as possible; one must be ready to look around it and sometimes to sweep the horizon far away from it.

One reads a book to obtain information on certain topics, but it is hardly possible to appreciate that information, without considering it in its setting. One must form an opinion of the whole book.

Reading a book, or simply using one, implies reviewing it, except that the review need not be written. As far as my own experience goes, I can truthfully say that I have seldom used a book — and this includes dictionaries and atlases — without having prepared a mental review of it.[2] Indeed, how could one use a book profitably without knowing what it contains, what one might expect from it and what not? The scholar must know the potentialities of his books even as a carpenter must know those of his tools. This remark may seem commonplace, and yet I have often witnessed the misuse of books by scholars who had failed to take those obvious precautions.

"Reviewing a book" in the technical sense, that is, writing and publishing a review of it, is only a particular case of the methodic examination which must be made of any book if one wishes to use it intelligently. In most cases, the results of one's examination, the final judgment, will remain in one's consciousness unformulated; some scholars may summarize their conclusions on a card or in a note-book, but even then they will not bother to make them easily intelligible to other people.

The purpose of "public reviewing," as we might call reviewing proper to distinguish it from the private reviewing which is the culmination of good reading, is simply to communicate to the public the results of one's analysis. The scholar doing that is accomplishing a very important social function. Thanks to him other scholars will be able to decide whether it is worth their while to obtain the book reviewed and to study it. Moreover, they will be able to appreciate the personality of the author and the value of his achievement. This does not mean that they will necessarily trust the reviewer and accept his verdict, but whatever he writes will help them to form their own judgment. In the first stage, that judgment is restricted to the solution of a simple problem: "Should I obtain the book and read it or try to read it?" The reviewer's judgment may help the reader in various ways. I have more than once bought a book on the strength of an unfavorable review of it.

Main points of a good review — The first point to remember is that a review should describe and characterize not only the book in question, but also the subject with which it is dealing. Of course, in some cases the subject is sufficiently indicated by the title. A biography of Faraday deals with Faraday and, if the reader is a chemist or a physi-

---

[2] It may sometimes be necessary to consult rapidly a number of books which one had no opportunity of "reviewing" but casual reference is not real use.

cist, the name of Faraday needs no more explanation than those of Washington or Lincoln to any American. Yet, if the reader were a French mathematician or a Hungarian zoologist a brief definition of Faraday would be useful. In the case of biographies of less illustrious men more information would be needed, and more readers would need it. Happily, it is very easy to give the essential in a few words: times of birth and death, nationality and places of activity, field of work, main achievements. The reader cannot be expected to take any interest in the biography of a man of whom he knows nothing.

In other words, the reviewer should not be too self-centered, and imagine that the people and the things which he knows so well are equally familiar to every reader of even the most learned journal.

Many books ostensibly deal with a very large subject, say, the history of alchemy. Such a title seems clear enough, yet the subject is incredibly vast and the chances are that the author did not try to cover the whole of it. It is necessary then to explain what the author's subject exactly is. What kind of alchemy? Where and when?

This brings us close to the second point. What is the author's purpose? What does he try to prove? And this introduces a whole series of questions which it is the reviewer's duty to answer.

What are the author's qualifications for the fulfillment of his purpose? What were the sources of his knowledge? Did he actually go back to the very sources or did be lean chiefly on secondary material? If he explored new sources, were these well chosen and sufficient? Has his book a deep and sound foundation, and if not, why on earth did he write it? Do not forget, however, that a book based on derivative material may still be a good and useful book, if the work was well done.

How did the author use his sources? What are his methods? How did he organize his results? Is the book well built? In some cases (as in a biography) the development is simply chronological, and nothing more need be said about that. Very often the chronological development is insufficient, or it is necessary to consider not a single sequence of events, but many which may interlock in various ways. It then becomes necessary to analyze the book and to consider whether the divisions and subdivisions of the field and the alternance of different points of view, were wisely chosen or not.

We may now return to the general purpose. How well did the author fulfill it? Did he introduce new facts, new ideas? Is the book a real addition to our knowledge, and if so, what exactly has been added? What is the book's place in the literature devoted to the same subject? Does it cover more ground or less ground than the other books? Does it cover its ground better or less well than they did their own?

The questions which have been enumerated are essential and the reviewer should try to answer most of them. A few subsidiary questions must still be considered. It is not enough that a book be well built and well documented, it should be well written. There is no excuse for bad writing, which is generally a symptom of poor thinking.[3] It is the reviewer's privilege (which he may exercise or not according to circumstances) to discuss the form of a book, its style and mood, its title,[4] its material presentation, paper, printing, illustrations.

The last word refers to the form of the illustrations, but in many cases the substance of the illustrations deserves full discussion. Some scholars are sadly deficient from the iconographical point of view;[5] others, on the contrary, take pains to select pertinent and original illustrations and to explain their provenience and meaning. Full credit should be given for that kind of merit.

Every review should begin with a complete bibliographical identification of the book reviewed. Full title and subtitle, size of the book and format (if unusual), name of publisher, place and date of publication. It is advisable to indicate the price and in the case of limited editions, the number of copies. The reviewer's guidance in all this is the desire to help the reader or prospective buyer, and give him all the information which he may require.[6]

[3] "Ce que l'on conçoit bien s'énonce clairement . . ." Boileau's saying does not apply as well to our contemporaries as to his. Men of substance, distinguished men of science, presumably educated, often lack a sufficiently deep knowledge of their own language. It may happen then that their clear ideas are betrayed by linguistic impotence, and steady thoughts, by wobbling expressions. Cf. S. E. Morison, *History as a literary art* (*Isis* 39, 197).

[4] Strangely enough, some books bear a misleading title. This should be pointed out, for it is a grave defect. Yet, the reviewer should not condemn the book, because it does not tally with the title; it is the title which is wrong, not necessarily the book itself. Let him thus condemn the title and then examine the book without allowing himself to be prejudiced by the inadequacy of its label.

[5] Sarton, Iconographic honesty (*Isis* 30, 222–235, 1935); Portraits of ancient men of science (*Lychnos*, 249–256, Uppsala, 1945).

[6] For example, the price should be quoted whenever it is possible to do so. The

From the editor's point of view much damage is done by scholars who agree to review a book and fail to do so. This is very shocking. The faithless reviewer obliges the editor to write to him over and over again, but that is nothing as compared with the harm he is doing to the author and publisher, and to all the people who are anxious that the book be known. Clearly, even the best book needs a modicum of publicity, for nobody will try to obtain it and to read it unless he is aware of its existence. If a scholar wanted to hurt the author and prevent the reviewing of the latter's work in a given journal, the simplest way of achieving his devilish aim would be to undertake to review it himself and then to dishonor his promise. As the review copy would be in his hands, the editor could not ask another scholar to handle the book. Such deliberateness must be rare, but the procrastination of many reviewers causes the same results, whether they be evil-minded, impotent, or lazy.

I have little respect for procrastinators, though I recognize that their guilt may be lessened by attenuating circumstances. Other duties may have been pressed upon them after their promise to the editor had been made in good faith; the general cause of delay, however, is mediocrity, weakness of will, or other mental deficiencies. It may occur also that a man agrees to review a book, because he had a false idea of it; after having obtained the review copy and examined it, he may discover that the book is not what he thought it was, lose interest in it, and shelve it. In such a case the honest procedure would be to return the book to the editor (or publisher) as fast as possible, just as he would do if he had bought the book. It is the buyer's and the reviewer's privilege to return a book when they don't like it; if they fail to return it in time, the buyer, at least, has paid for it, while the reviewer has obtained his own copy on false pretenses. That is not pretty.

I understand this kind of situation very well, because I am a reviewer as well as an editor. It has happened to me more than once that a book of which I had requested a review copy was not what I fancied it to be. In such cases, I gave it to somebody else to review (somebody who might like it), or if I thought that it did not deserve to be reviewed, I paid the cost of it to the publisher and that ended my obligation.

---

reader may be anxious to obtain the book, but he cannot buy it unless the price be within his means.

Procrastination is often due, I believe, to initial inertia. Many people have enough energy to continue a task, and even to carry it to completion, but not enough to begin it. Every scholar or writer is familiar with that kind of inertia. How hard it is to begin a new book, or even an article! The inhibition may be overcome in various ways: one may diminish one's exaggerated feeling of responsibility by undertaking the review somewhat casually, as if one were writing only for oneself or for a friend; or one may begin with the simplest preparatory investigations. By the time all the necessary investigations have been made, enough energy has been gathered to begin one's writing. Everybody will find similar tricks to outwit his own spiritual inertia, except that there is a degree of indolence and abulia which cannot be outwitted any more. The worst procrastinators are pathological specimens whom it is best to leave alone.

It is much easier to write a review soon after having studied the book, the sooner the better. One must strike the iron while it is hot, and write what one has to write when the ideas to be expressed are still bubbling. The longer the delay the more difficult does the task become. This helps to explain chronic procrastination; the longer it lasts the less shakeable it is. Spiritual debts are in that respect like other debts; the older they are, the harder and the more hopeless they become.

When I have to review a book my habit is to read it in the evening, writing notes or simply page numbers on a pad as I proceed. My review takes shape during the night, and I am ready to study my notes and write the review the following morning. If some other duty obliges me to postpone the writing for one or more days I am annoyed because I know that the task will become more difficult if it be delayed and may even lose a part of its freshness and goodness. Of course, a review may require new investigations the length of which cannot be foreseen, but I find it expedient to write it before the investigations are completed. Indeed, their results can generally be stated in a few paragraphs which it is easy enough to interpolate; they seldom oblige one to change his conclusions, or rewrite his review. Even in such extreme cases it takes less time and energy to rewrite the review than to postpone the original writing.

Soon after the foundation of *Isis*, I received a letter from a very distinguished scholar, a professor in one of the northern universities of Italy, asking me to obtain for him review copies of a number of important books. I wrote to the publishers and obtained these volumes for him, but he did not review a single one of them. From the publisher's point of view I had obtained these volumes under false pretenses, making promises which were never fulfilled. Though I was not the swindler, I was responsible for him. Did he ever think of the harm he was doing me? A young journal like *Isis,* whose reputation was not yet established, might have been dishonored by such swindles.

At the time of the first German invasion of Belgium, when I had decided to abandon my Wondelgem home and library, I made a note of a few volumes which I had received from the publishers and had not yet been able to review. When the publication of *Isis* was resumed five years later, the new number (no. 5) contained reviews of those volumes. My debt was paid.

Publishers of to-day are generally less interested in the progress of learning than in the earning of money. It is one of the ironies of the trade that while it becomes more and more difficult to publish an original book, the fruit of long and honest investigations, even if it be very well written, publishers are all the time instigating the production of hasty books on familiar topics, books which have to be composed as it were to order and "de chic" for commercial purposes. Some of these books written by good men, are good enough, but even then they are likely to be superfluous. When half a dozen books have been devoted to a definite subject, say the life and works of an illustrious man of science, the writing of a seventh one, according to the publisher's specifications, is merely a literary exercise. But what is the good of that seventh book, if it is simply based on the previous ones? It can easily be worse than they; it will rarely be better.

If the original and honest books, to which we referred before, are finally published, they deserve to be reviewed with special care. On the contrary, it is not necessary to review at length in learned journals the other kind of books, those which were brought into being by commercial enterprise. The publishers of such books hardly wish for learned reviews; they prefer superficial notices in the newspapers and the best that the literary editor can do to please them is to copy their own blurbs.

Let us examine now a few examples of the kind of reviewing which it is better to avoid. Consider first "James the Egotist," who does not think half as much of the book intrusted to him, and of the author, as he does of himself. His purpose is much less to explain the book than to show off his own qualities. His review may be interesting and even instructive, but does not answer the reader's main questions (the questions which have been outlined above). After having read it, one does not yet understand what the author really meant and what his work contains.

Then "John the Obscure" who tries to hide his own ignorance and meanness under a veil of spurious profundity. The "demi-savants" indulge in such tricks; they try to give the impression that their own knowledge is deep, so deep that clear speech could not reveal it. Their statements are ambiguous; they suggest and insinuate, and one does not know what to think of the book.

There is also the critic who is so "impartial" that he too leaves us in the lurch. He is afraid of committing himself to any opinion, for he might have to defend it. He says "yes" and "no" in the same paragraph. Such a critic reminds me of a Frenchman who refused to read the book which he had undertaken to review. "I am anxious to remain completely impartial," said he, "and I could not read the book without getting to like it more and more or less and less. Impartiality would become impossible." Of course, many critics follow the same course not because of any desire of impartiality, but simply because it is much easier to copy the jacket or the preface and let it go at that.[7] Some of them copy the table of contents; that is easy enough, but there are better and briefer ways of describing the contents of a book, and it is a shame not to use them.

Some reviewers indulge in superlatives. They will not say, "It is a bad book," but "It is the worst book ever written . . ." or else it is "by far the best one." How do they know? Have they read all the others? As Pliny the Elder remarked a long time ago,[8] no book is so

[7] In the Critical Bibliographies of *Isis*, the title of a book or article is often followed by an extract from the preface, the text, or even the jacket, the extract being quoted as such. That is not a review, but simply a statement of the author's purpose in his own words; no criticism of the book is implied.

[8] He died in 79. The remark has been transmitted to us by his nephew Pliny the Younger (*Epistolae* III, 5) "Nihil enim legit quod non excerperet; dicere etiam solebat nullum esse librum tam malum, ut non aliqua parte prodesset."

bad that one cannot find something good to glean from it. It is the critic's privilege to point out that which is good. On the other hand, no book deserves unconditional praise, and when a book is particularly good, it can stand any amount of adverse criticism. The author of a good book is anxious to be shown the errors which it contains in order that those errors may be corrected and the book improved.

Pedantic critics see nothing but the faults, however, and make capital of them. They insist so much on the errors (often trivial ones) that careless readers might be led to believe that the book is entirely untrustworthy. Wiser readers, who are able to detect at once the pedantic bias, are not so easily put off. They distrust the critic's judgment and wish to see the book themselves.

Some narrow-minded critics take a large book and, instead of considering it in its wholeness, do just the opposite. They look up their own names in the index, or the names of their friends, or their pet subjects, and judge the book (they often condemn it!) on the basis of a few unimportant samples. Their angle of vision is so acute that they are incapable of understanding the author's purpose; they do not even think of that, for it is only their own purpose which matters; they see only a very small part of the book, yet proceed as if that were the whole of it.[9]

Of course, when a book is very complex it is fair for any critic, after having described the whole of it, to restrict his examination to the segment which he is most competent to criticize. He should make it clear, however, that he is dealing only with a segment and should indicate the relationship and proportion of that segment to the whole.

The "Procrastinator" has already been mentioned, but if he fails to review a book he can hardly be reproached for having misunderstood it. His betrayal is of another kind and one might suggest that he betrays himself more than the author. His failure gives him away. It is sometimes claimed in his defense that he simply "forgot." The "Procrastinator" forgot nothing. He is like the people who borrow books and do not return them. They too "forgot." Did they? Any psychiatrist

---

[9] Confer the saying of the French critic Edmond Schérer (1815–1889), who was in some respects superior to his older and more illustrious contemporary Sainte-Beuve (1804–1869). Said Schérer, "Rien n'est plus répandu que la faculté de ne pas voir ce qu'il y a dans un livre, et d'y voir ce qui n'y est pas." (*Etudes critiques 1*, 195, 1863).

will tell you that they "forgot" to return the books which they wanted to keep. Even so, the "Procrastinator" is too lazy and too busy to keep his promise; yet he wants to keep the book. Therefore, he "forgets." This is an especially mean kind of prevarication.

In the criticism of any book, reviewers, especially the younger ones (who have not yet won their spurs), should remember that the writing of a tolerable book is no mean achievement.[10] It is irritating to listen to the "pooh-poohing" of a book by a man who has not yet proved himself capable of a similar effort. The writing of a book implies a greater continuity of effort than most people are capable of. Therefore, every honest book deserves some respect, in spite of its imperfection.

The inability to write a book, that is, to marshal a large number of facts and ideas in telling order, may be associated with great merits of other kinds and even with genius. The best example of such an association was given by Leonardo da Vinci. In most cases, however, the inability is not associated with genius, but simply with the lack of grasp and the lack of will. The difference between throwing out ideas and writing a well-organized book may be compared to the difference between casual flirtations and a responsible marriage.[11] Lots of people are ready to flirt with ideas, but do not go any further; curiously enough, such people, who could never gather enough energy and persistence for the writing of a whole book, are often the most severe critics of other people's books.

One should not confuse a popular or semi-popular book written, say, for a series of biographies, with an elementary textbook prepared by a master for the guidance of tyros. Such elementary books deserve to be criticized with particular care, but it is very difficult to find

[10] It is well to say the writing of a "tolerable" book, for the writing of a bad book may be easy enough (however, some bad books have been composed with extreme difficulty). The art of writing implies many steps: (1) orthography of words, (2) writing of correct sentences, (3) composition of paragraphs, (4) composition of articles, essays, or chapters, (5) composition of books. Some idiots have jumped to 5 in one leap; they have learned some tricks of strategy without bothering about tactics. They are ingenious enough to write books, plenty of them, and hardly think of their substance. Their books may be "paying" books, however, and publishers love them.

[11] That comparison has been ascribed to Freud, but as I don't know where and when he made it, I must assume responsibility for it, at least *pro tempore*.

reviewers who are willing, competent, and reasonable. Good scholars are often too snobbish and supercilious to judge elementary books as they ought to be judged, severely with regard to essentials, leniently with regard to details, kindly always. Perhaps the best judge of an elementary book is a young man, not yet too far removed from the elements, provided he is sufficiently modest and generous.

Some readers seem to think that the importance of a book is somewhat proportional to the length of the review devoted to it. That is a mistake. There is really no relationship between these two things. When a book is very good, it suffices to describe it, and to praise it briefly. On the contrary, if it is defective, the defects must be explained and discussed. If one says that a book is bad, one must be prepared to prove it. Hence, an imperfect book often requires a longer review than a book nearer to perfection. There are books which are so imperfect and superfluous, however, that they hardly deserve to be discussed; it is enough to include them in a bibliographical list.

Looking at the problem in a different way, one might claim that the better a book is the more it deserves to be criticized with severity. The errors to be found in "standard" books, which are often referred to, are far more dangerous than those obtaining in books which lack authority. It is thus worthwhile to point out, correct, and if possible to eradicate, those errors which may persist in the best books. The errors of bad books are relatively unimportant, and in any case there are so many of them that one could not enumerate them without waste of time and space; it is simpler then to condemn the whole book, and to forget it. If a new book must be written to cover the same field, let it be written without reference to the bad books.

A good review is descriptive and critical, but it should also be substantial and instructive; a distinguished review should include some novelty (fact or idea) on the subject dealt with, but only the experienced scholar can do that. In the case of important novelties, however, it would be better to publish them separately (and more briefly perhaps in the review) in order to focus the attention upon them; otherwise, they might be overlooked or wrongly credited.[12]

[12] A classical example is the review of Whitehead and Russell's *Principia mathematica* (2nd ed., vol. 1, 1925) by Henry M. Sheffer (*Isis 8*, 226-231, 1926).

It is better not to write too long a review of a book, for a short review is more likely to be read than a longish one. Reviewers often ask what is the optimum size; it is difficult to answer such a question, because the situation varies in each case, but it should be possible, I think, to do justice to almost any book, that is, to give a sufficient description and appreciation of it, in a thousand words or less. If the reviewer adds some original material of his own, the length of the review might be increased agreeably.

According to an old tradition, reviews appear in the leading English journals without signature. Such a practice is inacceptable in *Isis*, because, in the first place, the value of a review (as any other article) depends partly upon the qualities of its author,[13] and secondly, unsigned reviews are credited to the editor. Now, this is nonsense, for how could the editor be held responsible for the reviews of books which he has not read? The Editor of *Isis* prefers to leave the responsibility, where it belongs, upon the shoulders of the reviewer. He has often published favorable reviews of books which he did not like, and, what annoyed him more, unfavorable reviews of books he personally admired. It was necessary in each case to allow the reviewer to have his own say, without hindrance. The good reviewer may write what he pleases but only upon his own signature.

The reviewers are just as fallible as the authors themselves. In spite of every precaution, they are bound to commit errors — errors of fact or judgment. It is possible that some of the procrastinators delay their reviews, and even fail to produce them, because of the morbid fear of errors. Such a fear is obviously wrong. Human beings must learn to accept their imperfection. We should do all we possibly can to avoid errors, but recognize that the limitations of our nature are also the limitations of our duty. Nobody can be expected to do more than his best.

I may add that instead of being deterred by the possibility of error, I am rather encouraged by it. If I were certain of knowing the truth, the whole truth, I would not dare to criticize anything, because my

[13] Praise and blame have no absolute value; it all depends on who is praising or blaming. To be blamed by an idiot may be equivalent to being praised by a good man.

judgment would be final and inexorable. I am not afraid of expressing my candid judgment of a book, after having examined it carefully and honestly, because I know that such a judgment is at best, imperfect and precarious. It is the best I can do; yet, I may be wrong, and I am always deeply and humbly aware of that danger, and, of the non-finality of my criticism.

When a scholar has written a faithful review of a book, he has rendered a great service to the author and the publisher, and these should be the more grateful to him, because that service is generally a labor of love, which the learned journals cannot remunerate [14] except by the gift of a copy of the reviewed book; that gift can hardly be called a fee, for it is too small; we should consider it rather as a friendly gift for a friendly office.

Every scholar should produce a few reviews; it is part of his general responsibility to publish criticisms of the books which he is best prepared by his own investigations to criticize. No scholar should write too many reviews, for he could not do so without cheapening them and himself; he should write a few, and as well as possible.

Widener Library 185
July 1949

[14] It was not always so. A little more than a century ago Blomfield received 20 guineas for his review of Samuel Butler's *Aeschylus* in the *Edinburgh* and no less than 100 guineas for that of Barker's *Thesaurus* in the *Quarterly* (Martin Lowther Clarke: *Greek studies in England*, p. 6, Cambridge 1945; *Isis* 37, 232). This was truly a golden age for learned critics; but was it a golden age for criticism? I doubt it.

Incunabula Wrongly Dated[1]

T HE FOLLOWING notes are written less for the sake of collectors of rare books whose knowledge of incunabula is deeper than mine, than for historians of science who may be obliged to examine and describe early printed editions, yet are not and cannot be expected to be full-fledged incunabulists.[2] The young historian, whose training has been scientific rather than literary or historical, is likely to pay little attention to incunabula, or he may just mention them, without making any effort to identify them or even to check the dates. As his experience increases, he becomes more wary. He may even decide to examine carefully all incunabula and reproduce the date of each without bothering about other dates listed in bibliographies. That is a sound instinct. There is nothing like autopsy. The description of the real object cannot be wrong. Or can it?

When he has reached that stage, the young historian is not yet wary

---

[1] The following abbreviations will be used throughout this article:

ADB: Allgemeine Deutsche Biographie (Leipzig, 1871–1912);

BMC: Catalogue of incunabula in the British Museum (London, 1908 ff.);

Census: Incunabula in American libraries. A second census, edited by Margaret Bingham Stillwell (New York, 1940; *Isis 33,* 96);

GW: Gesamtkatalog der Wiegendrucke (Leipzig 1925 ff.);

Haebler: The study of incunabula (New York, 1933);

Introd.: Sarton's Introduction to the history of science (1927–1948);

Klebs: "Incunabula scientifica et medica" (*Osiris 4,* 1938);

Sarton: "Scientific literature transmitted through the incunabula" (*Osiris 5,* 1938).

A symbol such as (II-1) placed after a name, e.g. Ptolemy (II-1), means that Ptolemy flourished in the first half of the second century, and that he is dealt with in Sarton's *Introduction.*

[2] For a discussion of incunabula in general and scientific incunabula in particular, see *Sarton* (1938).

enough. He should remember that the date of a book is itself, not a natural, but an artificial fact. Printers were just as frail and liable to err as other men. The date printed in the colophon may be incorrect; that is, it may be different, even grossly so, from the date of actual publication.

There are two main causes of error. The first is the reprinting of incunabula either during the incunabula period or later. Some printers copied the old colophon, and some carried the carelessness to the point of copying the old register of gatherings though their reprint did not correspond to it; sometimes, they added a new colophon with a new date and then everything was clear; sometimes, they failed to add a new colophon, or they added a colophon without date.[3] Some "remainders" of incunabula were republished in the sixteenth century with a new title page.

Examples of incunabula of which two editions exist with the same date, one of the two being a later reprint of the other:

(a) Philippus de Barberiis:[4] *Opuscula.* Printed by Joannes Philippus de Lignamine in Rome, 1 Dec. 1481 (date in Roman). Another issue was printed somewhat later with the same date. In fact, some of the quires remaining of the first edition are included in the second; the end of the book is made up of the original stock and the old register is allowed to stand as it was in spite of the changes in the first two quires. (*BMC 4,* 131. *GW* 3386. *Census* B 105.)

(b) Andreas de Isernia.[5] *Super feudis.* There are two editions both stated to have been printed 5 Feb. 1477 at Naples by Sixtus Riessinger. One of these editions is printed in Roman type, the second in Gothic. It has been proved that the first was actually printed by Riessinger, while the second bearing the same colophon was printed somewhat

---

[3] In that case, the date can sometimes be provided by comparison with other dated books. When the book was reprinted with the old colophon, the situation was similar to some photographic reprints of today. For example, the reprint of my *Introduction,* vol. 1, bears only the original date 1927, though it was made twenty years later. There is an essential difference however. That reprint, being photographic, is perfectly accurate and for practical purposes may be considered as an original (as a delayed copy of the original edition). The fifteenth-century reprints, being made by hand, were never identical with the original and the pagination might be different.

[4] Filippo de' Barbieri of Syracuse, Dominican, Inquisitor in Sicily, 1462–1481.

[5] Andreas de Ysernia, Andrea Rampini of Isernia (Campobasso; not very far from Gaeta), jurist in Naples, died in 1353.

later by Ulrich Scinzenzeler in Milan. For the two printers, see *BMC* 6, 854–856, 761–776. *Haebler* 166, 199, 1933.

(c) Angelus de Aretio: [6] *De maleficiis*. There are two editions of this book, both of which claim to have been printed by Baptista de Tortis in Venice, on 22 May 1494. Only one of these editions can be genuine; the other must be a counterfeit. It has been proved that the second was issued by another Venetian printer, Paganinus de Paganinis, *c.* 1495. *BMC* 5, 458. *Census* G 55–56.

Example of an incunabulum reprinted in the sixteenth century with a new cover. — An edition of the *Imitatio Christi* was issued by Erhart Ratdolt in Augsburg in 1488, Roman date (*BMC* 2, 382; *Census* I 14). Some copies which remained unsold were reissued later "with a full title enclosed in a border of the Reformation period" (*Haebler*, p. 153, 1933).

The second kind of error was due to the printing of an erroneous date instead of a correct one, an error which we must assume was very seldom if ever deliberate, but unconscious. That kind of error is always possible (e.g., we ourselves may put a wrong date on a letter, especially at the beginning of a year when we are not yet used to the new millesim), but it was considerably easier when the dates were written by means of Roman numerals. Compare M.CCCC.LXXX.VIII with 1488; it was certainly more difficult to write exactly the Roman date for which 16 pieces of type were needed (or at least 13 if the dots were omitted) than to write the Arabic ones for which four pieces sufficed. One might claim that the chances of error increase in proportion to the number of pieces of type, or somewhat faster. As a matter of fact many such errors were committed by the early printers and the purpose of this article is mainly to describe a few examples of them in order to increase the historian's wariness.

Before doing that, however, it is well to anticipate a query which the attentive reader might ask us. Were all the incunabula dated with Roman numerals? No, not at all, but Arabic dates are very unusual. The first books dated with Arabic numerals are Regiomontanus'

[6] Angelo Gambiglioni of Arezzo, jurist, senator in Rome, questor in Norcia, d. *c.* 1461.

INCUNABULA WRONGLY DATED

Latin *Calendarium* and the Italian version, both printed by Ratdolt and Co. in Venice 1476 (*Klebs* 836.2; 838.1). What is more remarkable is that the date occurs on a title page, or on a decorated first page, not in a colophon . . .

That example remained isolated for a long time; curiously enough, it was not followed by Ratdolt himself in his later publications. The next title page appeared only at the very end of the incunabula period in 1500.[7] Arabic numerals may have been used a few years earlier (than 1476), in the Lactantius (Rome 1470) for marking gatherings; the matter is not clear. The use of figures for signatures (instead of letters) became a habit of Franz Renner in Venice in 1476. The same Renner and other Venetian printers began to use Arabic figures for leaf numbering at about the same time, and the same was done by a few German printers (*Haebler* 64, 71). The earliest example of pagination (numbering consecutively both sides of each leaf) occurs in Venice in 1499.[8]

We have already given an example of an incunabulum dated with Arabic numerals, and we shall give others, but these examples are very exceptional; almost all of the incunabula were either undated or dated by means of Roman numerals.

One more remark before we begin our exhibition. The author is concerned only with the yearly date, what the French call *millésime*, not with the exact date in terms of months and days. When the colophon includes a date, it is often a very exact one stating that the printing of the book was completed on such a day of such a year. The day may be indicated in Roman style "a.d. IV Non. Feb.," in our own way "2 February," or in terms of the Church calendar "Purificatio Mariae." The interpretation of that part of the date may involve

[7] Johannes von Glogau (XV–2), *Exercitium super tractatus parvium logicalium Petri Hispani* (Leipzig. Wolfgang Stöckel, 1500). Stöckel was printing in Leipzig from 1495 to 1520. (*BMC 3*, 653–56.) This particular book was printed by him for Johann Haller of Cracow. (*Haebler* 150.)

[8] Niccolò Perotti of Sassoferrato (1430–1480), *Cornucopiae linguae latinae* (Aldus Manutius, Venice, July M.ID) *BMC 5*, 561. (*Census* P 262.) Not only the pages, but the lines of each page, are numbered as is done in modern editions of the classics. The colophon ends with a "copyright," "Venetiis in aedibus Aldi mense Julio M.ID. Hunc librum non licet cuiquam in locis & dominio Illu. S. V. impune typis excudere."

various difficulties, as habits varied from time to time and from place to place.

A more serious difficulty was caused by the lack of unity in determining the beginning of the year. The year might begin as with us on the day of Circumcision (1 Jan.), or on 1 March (as was done in Venice until 1797), or on the day of the Annunciation (25 March), or on Easter, or on Christmas (25 December). The Easter beginning (generally practised in France) was the most confusing of all, for it varied from year to year and might occur on any date between 22 March and 22 April. If the beginning of the year was different from ours, all dates between 1 Jan. and that beginning must be corrected by the addition of one year to the year date.

E.g., 14 Feb. 1488 on a Venetian or French book, equals 14 Feb. 1489 according to our own usage (but Julian not Gregorian; there is no point in quoting a date in Gregorian style for dates anterior to the Gregorian reform, 1582). Ambiguities due to style never extend to more than two years, i.e., assuming that no other mistake has been made, the year is 1488 or 1489; it could not be 1487 or 1490.

The calendar style (*a navitate, ab incarnatione, etc.*) and the ecclesiastical means of designating each day [9] varied from place to place, and what is even more confusing, they were not followed consistently in any one place, not even in Rome.[10] The art of printing was carried from one city to another by master printers who sometimes continued the use of their own local style in their new residence (even when they set up their presses in another country). That was for them a natural thing to do; they did it innocently without attempting to deceive anybody; everything in their own original style was so clear to them that they did not feel the need of any explanation. Moreover, a printer might use one kind of style to date a book and another style to date another book, and then come back to his first style, and so forth.

To return to our main subject, the historian of science is generally not interested in the day-date but only in the year-date, and it is important for him to realize that the year-date printed in the colophon of

[9] For examples of these designations and their variations, see Frederick R. Goff, The dates in certain German incunabula (*Papers of the Bibliographical Society of America 34*, 17–67, 1940; *Isis 36*, 182).
[10] The papal chancery used one kind of style in the Bulls and another in the daily records (*Haebler*, p. 169).

an incunabulum is not necessarily the year in which the book was actually printed.

[1949]

Example 1

Ptolemy (II–1), *Cosmographia*. Second edition, the first with maps. Bologna, Lapis, 23 June 1462 (the correct year is 1477).

The most interesting example to historians of science concerns one of the outstanding classics of science, the geography or "cosmographia" of Ptolemy. There are seven incunabula editions of it in Latin ranging from 1475 to 1490, plus one German abstract, 1493.

One of the Latin editions, the second, bears the date Bologna 23 June "1462." If the date were correct, that edition would naturally be the first, anticipating the real first by thirteen years. That was very puzzling, because the real first, Vicenza 1475, has no maps, while the edition of "1462" has 26 maps. It was soon suspected that the (Roman) date was incorrect, and it was first thought that XX had been forgotten or dropped and that the real date was thus 1482 (in that case that edition would have been the fifth); what really happened is that XV was dropped and the date is thus 1477 (that edition is thus the second).

See facsimile of colophon in Sarton, *Study of the history of science* (p. 13, 1936).

The real date of the first edition of Ptolemy's geography with maps, 1477 not 1462, was definitely established by Lino Sighinolfi, I mappamondi di Taddeo Crivelli e la stampa bolognese della Cosmografia di Tolomeo (*La bibliofilia 10*, 241–269, Florence 1908).

BMC 6, 814; *Klebs* 812.2; *Census* P988.

[11] [*][Examples 2–15 omitted. See *Isis 40*, 231–240.]

Iconographic Honesty

(Followed by a Bibliography of iconographic studies and a Note on altered portraits)

THERE are between men infinite differences in kind and even more so in degree. For it could be claimed that we all have very much the same qualities, though these qualities vary exceedingly in extension and intensity. For example, it is possible that even the meanest of men have some sparks of generosity; it is possible that all men are generous, though when we try to analyze that single quality we realize the existence of endless diversities. The one man is generous with his time, while the other is very greedy of it but generous with his money, and others still are generous only with their advice. As our analysis goes deeper we realize the increasing complexity of the differences. Some men are always ready to spend lavishly for their friends' sake but only in the form of dinners or other entertainments. The specialization of that quality goes even further. I was told the story of a rich man who loved to order extravagant dinners and spared no expenditures for such friendly occasions, but when it came to cigars (he was not a smoker) he was as avaricious as could be, and thus he more than once spoiled a princely repast with atrocious stogies.

Similar remarks will occur to the reader's mind with regard to other qualities, each of which is capable of infinite variations. Thus truthfulness; it is not enough to say that men are more or less truthful, and to try to measure the intensity of their truthfulness; one must try to determine the field of it. Some men may be depended upon to tell the truth in matters of business, but not in war or love or fishing. Some report truthfully their scientific investigations, but their intellectual probity loses its keenness or vanishes altogether under the influence of passions, such as political hatred or professional jealousies. Scientific

326

truthfulness is capable of further differentiations. I have repeatedly insisted on the distressing fact that the very man who will make and report physical measurements with pedantic accuracy, is capable of picking historical data and recording them in the most careless manner without any attempt at verification or precision.

The most remarkable differentiation is the one which I propose to discuss to-day, the restriction of historical scholarship and honesty to texts, that is, to words versus pictures. Some historians will take considerable pains to insure the accuracy of each and every statement and then select relevant or irrelevant illustrations with the utmost laxity.

The explanation of such an aberration is natural enough. There is an established tradition for historical records expressed by means of words; that tradition is carefully taught in seminaries, and young historians, eager to earn their spurs, are deeply imbued with it. A similar tradition has not yet been developed with regard to iconographical documents, or it has not been explained as frequently and as deeply. The problem of how to illustrate a text is often completely neglected in historical seminaries. Indeed in earlier days the illustration of books offered too many technical difficulties and was likely to increase the cost of publication overmuch; hence the majority of historical memoirs lacked illustrations, or had only a few; and there was no temptation to investigate iconographical problems. On the other hand when historical books were illustrated, the illustrations were often selected by men other than the authors, and their connection with the text was not always so clear and strong as one might have wished.

In our days, it has become possible to reproduce images so cheaply by means of microfilms and photostats, and to print them sufficiently well at a low cost, that there is no excuse for omitting iconographic evidence whenever it is available. To be sure some processes of reproduction are expensive and will presumably ever be so, but for plain scientific purposes (as opposed to artistic ones) they are but seldom needed. For example, a portrait should be reproduced clearly, but it is not necessary for the scientific argument that every nuance of the painting be recorded . . .

It is possible now to provide as many illustrations sufficient for scientific purposes as may be necessary for the completion of the argument, and it is the historian's duty to provide them. This increases considerably his opportunities of giving richer and better information, but it increases his responsibilities in proportion. For example, compare the most fastidious description of a title page with a facsimile of it. Not only does the latter give information which could hardly be conveyed by means of a multitude of words, but it gives it immediately.

This is the heart of the matter. Information given by means of printed words is necessarily slow and gradual; one must wait for the words to succeed each other one by one, and we cannot be sure of any thing until the last word has been read. On the contrary, every picture says all it has to say at once. The wordy message is analytic, the pictorial one, synthetic. The text is an evolution of ideas; the image, an involution.

The preceding remarks apply with especial force to portraits. Compare a written portrait with a painted one, or even with a photographed one! What an abyss between the two! Let us take them both at their best, and consider on the one hand an excellent biography and on the other a masterly painting. The best biography cannot be appreciated without being read slowly, annotated and analyzed. If we wish to assimilate its substance we must be prepared to make a great effort of concentration, or rather a whole series of rhythmical efforts, in turn analytical and synthetic. Now look at the painting, let us say, Franz Hal's portrait of Descartes in the Louvre, and lo! there you have the whole man at once, — that intelligent yet crossgrained and cantankerous man, almost alive. You are given immediately some fundamental knowledge of him, which even the longest descriptions and discussions would fail to evoke.

The same thing cannot be said of many portraits. Even as the written biographies may vary along the whole gamut from ultra-goodness to infra-mediocrity, even so paintings and photographs differ exceedingly. Some are extraordinarily revealing as Hal's portrait of Descartes or the photographs of Pierre and Marie Curie which it was our privilege to reproduce recently in *Isis* (28, 480–481, 1938); others are just satisfactory, and others still are curiously silent and meaningless. We must bear in mind when judging them, that a portrait can hardly be more attractive than the personality which it represents, and living

328

men are not by any means equally alive. It is true enough, whether we like to admit it or not, that many distinguished scientists, though great discoveries have immortalized their names, were singularly inarticulate and unimpressive, and we cannot expect their portraits to speak more clearly to us than they would have spoken themselves.

A good portrait is almost as good as a biography, and in exceptional cases, it is better. Hence it is hardly necessary to emphasize the importance of portraits save to insist that our critical use of them must be on a level with it. Yet paradoxically enough, there are many historians who if they had to describe an individual would weigh pedantically every word, and yet will accept any portrait of him almost blindly. Think of those mussitating idiots who strain at a gnat and swallow a camel! They will hesitate interminably for this or that word of their description (is it quite correct to call him a short man, or to say that his eyes were dark, and his eyebrows very arched?) and then accept uncritically a wholesale and final account of him in the form of a portrait.

The best proof that I am not exaggerating is that there are many examples of portraits which have been wrongly identified with individuals they do not represent at all! Not errors concerning details these, but wholesale, immense errors, as if one wrote with painstaking precision the biography of John Doe and then called it "The life of William Smith." For example, the *Photographische Gesellschaft* of Berlin published a portrait of Berthelot, a very good portrait indeed (I have a copy of it), the only defect in it being that it does not at all represent Berthelot whose name it bears, but Berthollet! I often think with a mixture of amusement and sadness of the chemists who have framed that portrait and hung it in their laboratory. If they have a good visual memory, they have in their mind an image of "Berthelot" — which may be very precise, but is all wrong! It is almost as irremediably bad as if one were to love a strange woman in the darkness instead of the beloved one.

Another example is Jan Stolker's fraudulent transformation of one of the heads in Rembrandt's "Anatomy lesson" into a portrait of Swammerdam.[1] That portrait has been many times reproduced in

[1] J. F. van Someren, *Beschrijvende catalogus van gegraveerde portretten van Nederlanders* (vol. 3, no. 5431, Amsterdam, 1891). G. H. Parker, A spurious

textbooks on the history of science and the history of biology, and textbookmakers being what they are, we may expect to see it reappear from time to time.

No portrait should be published without having been carefully identified. This is relatively easy for modern portraits, though one's wariness should never be relaxed; it is more difficult for earlier (pre-photographic) ones, and the difficulty increases rapidly with the depth of time. I do not believe there is a single ancient scientist of whose lineaments we have any definite knowledge; thus to publish "portraits" of Hippocrates, Aristotle, or Euclid is, until further notice, stupid and wicked. The man who does that is nothing but a liar, and a particularly silly one at that. Authentic portraits of mediaeval times are very few. We may perhaps accept that of Richard Wallingford and a few others; how many or rather how few I am not prepared to say. It should be noted that the identification of a mediaeval portrait is generally a difficult task, and often a hopeless one. The reader wishing to measure those difficulties is advised to read Holbrook's book on the portraits of Dante (1911). He may remember also the endless discussions anent Shakespeare's features.

Beginning with the fifteenth century, as the art of painting develops in the West,[2] the number of identifiable portraits increases, slowly at first, then more and more rapidly. The portraits of some illustrious scientists were reproduced repeatedly, and that very richness of evidence, sometimes conflicting, introduces many new difficulties. The critic having to choose between many portraits must determine their relative values, and select the best one for each purpose. The way to initiate one's self in these fascinating studies is to read the iconographical analyses which have already been published apropos of Vesalius, Galileo, Harvey, and Linné (see bibliography below).

It is high time that a historian of science endowed with a sufficient amount of artistic feeling and experience, devote himself to the study of scientific portraits, or to what might be called more generally

portrait of Swammerdam (*Quarterly review of biology*, vol. 12, 206–209, 1937).

[2] I have not considered Eastern portraits. There are no Islamic portraits, except relatively late Persian and Hindu ones, none of which, as far as I know, concerns the historian of science. As to Far Eastern portraits I am not qualified to investigate them. A special group of them, Japanese Confucian physicians, was dealt with recently by G. Fujinami (Tokyo, 1937; *Isis 82*, 504–506).

"iconography of science." A great opportunity is waiting for the right man. If I had more time for such systematic investigations I would begin with a definite period and country, say, the Netherlands in the seventeenth century, a field of special promise because of the large number of excellent paintings and engravings which were created there and then. The best procedure would be to explore the museums and collections of engravings of that country, but a good beginning might be made if one established his headquarters in or near any collection of engravings and photographs of sufficient wealth (there are many in America). One's field might then be gradually extended to other periods or to other countries. The experience and the "flair" obtained through the iconographic study of any scientist (or any scientific event) would be of some advantage for the study of a second one and so on.

I tried to start an iconographic tradition in *Isis* some years ago when I began the publication of the series entitled "Medallic illustrations of the history of science." [3] The series was restricted to the nineteenth century in order to simplify iconographic investigations as medals of the nineteenth century would presumably be based on the best available portraits. I was obliged to stop the series because of the lack of money, and even more so, of time, but I would be delighted to renew it, if I could find a capable and enthusiastic collaborator for that purpose. This would be the natural preparation for a regular "iconographic" department in *Isis*, the scope of which would be the discussion of every iconographic problem or controversy concerning historians of science, or scientific events, and the reviewing of relevant publications . . . See for example Gino Loria's recent study on Lagrange (*Isis 28*, 366–375, 1938, with six portraits and three facsimiles); this is not quite satisfactory from the purely iconographic point of view as the portraits were not discussed as I should like them to be, but it shows that the portraits can be sufficiently well reproduced for any scientific purpose without unnecessary luxury.

I still believe that an exceptionally good portrait should be published as beautifully as possible and that the expenditure involved, if we could but afford it, would be wholly justified, for it would be an

---

[3] *Isis* vols. 8 to 14 (1926 to 1930); 53 medals were completely identified, described and photographed.

excellent means of putting art to the service of science and scholarship, and of making men of science realize more keenly the immeasurable value of beauty. However, in such cases, even more so than in others, the authenticity of the portrait should be ascertained first, and its credentials should be fully set forth. It would not suffice, for our purpose, to publish a beautiful portrait, however beautiful it might be; we should be able to explain its provenance and vicissitudes, to name the painter or the engraver (or both in the usual case of an engraving made from a painting), to discuss the time and place of its making; in short to give all the information which an art critic would expect plus that needed by the historian of science.

The need of precision in this field is the same as in any other field. Vague knowledge is always open to suspicion. You say "This is the portrait of Donald Smith" without adding any information relative to it. We cannot help wondering then: "Is it really? How do you know?" But if you are able to state, "This portrait of Donald Smith was painted by Reynolds in the year 1770, we have records of the sittings . . . The portrait was exhibited there and there. It was owned by the family until 1853 when it passed into the possession of Lord Buck, . . ." then we feel that we are on safer ground, and we do not hesitate to accept your statement.

I have often been thinking of these questions for the last twenty-five years, but my reflections were quickened recently by the examination of an album entitled "Pictorial mathematics. Portfolio number one. Portraits of eminent mathematicians. With brief biographical sketches by David Eugene Smith. Scripta Mathematica, New York, 1936." I opened that volume with keen anticipation but was deeply disappointed; indeed I could hardly believe my eyes, for it would be difficult to imagine anything more topsy-turvy. This portfolio number one contains twelve portraits, to wit, of Archimedes (!), Copernicus, Viète, Galileo, Napier, Descartes, Newton, Leibniz, Lagrange, Gauss, Lobachevsky, Sylvester. The portraits are well reproduced, and within the limitation of their relatively low price, as good as one might wish, but believe it or not, not a single one is explained! Though some were created by great artists, such as Hals or Sustermans, these artists are not even named, and I could discover — in that iconographical collection — no information whatsoever about the portraits included! Instead of which, the reader is given biographical sketches which are far too light to have any value and are moreover entirely superfluous, as more abundant information of the same kind can be obtained immediately in a number of common books! From the point of view of scientific iconography, that publication is not simply wrong, but fundamentally wrong. It will enable uneducated mathematicians to frame a dozen pictures, if they wish to embellish their classroom, but these pictures will be almost meaningless, like museum objects the labels of which have been lost. It is deplorable that so good a man as our old and great friend, Professor Smith, allowed himself to countenance such a backward undertaking.

Let us forget "Portfolio number one" as promptly as we can and return to our main argument, which it is time to conclude. Iconographical documents are very important and very impressive, but only if they are genuine and relevant. Considering the easy and cheap means of reproduction available to-day, no biography or monograph on almost any subject of the history of science, should be deemed complete to-day without illustrations which tell in a different way another part of the story and which literally illuminate it. Yet illustrations, whatever their potential value, which may be very great indeed, are worthless unless they are authenticated, explained with sufficient detail, and every doubt removed or discussed. This may entail many difficulties but the reward is great, and nobody is obliged to assume them. In the same way it is a good deal better to be silent, than to speak without knowledge. If one lacks the time, energy, or capacity to investigate the illustrations, it is better to do without them. In that case, no harm is really done, except that the article is less complete than it would be, but one can never exhaust a subject anyhow; the illustrations may be published and explained later by another scholar. To publish unaccounted for illustrations is just as bad as, or rather worse than to publish facts for which one cannot vouch. It is a specially heinous kind of bluffing and lying which should be condemned, as I do condemn it, wholeheartedly.

Rockport, Massachusetts,
August 13, 1938.

BIBLIOGRAPHY OF ICONOGRAPHIC STUDIES

Browne, Sir Thomas. — Miriam L. Tildesley, Sir Thomas Browne, his skull, portraits and ancestry. With an introductory note by Sir Arthur Keith. 78 p., 35 pl., reprinted from *Biometrica*, vol. 15, Cambridge, 1922.

Dante. — Richard Thayer Holbrook, Portraits of Dante from Giotto to Raffael. A critical study with a concise iconography. Illustrated after the original portraits. xix + 263 p. many illustr. London Medici Society, 1911.

Galileo. — J. J. Fahie, Memorials of Galileo Galilei, 1564–1642. Portraits and paintings. Medals and medallions. Busts and statues. Monuments and mural inscriptions. xxiv + 172 p., 20 portraits, 42 other illustrations. Leamington, The Courier Press, 1929 (*Isis 14*, 250–251).

Goethe. — Hermann Rollett, Die Goethe-Bildnisse. Biographisch-kunstgeschichtlich dargestellt. Folio, xii + 312 S. Mit 78 Holzschnitten, 8 Radierungen von Wm. Unger und 2 Heliogravuren. Wien, W. Braunmüller, 1883.

Fritz Stahl, Wie sah Goethe aus? Mit 28 Tafeln, 66 S. Berlin, G. Reimer, 1905, Small-sized popular publication.

Ernst Schulte-Strathaus, Die Bildnisse Goethes (Propyläen-Ausgabe von Goethes sämtlichen Werken, Erstes Supplement). iv + 100 p., 167 pl. München, Georg Müller, 1911.

Hans Timotheus Kroeber, Die Goethezeit in Silhouetten. 74 Silhouetten in ganzer Figur vornehmlich aus Weimar und Umgebung. 180 S., 70 Taf. Weimar, Gustav Kiepenheuer, 1911.

Franz Neubert, Goethe und sein Kreis. Erläutert und dargestellt in 651 Abbildungen. Mit einer Einführung in das Verständnis von Goethes Persönlichkeit. xxx + 220 p., small folio. Leipzig, J. J. Weber, 1919.

Hans Wahl, Goethe. Die wertvollsten Goethebildnisse. Ausgewählt mit Unterstützung des Goethe-National-Museums in Weimar herausgegeben. 19 pl., 15 p. München, Einhorn Verlag, 1919. Folio.

Hans Wahl, Goethe in Bildnis. Herausgegeben und eingeleitet. 70 p., 120 pl. Leipzig, Insel Verlag (no date, 1930).

Hans Wahl und Anton Kippenberg, Goethe und seine Welt. Unter Mitwirkung von Ernest Beutler. 306 p., 580 ill. Leipzig, Insel Verlag, 1932.

Haller. — Arthur Weese, Die Bildnisse Albrecht von Haller, 282 p., ill. Bern, Francke, 1909.

Harvey. — Portraits of Dr. William Harvey. Published for the historical section of the Royal Society of Medicine. Folio. v + 50 p., 20 pl. Oxford University Press, 1913.

Linné. — Tycho Tullberg, Linnéporträtt. Vid Uppsala universitets minnesfest på tvåhundraårsdagen af Carl von Linnés födelse. 187 p., many illustr. Stockholm, Ljus, 1907.

Newton. — David Eugene Smith, The portraits of Isaac Newton (*Bibliotheca mathematica*, vol. 9, 301–308, 1909). The portrait medals of Newton (14 p., Boston, Ginn, c. 1912); Portraits of Sir Isaac Newton; the portrait medals. In the memorial volume edited for the Newton bicentennial commemoration by W. J. Greenstreet (London, 1927; *Isis 11*, 387–393). Smith's papers are brief lists, largely based upon his own collections, forming a good introduction to the subject, but we need more, much more.

Paracelsus. — Karl Aberle, Grabendenkmal, Schädel und Abbildungen des Theophrastus Paracelsus. 580 p., ill. Salzburg, Dieter, 1891.

Pascal. — Augustin Gazier, Port Royal au XVIIe siècle, images et portraits avec des notes historiques et iconographiques. Introduction par André Hallays. Folio, xii + 20 p., 130 pl. Paris, Hachette, 1909. Published to commemorate the second centenary of the destruction of Port Royal.

Albert Ojardias, Divers portraits de Pascal et des siens. (*Gazette des Beaux arts*, vol. 4, 195–207, 10 ill., Paris 1910).

C. A. Sainte-Beuve, Port Royal, Édition documentaire établie par René Louis Doyon et Charles Marchesne. 10 vols. Paris, La Connaissance, 1926–1932. The first edition of this classic began to appear in 1840. The "édition documentaire" is richly illustrated.

Léon Brunschwig, Pascal (86 p., 60 pl., Paris, Rieder, 1932; *Isis 21*, 375).

Vesalius. — M. H. Spielmann, The iconography of Andreas Vesalius, 1514–64. xxxvii + 243 p., many illustr. London, John Bale, Sons and Danielsson, 1925.

I owe a part of this bibliography to the kindness and learning of Dr. Arnold C. Klebs of Nyon . . . It is meant to include not every paper dealing with iconographical problems (many such ones are recorded in *Isis* as they appear) but only general studies of the portraits of great scientists . . .

NOTE ON ALTERED PORTRAITS

American scholars who know their classics remember the story of Rip Van Winkle. When Rip awoke from his long sleep in the Catskill Mountains and walked down to his old village on the Hudson he was amazed at the changes which he witnessed everywhere. For example, when he reached the old inn where he had whiled away so many an afternoon he could scarcely recognize it. Says Washington Irving, "Instead of the great tree that used to shelter the quiet little Dutch inn of yore, there now was reared a tall naked pole, with something on the top that looked like a red night-cap, and from it was fluttering a flag, on which was a singular assemblage of stars and stripes — all this was strange and incomprehensible. He recognized on the sign, however, the ruby face of King George, under which he had smoked so many a peaceful pipe; but even this was singularly metamorphosed. The red coat was changed for one of blue and buff, a sword was held in the hand instead of a sceptre, the head was decorated with a cocked hat, and underneath was painted in large characters, General Washington."

This is a very good example of an altered portrait. The reader should not imagine that it was very unusual. The practice was not uncommon in earlier days. There was another practice coming close to it of preparing portraits in advance for the accommodation of unknown sitters. Thus in early colonial days enterprising painters would roam across the American colonies with canvasses upon which they had already painted the bodies of fine gentlemen and ladies, dressed in the latest fashion; all that was lacking was the head which was then filled in to accommodate the patron. Similar customs, or worse ones, obtained in China in the case of the so-called funeral portraits.[4]

While I am talking of fancy portraits, I might say a few words of the naive procedure followed by some of the early printers, who reproduced repeatedly the same portrait, even in the same book, to represent different persons! The best example I know is the *De claris mulieribus* of the Augustinian Iacopo Filippo Foresti (1434–1520), generally called Bergomensis because he hailed from Bergamo in Lombardy. The edition of that book printed by Laurentius de Rubeis on April 29, 1497 is said to be the most beautiful book printed at Ferrara.[5] It contains no less than 172 woodcut portraits of famous women of all times, but these portraits were printed from 56 blocks. That is, each woodcut had to serve for many women. "The cut depicting Niobe for instance, is used also to adorn the biographies of Arachne, Argia, Mantho, Nicostrate, Helen, Polyxena, Penelope, Veturia, Sophonisba, Portia, Faustina, and Griselda. The picture of Sulpicia, the wife of Lentulus, is also the likeness of Antonia, the daughter of Marc Anthony, and of Maria Puzzoli, a contemporary of Petrarch. Similarly, the portrait of Saint Petronilla serves for seven other Christian saints: Domicilla Flavia, Martina, Justina of Antioch, Christine, Euphrasia, Marcellina, and Elizabeth of Hungary." The picture of Eve between two palm trees holding Cain by the hand and Abel on her arm, is very plausible; and that particular cut was

[4] Arthur Waley, *Introduction to the Study of Chinese painting* (p. 160, London, 1923).
[5] Facsimile of one page and descriptions of the work, by Zoltán Haraszti in *More books, The Bulletin of the Boston Public Library* (June 1938, 235–239).

used only for Eve, but even in that case I am not prepared to say that it is a genuine portrait.

To return to *altered* portraits, the practice was often indulged in by mezzotinters and other engravers. Copper plates were very expensive, and the demand for definite portraits would change capriciously as the persons delineated became more or less popular. The engraver would be very tempted to transform an obsolete copperplate and produce with a minimum of alterations a new portrait for which there would be a better market. We are very well informed with regard to that practice as it obtained in England because the late George Somes Layard had made a collection of such plates now in the possession of the marquess of Sligo. Layard prepared a "Catalogue raisonné of engraved British portraits from altered plates" edited posthumously by H. M. Latham, with a preface by the marquess of Sligo (xii + 134 p., quarto, 43 pl., London, Philip Allan 1927, 300 copies).

The Catalogue includes plates in mezzotint, line, and stipple in which the figure, or some part of the pictorial surface has been altered in a later state to represent a different person. It is confined to plates either engraved by a British artist, or representing in one state persons of British birth or connected with the British royal family. It does not include plates in which only the title has been altered. There are 118 plates in all. Every known state of each plate is described, and the Catalogue contains descriptions of many states which have not hitherto been recorded by Chaloner Smith or by other authorities. The earliest plate described is the line portrait of Queen Elizabeth enthroned which was subsequently altered to James I; the latest is the mezzotint of Queen Victoria riding in Windsor Park, in the first state with Lord Melbourne, and in the second with the Prince Consort.

In some cases the plates were not altered once but many times. For example no. 35 (in Layard's Catalogue) is a plate of which seven successive states are known, that is, which was altered six times to meet changing needs. The seven states represent, respectively, Cromwell on horseback, a headless rider, Louis XIV, Louis XIV again, Cromwell, Charles I, Cromwell again! No. 9 represented successively the Duke of Schomberg, William III, Marlborough, the prince of Orange, and Field marshal Keith.

There are also examples of double portraits, both altered. No. 64 illustrating James I and Anne of Denmark was changed to represent Frederick and Elizabeth of Bohemia, then again to represent Cromwell and the symbol of Justice! No. 87 served in turn for the Princes Maurice and Henry of Orange, then for the Earls of Oxford and Southampton, finally for Gustave Adolphus and John George I, Elector of Saxony!

Thus far, I know of only one altered plate of interest to the historian of science, that is no. 113 of Layard's Catalogue, engraved by T. Cecill. It was first used for the portrait of the poet and antiquary John Weever (1576–1632). When that portrait did not sell any more, the skillful artist contrived to transform the poet Weever into the mathematician William Forster (fl. 1632). The Forster portrait was published in the latter's posthumous(?) *Arithmetick* (London 1673).[6]

It is quite possible that some of these altered portraits are good and authentic likenesses, even as the portraits of George III and George Washington which Rip Van Winkle beheld before and after his long sleep may have been faithful and living images, but we have the right and the duty to be doubtful.

I have told the curious story of the altered plates in order to awaken the reader's skepticism with regard to portraits in general and teach him to be as critical in such matters as in any other historical matters.

Cambridge, Mass.
Dec. 4, 1938.

[6] I have not seen that *Arithmetick* nor the portrait, but I have consulted in the Harvard Library Forster's English translation of Oughtred's *Circles of proportion* (London, 1632). There is a short biography of William Forster in DNB (20, 24, 1889); see also Florian Cajori, *William Oughtred* (Chicago, 1916). The title of *Circles of Proportion* is wrongly quoted by both scholars.

The Study of Early Scientific Textbooks

Wʜᴇɴ one reads an elementary history of science wherein the account is necessarily restricted to the "great discoveries," one has an impression of discontinuity, as if men of science had been jumping from one mountain top to another. Each great discovery is indeed a discontinuity, or to use a mathematical term, a "cut," in the history of thought. Think of the following dates: 1543, 1628, 1637, 1638, 1687, 1800, 1859, 1895, each of which recalls a great spiritual victory. It is as if astronomy (and anatomy) had been suddenly lifted up to a higher level in 1543; it is pertinent to speak, as if they were distinct, of physiology before 1628 and after, of electricity before 1800 and after, and so on. That is all right, and may serve as a first approximation, but one should not confuse the approximation with reality.

We should always bear in mind two restrictions, or two sets of restrictions. In the first place, the great discoveries or the great classics of science did not come suddenly out of the blue sky. On the contrary, each was prepared by a long evolution; much of that evolution might be underground or secret, or more simply, it might concern only very few men. These men were not hiding anything, but the rest of the people — that is, practically all the people — were not interested in them and their doings and left them alone. Thus, if one had time and space to tell the whole story, the "cuts" would still exist, but they would not be as deeply isolated as they seem to be in the elementary picture.

This remark does not apply only to the history of science, but to history in general. Our generation is so much in a hurry that there are increasing tendencies to restrict education to the "high lights." That is good as far as it goes, and certainly better than nothing, but misleading. Thus, one might explain American history in a series of lectures chiefly devoted to Franklin, Jefferson, Washington, Lincoln, Woodrow

Wilson, and Franklin Roosevelt. Such lectures might be very interesting and very moving but however good, they would not cover the field of American history, nor explain that history sufficiently well. After all, many things happened between Washington and Lincoln, or between Lincoln and Wilson.

The same fallacy underlies the idea of teaching based on the "hundred" most important books. Must we emphasize the discontinuities, the revolutions, of history, or its essential continuity? I believe that no education is complete without frequent shiftings from one of these methods to the other. The discontinuities must be fully described, but that very description becomes meaningless if the fundamental continuity does not serve as their background. The mountain tops are exhilarating, but they could not exist by themselves; they imply vast plains around them, deep and lovely valleys, meandering rivers and graceful lakes, and an abundance of smaller hills. We should be ready to praise the heroes and to illustrate their greatness, but we can not do so without speaking of the people from amongst whom they emerged, whom they served or fought.

In the second place, we must bear in mind that just as the people were unaware of the long incubation of the great discoveries or intellectual revolutions, they were equally unable to realize their very existence except after a lag of variable length. In this respect, there is an essential difference between political or military history on the one hand, and the history of science on the other. Wars and social revolutions are obvious enough to all the people, for all the people suffer from them and help to pay the price. That price may be enormous and is distributed with remarkable impartiality; the rich are decimated as well as the poor, and the wise pay as much as the fools; people of all kinds and classes are ready or obliged to forsake their material goods, their health, their joys, their very lives. The catastrophe is general and concerns everybody without discrimination. On the other hand, intellectual revolutions are hidden from the eyes of the multitude. Thousands of people could witness the beheading of Lavoisier, but only a very few were aware that this man had completed another revolution, the "chemical revolution," more pregnant than the social revolution in which they were taking part. And so it is for every scientific discovery. The mass of the people do not begin to

340

think of it until it touches their interest, affects their health, their comfort, or their purse.

It is not clear then that a list of discoveries is only a very small part of the history of science? To put it otherwise, we may try to visualize mankind, the whole of it, on its pilgrimage in the search of truth. (The whole of mankind is engaged in that pilgrimage but only very few are conscious of it.) It is guided by leaders, and ahead of those leaders are many scouts. The whole body follows the leaders with more or less speed and compactness. Groups of various sizes are distributed along the road and, however long the procession may be (it is extremely long indeed and it may take God many centuries to see it pass), there are still a number of stragglers drifting in the rear. We may overlook those stragglers who are not representative and are hopeless, but we can never overlook the main groups, however belated, for it is they who make the laws, fix the customs, pay the taxes, and incidentally it is they also who provide the wages of the leaders and of the scouts.

A history of science dealing only with the leaders and scouts gives one a wrong view of the whole procession, and yet that is the way most histories are written. A good history should speak of the main body as well. In other words, it is not enough to tell the story of the discoveries; one must explain how these discoveries were received by the people and transmitted by them to their neighbours or to the coming generation. The history of science must include the history of scientific education, the term education being taken here in its broadest sense.

Mankind's destiny is to find the truth (goodness and beauty will be obtained in the bargain, but truth is the basis). To find and establish the truth is man's highest task, but the discovery of it is only a part of the task, and often that is neither the largest nor the most difficult. When the truth has been discovered it remains necessary to explain it to other people, in increasing numbers, and to obtain their acceptance of it. Nor is it generally enough to establish the truth; one must also disestablish the errors and superstitions which prevent, and may even stop, its diffusion. The discovery of the truth is one thing; its transmission another, equally necessary.

The two things are more closely dove-tailed than most people imagine. Indeed, the discovery of truth is not simple — as if truth were a tangible monument; a new piece of truth is hardly ever seen in its integrity from the first moment. One sees this aspect of it or that and only gradually are its implications realized. Now that realization is very often accessory to the process of transmission. The discoverers are not always able to appreciate what they have discovered. Columbus may be the father of America, but he never acknowledged his own daughter. The discoveries begun by great men of science are very often implemented by other men, maybe lesser men, and sometimes they are not understood until they are explained by teachers. After all, that is natural enough; we can never be sure that we understand a thing until we succeed in explaining it to others.

There are many ways of investigating the scientific knowledge of a group of people (say, the élite, the group of students or educated men who follow, or at least try to follow, the leaders most closely). Some idea of the scientific atmosphere may be obtained from contemporary non-scientific writings, such as the *Divina commedia*, the essays of Montaigne, the plays of Shakespeare or Molière. Many investigations of that kind have been made and the results are often entertaining as well as instructive. Another method, less amusing but more rewarding, consists in analyzing the contemporary textbooks, which were compiled for the purpose of explaining the new ideas, of popularizing these ideas or sometimes of resisting them.

Before going further, it is necessary to make a distinction between modern textbooks, say those of the second half or end of the last century and even more so those of this century, and the textbooks of earlier times. Within the last hundred years, and chiefly within our own days, the making of textbooks has become a highly competitive business. Textbooks are produced in increasing abundance and new editions of the successful ones appear at short intervals. Moreover, there are so many means of diffusing new ideas, that these ideas can be checked and rechecked by the experts of many countries within a few years, even within a few months. The final acceptance or rejection of those ideas is equally rapid. The scientific spirit of our men of science, at least of the leading ones, is so strong and well-disciplined that the inertia to novelty, *qua* novelty, is reduced to very little. Far from being annoyed or disconcerted by a new idea which threatens to supersede his own, the well-trained man of science of today is often delighted; to be sure, he examines the newcomer with caution and at first with suspicion, but once his reasonable fears of experimental error, levity, or quackery have been allayed, he welcomes the newcomer with pleasure and enthusiasm. He welcomes the new idea exactly as he would welcome a new tool enabling him to do better work. Under those circumstances, new ideas are quickly integrated into the textbooks, and the lag between the discovery of such an idea and its teaching tends to decrease. (There will always remain a lag, if only because the writing, editing, and printing of a textbook takes a not inconsiderable time). Therefore, analyzing the textbooks of today would not be very profitable; it would add relatively little to our knowledge of scientific evolution obtained in other ways.

If we turn to the earlier textbooks, even those of the seventeenth and eighteenth century (i.e., relatively modern), the situation is very different. During those centuries, in spite of the functioning of a few academies (which were clearing houses, their fellows acting as moderators and critics), the scientific spirit was not by any means as strong and as pure as it is today, the resistance to novelty was still enormous, even among men of science, and above all the diffusion of new ideas was still very slow.

In particular, textbook-makers were often schoolmen who had not yet been able to abandon scholastic methods, and were inclined to discuss scientific ideas in the same manner as they would have discussed philosophic or theological theories. The mention of theology reminds us that theological and religious obstacles were still limiting the exercise of thought and were often making that exercise dangerous.

For example, we might examine a number of textbooks discussing astronomical hypotheses. How was Copernicanism gradually introduced into the French schools? Boutroux has examined a number of treatises and theses beginning with that of Oronce Fine (d. 1555) and extending throughout the seventeenth century.[1] I summarize his conclusions. The early textbook-makers proceed very cautiously. They show the different astronomical systems, side by side, to wit, the sys-

[1] Pierre Boutroux, L'enseignement de la mécanique en France au XVII⁰ siècle (*Isis 4*, 276–294, 1922), an excellent article which every student of the subject should read carefully. I owe much to it. The astronomical treatises used by him are enumerated on p. 283.

tem of homocentric spheres, that of Ptolemy, the system of "the Egyptians" (the geo-heliocentric compromise of Heraclides of Pontos), the system of Aristarchos and Copernicus, the system of Tycho Brahe. They often refuse to choose between those systems. A little later they will perhaps admit that the system of Copernicus is the most likely to be true and the most satisfying to the human spirit, yet as late as 1685, one Pontchartrain feels obliged to add that the system of Copernicus, while apparently the best, cannot be accepted, because it does not tally with the Scriptures.

You realize the difficulties implied. How shall we compare those treatises? It is not simply a matter of deciding which of them is introducing Copernicus, but how does each of them introduce him? How many reservations do they feel obliged to add, and how shall we compare and classify those reservations?

It is clear that the history of Copernicanism cannot be properly elucidated before a large number of post-Copernican textbooks have been analyzed and compared. The method must be applied to every one of the countries where such treatises were published and where astronomers were at work. Final conclusions concerning the diffusion of Copernicanism in Europe and America could not be reached until a long series of such monographs had been completed.

The same method could and should be applied to every scientific theory, and especially to those theories which implied technical difficulties and the possibility of misunderstandings, and which evoked philosophical, theological, or political controversies. The case of the teaching of mechanics in the seventeenth century is peculiarly interesting because mechanical principles are apparently so simple; but it has been well outlined by Boutroux, as far as his own country was involved, and I refer the reader once more to his article.

I suppose that in almost every case, one would come across the compromising and ambiguous attitude of textbook-makers (timid people most of them, but we must admit that they had sometimes very good reasons for being timid). This might discourage the student in search of clear-cut allegiances, but he should be fully prepared for their exceptional nature and change his point of view accordingly. Take the wave theory of light which Huygens had brilliantly (if incompletely) explained in 1690, but which Newton's authority had pushed back into obscurity. What do the many writers of physical textbooks in the eighteenth century think of it? What position do they take between the two giants, Huygens and Newton? It is interesting to know that two other giants, the electrician Franklin and the mathematician Euler, did not hesitate to defend the wave theory, but how many of the scientists and virtuosi did they convert? One might burrow into the main literatures of Europe for that purpose, but the most valuable and instructive results would be obtained from the comparative analysis of the textbooks.

Let me give another curious example of the compromising attitude of the textbook-makers. This is done to illustrate the complexity and difficulty of the undertaking, for things that are too easy are hardly worthwhile. In my opinion, the textbooks have been unwisely abandoned because of their timidity and lack of decision; the historian should not allow himself to be put off like that, but should be more persistent; he should take pains to interpret exactly the lack of decision or the disguised scepticism of the authors as well as their occasional dogmatism.

This suggests that it might be particularly useful to examine unpopular textbooks. The most popular textbooks were not necessarily the best; their popularity might be due in part to their mediocrity or to their syncretic and accommodating tendencies. While the more original and independent authors would necessarily antagonize some of their readers, the clever textbook-makers would try to please everybody and often succeeded in doing so.

To return to the example which is the most amusing as well as the most instructive I know of: it concerns the gradual transition from Cartesianism to Newtonianism. It is an irony of fate that Cartesian physics did not find general acceptance except a short time before it was to be invalidated by Newtonianism; that invalidation was not readily accepted, however, even by competent scientists, even by Newtonians!

The story of that imbroglio is very complicated,[2] and I can deal here

---

[2] Much information *ad hoc*, but not by any means the whole story, may be found in the books of Pierre Brunet, *L'introduction des théories de Newton en*

only with a few events. Jacques Rohault (1620–1675) of Amiens, son of a rich merchant, studied philosophy and mathematics and was finally converted to Cartesianism. His conversion was perhaps favored by his marriage with the daughter of Claude Clerselier (d. c. 1685), who was a Cartesian of the first generation, Descartes's correspondent (the main one after Mersenne's death) and the editor of his post-humous works. Under that patronage Rohault became himself a Cartesian enthusiast and published a *Traité de physique* [3] (Paris, 1671) wherein everything was explained in Cartesian terms. Rohault ended his preface with the words "cependant je prépare une version latine en faveur des étrangers chez qui j'ose me promettre un accueil assez favorable," [4] and this implies that he was not too sure of obtaining a welcome in his own country. It is said that the calumnies of the anti-Cartesians advanced his death; it is certain that when he died in 1675 he could not obtain the extreme unction before having satisfied his confessor with a new profession of faith. Yet the treatise was very popular; it was perhaps the best means of establishing the superiority of Cartesian physics over the earlier systems. (The anger of the anti-Cartesians was thus natural enough.)

The French original was reprinted in Paris in 1672, 1675, 1682, 1705, 1708, 1723, 1730; other editions appeared in Amsterdam 1672, 1676; there are probably still other editions, since the one of 1708 (à Paris et se vend à Bruxelles) was called the twelfth. In the meanwhile, it was translated twice into Latin. The first translation was prepared by the Genevese physician Théophile Bonet [5] and published in Geneva in 1674; it was reprinted in

---

France au XVIIIᵉ siècle avant 1738 (viii + 355 p., Paris, 1931; *Isis 17*, 433–435) and Paul Mouy (d. 1946), *Le développement de la physique cartésienne, 1646–1712* (343 p., Paris, 1934; *Isis 33*, 104).

[3] "Physique" *largo sensu*, like "natural philosophy" in English. Rohault's treatise is divided into four parts dealing (I) with generalities, matter, motion, reflection and refraction, elements, heat, vision and optics, (II) with cosmography and astronomy, (III) with meteorology and geography, (IV) with physiology and medicine. The circulation of the blood is explained in chs. 14–15 of part IV (p. 342–345) in a very strange manner. Ch. 14 is entitled "Du poux, ou battement du coeur et des artères" and the circulation is not mentioned; the language is still curiously Galenic; in ch. 15, however, "Durée de la circulation du sang," it is clearly implied. That manner of explanation was preserved in later editions, including the English translation published in 1723 almost a century after the *De motu cordis et sanguinis*.

[4] ["However I am preparing a Latin version for the benefit of foreigners among whom I dare promise myself a fair enough welcome."]

[5] Théophile Bonet or Bonnet, born in Geneva in 1620, died in 1689. One of

London 1682; and in Amsterdam 1682 and 1700 with notes of the Franciscan Antoine Le Grand; [6] then again with the notes of Le Grand and Samuel Clarke in Amsterdam 1708 and Cologne 1713. A second translation, to which we shall come back presently, was made by Samuel Clarke and published in London 1697, reprinted there in 1702, 1710, 1718; a "sixth edition" with additions by one Charles Morgan is dated Leiden 1739. That is not all; an English translation by Samuel's brother, John Clarke, appeared in London in 1723, 1729, 1735. I have handled many of these volumes but not all, and do not offer this as a complete bibliography (which would be desirable) but rather as an outline, sufficient to prove the popularity of Rohault's textbook. That textbook could be read by any cultivated person in French, Latin, or English, and the publishers of France, Holland, England, Switzerland, and Germany vied with one another to increase its availability.

In the meantime, the *Principia* had appeared (1687) and Newtonian physics did not simply disagree wth the Cartesian, it was in some respects fundamentally opposed to it. As Voltaire put it in his characteristic manner,[7] "A Frenchman who arrives in London finds matters as different in philosophy as in all the rest. He had left the world full, and he finds it empty. In Paris, one sees the universe filled with vortices of a subtle matter; in London one sees nothing of the kind. For us, it is the moon's pressure which causes the tides, for the English it is the sea which is attracted by the moon . . ." I am afraid that Voltaire exaggerated a little as was his custom, or that he generalized the results of his own experience in selected circles, as we all do. The difference was not as sharp as he represented it to be; the English were not so progressive, nor the French as retrograde as he would have us believe.

In the first place, the *Principia* being published in Latin could be read as easily in France as in England; there were more readers in the second country than in the first, but in both countries the readers remained very few in numbers for a long time. We must assume that the men of science using Rohault's textbook after 1687 were aware, how-

---

the founders of pathological anatomy, a forerunner of Morgagni. He wrote many medical treatises all of which were first published in Geneva (*NBG 6*, 632, 1855).

[6] Antoine Le Grand (d. 1699). Born in Douay, assumed the Recollect habit and moved to England. He was the author of an *Institutio philosophica secundum principia Renati Descartes* (1672), translated into English (1694). A Franciscan defender of Descartes at the end of the seventeenth century! (*NBG 30*, 422; *DNB 32*, 421).

[7] *Lettres philosophiques*. Lettre XIV, sur Descartes et Newton, 1734 (*Oeuvres de Voltaire*, édition Beuchot, vol. 3, 186–194, 1829).

ever vaguely, of Newtonianism. Remember that out of some thirty editions of it, less than ten were anterior to the *Principia*. Thus, Rohault's success was not diminished by the introduction of Newtonianism, but increased, and his Cartesian textbook continued to be reprinted until twelve years after the death of Newton in very old age (*aet.* 85), or until more than half a century after the first edition of the *Principia*.

That aberration appeared in its most curious form, not in France, but in England, in the very University of Cambridge, where Newton had been teaching. Samuel Clarke (1675–1729) of Norwich, who was to distinguish himself later as a theologian and metaphysician (during the twenty-five years elapsing between Locke's death and his own he was considered the leading English metaphysician), began his career as a mathematician and natural philosopher. He studied Newtonianism in Cambridge (not in Trinity, but in Caius) and defended it for his bachelor's degree in 1695. Yet, upon the advice of his tutor, he made a new Latin translation of Rohault's physics, which was published a couple of years later (1697). This edition of 1697 is apparently not available in America, but Dr. Agnes Arber kindly examined for me the copy kept in the University Library of Cambridge . . . According to her report, there are references to Newton in the notes. By the time a second edition was called for (in 1702), Clarke had realized more keenly the necessities of those Newtonian notes and their presence was advertised in the title page. The Rohault-Clarke treatise became the outstanding scientific textbook in England (and America) in the first half of the eighteenth century. At the beginning of that century, however, English students were already losing their hold on Latin. John Clarke (1682–1759), who became in 1728 dean of Salisbury and is better known as such, translated Rohault into English, together with the Newtonian animadversions of his older brother. The English text was first published in 1723 and twice again in 1729 and 1735.

Now the Rohault-Clarke treatise could be defined not as a Cartesian Newtonian textbook (that would be nonsense) but as a Cartesian textbook including, in the footnotes, a Newtonian refutation. Please note that that ambivalent book continued to be printed in England until 1735 and in Holland until 1739. Many generations of English and

American students (in Yale until 1743) learned Newtonianism in a Cartesian textbook.

It is sobering to compare the popularity of Rohault with the unpopularity of Newton. By 1712, some twelve editions of Rohault's book had already appeared in French plus eight in Latin, while the *Principia* had still to be read, if at all, in the first edition of 1687. In 1709, Newton had been persuaded by the Master of Trinity (Richard Bentley) to permit the preparation of a new edition with the assistance of Roger Cotes.[8] The printing, much delayed by Newton's reflections and hesitations, took three years and a half; the second edition of the *Principia* appeared finally in June 1713. Cotes had contributed a long preface (dated 12 May 1713) the main purpose of which was to attack the theory of vortices. Thus as late as 1713 Newton and Cotes found it still necessary to combat Cartesianism. It was very necessary indeed as long as the young men continued to study natural philosophy in Rohault, and they continued to do so almost until the middle of the century.

Conditions being such in England we could not expect them to be better in France, for Descartes after all was one of their own, while Newton was a foreigner. The Cartesian resistance has been very well described by Brunet, but unfortunately he stopped his account in 1737 and many Cartesian rearguard actions were fought after that year.[9] The two following items give an idea of the situation in that year. In his eulogy of the geometer Joseph Saurin (1655–1737),[10] Fontenelle remarked, "Everything begins to clear up, and there is reason to believe that the Cartesian universe, violently shaken and strangely disfigured, will be strengthened and reassume its old form."

[8] Roger Cotes (1682–1716). Mathematician, Trinity College, Cambridge. When Cotes died suddenly at the age of 34, Newton exclaimed, "Had Cotes lived we might have known something" (Miss A. M. Clerke in *DNB 12*, 282–284, 1887).

[9] As a matter of fact, even the Aristotelians continued to fight, except that now they might be engaging not only their older enemies the Cartesians but also the younger ones, the Newtonians. The *Philosophia ad usum scholae accomodata* of Guillaume Dagoumer (d. 1745) first published in 1701 was still reprinted in 1757. Dagoumer was not by any means alone. Then came the "compromiser," the surgeon, J. C. F. Caron (1745–1824), who in his *Compendium institutionum philosophiae* (Paris, 1770) explained both systems, Cartesian and Newtonian, admitting their equal probability! More information in Daniel Mornet, *Les origines intellectuelles de la Révolution française* (p. 179–180, Paris, 1933; *Isis 23*, 463–467).

[10] *Histoire de l'Académie des sciences 1737*, p. 159. Quoted by Brunet (p. 340).

When Voltaire had completed his *Elements of the Newtonian philosophy*, he was refused license to print it by the Chancellor of France, Henri d'Aguesseau, who was a good and great man but a faithful Cartesian. Voltaire's reaction to that is as piquant as we might expect it from him; he wrote to his old friend Thiriot, "The Chancellor has not thought it permissible to grant me the privilege . . . and perhaps I should be obliged to him. I dealt with the philosophy of Descartes as Descartes dealt with that of Aristotle . . . I would have gained nothing but new enemies, I shall keep for myself the truth which Newton and 's-Gravesande have taught me." [11] The *Eléments de la philosophie de Newton* was published in Amsterdam in 1738, and reprinted the same year in London both in French [12] and in English translation. This did much to popularize Newtonianism not only on the continent but also in England.[13]

Brief as it is, this sketch will show how profitable it would be to investigate more in detail, in the many textbooks of philosophy and of natural philosophy, the gradual and ambiguous shifting from Aristotelianism to Cartesianism and from Cartesianism to Newtonianism. At the turn of the seventeenth century and well into the eighteenth the majority of natural philosophers were Cartesians but those Cartesians were subject to the attacks of two minorities, the belated Aristotelians to the right, and the adventurous and "radical" Newtonians to the left.

The study of early scientific textbooks is a wide field, which has hardly been exploited, and which promises a rich harvest of facts for the better understanding of scientific development and also for a better knowledge of man with all his desire for truth, his good and bad velleities, and his incongruities. It is only after many monographs have been patiently completed that it will be possible to describe with any fidelity the gradual acceptance of Copernicanism, Vesalianism, Cartesianism, Newtonianism, or whatever you please.

[11] French text in Brunet (p. 341).
[12] The French edition dated "London 1738" was printed and published in Paris.
[13] The English could read the *Principia* in their own language, for Andrew Motte's English translation had appeared in London in 1729. The French translation by Voltaire's friend, the marquise du Châtelet, was published in Paris in 1759. A Spanish translation of such a pernicious book would have been unthinkable.

Let us now try to explain briefly how such investigations should be conducted. Suppose we want to understand the development of optical theories, as set forth in the textbooks in the eighteenth century in France. The investigation would require seven steps:

(1) A study of the history of optics in the eighteenth century (or better from 1675 to 1825) leading to a list of the main discoveries, original memoirs or books, and controversies. (This would provide the fundamental frame of reference). It would be convenient to have also ready at hand a list of the main political, social, and religious events which may have affected the opticians and textbook-makers. The chronological summaries already published are not sufficient, because they were made from other points of view in order to satisfy other needs. Each student must construct his own summary, appropriate to his own purpose.

(2) Preliminary list of the main textbooks to be considered. Many such books are mentioned in the histories of physics or may have been discovered during step 1. This list will eventually be modified by addition or subtraction.

(3) Study of the lives of the textbook-makers and of their assistants. How did they come to write textbooks? What were their peculiar background and orientation? Did some events of their lives influence and guide their thinking?

(4) Bibliography of the textbooks selected. Description of their editions, translations, adaptations and of the commentaries or controversies to which they were eventually submitted. Polemics caused by textbooks are peculiarly interesting, not only in themselves, but also because they help us to determine the sensitive points, and thus facilitate the remaining steps. The descriptions should be accurate but bibliographical minutiae may be abandoned to bibliomaniacs. It is hardly necessary to describe a title page according to the formulae of bibliographers; it is simpler and better to publish a facsimile of it. The minute description of a book (how it was built by the printer) is of no interest for our purpose; its size and number of pages are relatively unimportant; but it is always worthwhile to give some indication of its length (say, about 200,000 words).

While the typographical features of the book may be omitted (except if they be of a very unusual kind), it is very important to set forth its logical structure. What was the author's purpose as revealed by the title, preface, table of contents, and chiefly by the book itself? How is the argument built up? Are new experiments described and discussed? Are authorities quoted, and if so, which are the main ones? What is the general outlook of the author? his tone and style? What are his attitudes to science, education, philosophy, religion, and politics? Is the book illustrated and how? In short, the internal structure, the purpose and meaning of the book should be analyzed as completely as possible.

(5) Examination of each textbook (and eventually of their sundry editions and translations) from the point of view of the critical question listed in step 1 or discovered later. What were the author's views on the speed of light, the aberration of light, the nature of color (e. g., of thin films) the intensity of light, the wave theory or alternate theories on the nature of light, etc. Each such question is a touchstone, and when a textbook has been examined with every touchstone applicable at the time of its publication we can formulate a well-considered judgment of it and of its author.

(6) Comparison of the textbooks with reference to each touchstone or to all of them. Classification of the textbooks from various points of view.

(7) Conclusions — This will include a list of the best textbooks, and of the best editions of each. Such a list will be valuable for other investigations of the same nature. A student of the history of physics (in a definite country and in a definite period) should try to have a set of those standard textbooks ready at hand; this would be an essential part of his apparatus.

The method just outlined is tentative and subject to modifications of various kinds. It is the method which I would follow, at least to begin with, but I am not dogmatic enough to claim that it is the best method or the only one. Any intelligent scholar applying it to the problem mentioned above or to any other would be led to modify it somehow. Moreover, each new problem requires a special handling and suggests additional inquiries peculiar to itself.

A method is like a tool; its goodness is a function of the qualities of the craftsman using it. As in the case of natural history, the main quality of the scholar is the ability to observe significant variations in the midst of an infinity of insignificant ones, the ability to remain critical, to take nothing for granted but to check everything down to bedrock.

It was told of the distinguished naturalist, Henry Nottidge Moseley (1844–1891) [14] by one of his teachers:

> He had somehow developed in early youth the most deep-rooted scepticism which I ever came across among men of my own age; hence it was the REALITY of the work which he did in the dissecting room at the Museum which delighted him and gave confidence that there was "something in it" worthy of his intellectual effort. With unfeigned astonishment he would say, on dissecting out the nervous system of a mollusk or some such structure, 'It is like the picture, after all!'
> He had a profound disbelief in the statements made in books unless he could verify them for himself, and it was this habit of mind, perceived and encouraged by Rolleston, which made him in after life so admirable an observer and so successful as a discoverer of new facts. Rolleston used to say that you had only to put down Moseley on a hillside with a piece of string and an old nail, and in an hour or two he would have discovered some natural object of surpassing interest. (*Isis* 9, 98, 1927.)

That attitude of mind is well known among students of natural history, but not so well among students of the history of science. Young historians must be trained to use it; if they have the aptitude to use it, they will learn to use it better and better by using it, not otherwise.

In order to complete the definition of the kind of monographs which I am recommending let us compare them with two other kinds, which may be said to limit them to the right and to the left.

In the first place, consider the bibliographical investigations of John Ferguson, *Bibliotheca chemica* (Glasgow, 1906); David Eugene Smith, *Rara arithmetica* (Boston, 1908); and Louis C. Karpinski, *Bibliography of mathematical works printed in America through 1850* (Ann Arbor, 1940; *Isis* 33, 293). Such works are bibliographical introductions to the monographs which I have in mind; they are exceedingly valuable but do not solve our problems. They contain elements indispensable for our investigations and facilitate the latter considerably. Happy the scholars who are given such excellent tools with which to begin their own work.

[14] Father of the more famous H. G. J. Moseley (1887–1915). See my article, Moseley and the numbering of the elements (*Isis* 9, 96–111, 1926) [pp. 268–283 above].

To the historian of science, bibliography is only a tool for a higher purpose; such tools are always welcome, we need plenty of them, but they can not satisfy us, except as means to other ends.

In the second place, consider an essay like the one by Pierre Boutroux, praised at the beginning of this article. This is too much like a conclusion offered to us without the material upon which it was based, and therefore unsatisfactory to the critical investigator.

Karpinski gave us the beginning of a monograph, Boutroux the end of one. We need the whole body . . . The preparation of such a monograph may be considered an excellent training for every aspect of our field, fundamental bibliography, chronological precision, appreciation of scientific ideas in their various stages of development, familiarity with scientific terms and their variants, description of the social background, psychology of discoveries and of their traditions, understanding of human character and its singularities, in short all the interactions between scientific efforts on the one hand and personal or social behavior on the other . . .

24 September 1946

Remarks Concerning the History of
Twentieth-Century Science

In spite of the fact that my main duty at present is the study of mediaeval science, and especially of fourteenth-century science, my work as a teacher of the history of modern science in Harvard University and my responsibilities as editor of *Isis* oblige me to follow as closely as possible the exuberant development of living science, and to connect and integrate that development with our traditions. Thus I cannot help wondering all the time,

If the growth of science continues at the present rate, will it remain possible for any historian, however deep his scientific preparation, to understand and record further progress? And will the historian of say, the twenty-first century be able to write the scientific history of our times? How will he manage to do it?

Leaving aside technical difficulties and assuming that the historian has no trouble in understanding the scientific achievements of to-day (which is a big assumption), he must still face a very complicated problem: he must *select* a relatively few representative documents from among a large mass of others which must of necessity be neglected, otherwise a clear account becomes impossible. In order to understand this better one must realize that his troubles are essentially different from those of the historian of ancient and mediaeval science. As the vicissitudes of time have already destroyed the great majority of ancient documents, the historian dealing with the distant past is obliged to make the most of the extant ones. He does not choose these, they have been chosen for him by an inexorable fate. On the contrary, the historian of modern science is literally submerged by the mass of documents. Assuming that he had no difficulty in understanding each and every one, it would still be physically impossible for him to consider them all. In this case, the natural selection effected by time must be replaced by an artificial selection. One might make it blindly, as Father Time made his [1] but that would be a desperate procedure, which could not satisfy anybody. Our fundamental problem then is to select as well as possible the main scientific documents and monuments of our time.

It may be objected that historians of science are as little able as the scientists themselves to appraise correctly contemporary efforts. As the historian well knows, this can be proved, as far as the past is concerned, by the comparison of contemporary appreciation, with later ones. The blindness of contemporaries is to some extent unavoidable because the value of a theory or of a discovery is a function of its fruits — some of which may be considerably delayed. However good their knowledge of the past, historians cannot penetrate the future, and hence, however wise their analysis and interpretation of contemporary theories, their conclusions are necessarily incomplete and tentative. We can hardly expect these conclusions to be more mature than the theories themselves.

That objection is specious. If it were allowed to stand, the writing of the history of science would have to be abandoned. Indeed that objection does not affect contemporary events alone. In a sense no scientific theory is ever final; it is always liable to criticism, modification, and even repudiation; hence historical judgments are at best tentative. The wisest historian writing toward the end of last century would have appreciated optical theories in a manner which would not be acceptable today. Science is gradually built up by the method of successive approximations; the history of science is necessarily built up in the same way. It can never be considered perfect but it may be indefinitely perfected.

It is not correct to say that the historian cannot appraise contemporary achievements. He can and does appraise them, but his appraisal

---

[1] Father Time's selection is not completely blind. Important and beautiful things have on the whole a greater survival value than unimportant and ugly ones. Father Time's selection is somewhat rough and careless, but it is effective in the long run. Hence our familiar illusions concerning the past. It is glamorous because the mediocre elements have been gradually sifted out, while the present is often dull and oppressive because all that is good and beautiful is submerged by the flood of mediocrity.

is necessarily approximative and tentative. It may have to be revised time after time, but in the meanwhile it may do good service.

A selection must be made, and every precaution should be taken to make it as well as possible. In spite of these precautions it is bound to be imperfect in many ways. However, an imperfect selection is better than none, and is itself a means of gradual improvement.

It is true in a general way that we must be at a certain distance (in space and time) in order to view things in proper perspective, and the bigger they are the greater must be our distance from them if we wish to see them in their wholeness and to appreciate correctly the relationships of the different parts to each other and to the whole. Thus it is certainly easier to appreciate the scientific achievements of the seventeenth century than those of the nineteenth and our judgment is likely to be more often correct in the first case than in the second. Moreover our judgment of contemporary personalities is more likely to be vitiated by irrelevant considerations, to be more partial — less objective — than our judgment of men with whom personal contacts have been completely eliminated. The great men of to-day may seem less great to-morrow, and others whom we have despised or overlooked may become more and more important as the centuries go by.

Nevertheless our judgment of our contemporaries will always remain interesting, even if it needs correction or is proved to be completely wrong, for that judgment will help to judge us. Thus in our appreciation of the past we take into account not simply the achievements themselves, but the contemporary criticism of them.

While we realize the great difficulties of our task, and the many chances of errors, we realize with equal strength our responsibilities. For the guidance of the scientists themselves, as well as for the guidance of philosophers and educated men, it is necessary to apply historical methods to the study of living science. We must at least write *chronicles* of it, and thus facilitate the task of later historians.

Let us consider the preparation of chronicles of the development of science from 1901 to 1940 (inclusive). I write "1940," for if my suggestions were carried out at once, the survey could not be completed within less than five years. The method would consist essentially in compiling a chronological list of the scientific achievements of those forty years, somewhat in the way it was done in Ludwig Darmstaedter's *Handbuch zur Geschichte der Naturwissenschaften und der Technik* (2nd ed., Berlin, 1908) but with far greater thoroughness and precision.

Darmstaedter's collaborators did only the first part of the work, and even that not too carefully. A similar list of main achievements should be compiled on the following bases: annual surveys of various sciences published in various journals, or in the form of presidential addresses to various societies, or otherwise; annual lists such as those published in the *Monthly Notices of the Royal Astronomical Society*, or in *Science News*, or elsewhere.

A large-sized card would be devoted to each discovery or achievement, and would bear the following indications: date; definition of the achievement; determination of its publication; various remarks clarifying the meaning of the achievement and indicating its relationship (cause, effect, simultaneity, degree of dependence or independence) with other achievements. The date might need qualification too. Indeed when one speaks of the date of a discovery, more than one date may be meant: date of actual discovery, date of communication to a learned body, date printed on the published account, actual date of publication. The names of the scientists should be quoted completely, together with the dates of birth (and eventually of death), but no other biographical information, except details which might throw light on their particular achievement.

The redaction and classification of those cards would constitute the first stage of the work. The second stage would consist in taking out all the cards relative to a special subject, and studying the original memoirs in due sequence. This would make it possible to correct and complete the analytical notes already included in the cards. In addition to this, advantage should be taken of the historical indications which are given in almost every memoir. The author indicates the source of his investigations, or he refers to other investigations of a similar kind and so on. On the basis of such references new cards would eventually be prepared, or earlier ones corrected and annotated.

With regard to the dead scientists, the general appreciation of their work contained in biographies or obituaries would improve our focussing and frequently would help us to restate the achievements with more clearness and authority.

As to the living scientists, after having taken all these preliminary pains, we would feel justified [2] in writing to them — explaining our general purpose and asking for their personal coöperation. They would be asked (1) to define their main achievements adding the necessary bibliographical references and the qualifications suggested by later experience, (2) to indicate other achievements of contemporary scientists to which they attach special importance, (3) to offer any other pertinent suggestions.

These inquiries might be completed by similar ones addressed to other members of the main scientific academies or societies. The critical spirit is very different from the creative one; some people are richly endowed with the former though not with the latter: their coöperation would be very useful.

All the data thus obtained would be reclassified, and it would then be realized that certain achievements are referred to more frequently, and with more emphasis than others. This would enable us to put a star (or two stars, or more) on certain cards, and thus to begin a preliminary graduation of these achievements. Other cards on the contrary would bear a question mark (or more marks), to indicate that their final inclusion is or is becoming questionable.

The patent literature might be searched and would probably introduce some items of true scientific interest. Basic patents are likely to contain new scientific ideas. The study of that special literature offers great difficulties of its own, of which I am aware because of long conversations with a great inventor (L. H. Baekeland), but I am not sufficiently familiar with them to venture any discussion of them. An officer of the Patent Office or another specialist of patent literature might be invited to give his own views of the subject.

The final classification and editing of all these cards should be done by a group of first-class scientists — men of broad knowledge and

[2] There has been considerable abuse of questionnaires by lazy authors who exploited that method in order to accumulate easily and rapidly the substance of a book. In this case however our questions would only be a means of obtaining additional information and improve our selection. They would be justified on the one hand by the quantity and earnestness of our own investigations, and on the other hand by the need of eliciting the scientists' own reactions to the achievements of their contemporaries.

experience, who would obtain the advice of specialists whenever they would be in doubt with regard to technicalities.

The chronological list of achievements — constituting a "chronicle of science" — would finally be published, together with a summary of all the explanations and abundant cross-references. The publication should be completed with two indices (1) of authors, easy to establish, (2) of topics, very difficult and delicate.

After the publication, about the year 1945, of those *Chronicles of science from* 1901 *to* 1940, the same staff — who would have obtained in the meanwhile very valuable experience of a new kind — would be utilized for other similar undertakings which I shall now proceed to describe.

In the first place, they would prepare in a similar way a chronology of science in the nineteenth century. In the second place, they would continue the same kind of survey year by year, and publish the corrected results soon after the completion of each decade. For example, it would be possible to publish about 1952, a new edition of their Chronicles extended to the first half of the century, with cumulative indices. New editions would appear in 1962, 1972, etc. — with new cumulative indices from time to time. Each of these successive editions would also contain addenda and errata relative to the previous ones.

At the time of their publication the Chronicles might be preceded by synthetic accounts which would be tentative sketches of the history of science during the period considered. This would be done or not according to possibilities, the main variables being the personalities engaged in the work. The learned scientists (or scientific historians) in charge of it might easily be so analytically minded, so conscientious or fastidious, and so timid that they would shrink from generalities, or on the contrary, they might be more philosophically minded, and sufficiently adventurous to feel the need of intermittent generalizations — if not every day, at least on Sundays and great holydays!

Thus far I have not laid sufficient stress upon the biographical investigations, which are nevertheless very important. We cannot understand achievements completely, or at least appreciate their finer points, their human aspect, without knowledge of, and some familiarity with, the men who were responsible for them. The scholars engaged in the compilation of our Chronicles would thus be obliged to undertake considerable biographical investigations: in some cases sufficient biographies would be available, in other cases, they would have to be provided.

Thus the preparation and edition of biographies of contemporary scientists would be an indispensable accessory and by-product of their activity. It is just as well to recognize the need of biographical information at once, and to organize its satisfaction instead of allowing it to become a hindrance.

A great waste of time and energy is taking place in that very field. Most academies and scientific societies try to publish biographies or at least obituaries of their members. That tendency is responsible for the futile sidetracking of many scientists — who are gifted for that sort of thing — and for the production of many poor biographies, in addition to a few good ones, and very few which are excellent. Moreover, most of those biographies, being buried in academic publications, remain practically unknown except to the members of the academies concerned.

It is clear that one might expect to obtain better biographies if these were centralized in a single authoritative publication, known all over the Republic of Letters. Many would be prepared by professional biographers (members of our office), well aware of the special difficulties and pitfalls of such work, and accustomed to aim for relatively high standards of accuracy and completeness.

The idea would be to publish within a single volume all the information relative to men of science and learning who died in a single year. The *Scientific Necrology* for the year 1940, let us say, would appear in 1945; as the staff would become more experienced the delay might be gradually reduced from five to three years. It would not be wise to reduce it more, as premature publication would tend to increase the number of addenda, especially with regard to the lesser known men of science whose death may remain unnoticed for a longer while.

Each volume would contain brief "who was who" biographies of all the men of science and learning known to have died within a given year, plus longer biographies (from fifty to a hundred) with portraits and bibliographies of the most prominent among them.

A good model for this part of the undertaking is furnished by the *Deutsches Biographisches Jahrbuch* published by the union of German academies. The German Jahrbuch deals only with Germans, but it includes men who have distinguished themselves not only in the field of science and learning but in other fields as well. Our Necrology would be restricted to science and learning, but extended to the whole world.

The two undertakings *Chronicles of Modern Science and Learning* and *Scientific Necrology*, being complementary, it would be expedient to conduct them in the same offices, though some officers would devote themselves more exclusively to the one or to the other.

The expense would not be inconsiderable. Accurate scientific work is always expensive (even if it be cheaper in the long run), and this task could only be accomplished by first-rate men. However, the expense would be restricted to salaries and office needs; the offices would be located in or close to a large library, hence a small number of reference books would suffice; there would be no expenses comparable to those incurred in laboratories or observatories.

The *Chronicles of Science and Learning* and the *Scientific Necology*, if they were well done, would soon prove to be very valuable and their need would be felt in every laboratory and reference library. Hence without being unduly optimistic, we may say that they would probably pay for themselves — in whole or in part — after a reasonable interval of time.

The intellectual value of these two parallel undertakings would be considerable. They would help the historians of science of to-day, and even more so those of the future, to find their way among our innumerable scientific publications, and would make possible the writing in due course of an adequate history of some of the most praiseworthy achievements of our own times. They would lift up the standard of every kind of historical writing and provide an especially strong stimulus to our studies.

People who have not forgotten the tragic failure of the *Interna-*

tional Catalogue of Scientific Literature,[3] and who remember the large amounts of money and energy which were sunk in that ambitious undertaking, may be in a hesitating mood with regard to this one. There is an essential difference between the two. The *International Catalogue* was purely analytic; its purpose was to record every scientific publication duly classified in topical order. In the meanwhile the number of items increased by leaps and bounds, not only in a normal way, but also abnormally because of racial, national, and linguistic competitions. The *Catalogue,* useful as it was, and however well it was done, could not help the historian and the philosopher, nor even the scientist, very much. It put some order in the chaos, but did nothing to cure or alleviate the main evil: the superabundance of futile and second-rate publications.

Our efforts on the contrary are distinctly synthetic. Our fundamental idea is the need not only of order, but of choice, and the problems which we are trying to solve and which we could solve with a fair degree of approximation, would be largely concerned with selection rather than classification. Of course classification is important enough, but it is easier to accomplish — it may be done, if not automatically (far from it), at least with less intellectual effort. The selection is extremely difficult and calls for a good deal of wisdom, ingenuity, integrity, and courage. The method which I have outlined would enable good scholars to establish on a sound basis a selection which would be as correct as possible and constantly submitted to revision. Thus we would not only prepare the historical synthesis of to-morrow, but clarify the scientific thought of to-day, and, to some extent, we would even help in guiding it.

Harvard Library, 185.
January 20, 1936.

[3] Sarton, *The study of the history of science,* p. 59 (Cambridge, Mass., 1936).

[The Work of a Historian of Science[1]]

Sᴛᴜᴅɪᴇs ɪɴ the history of science imply the correct application of methods, some of which are identical with the methods used by other historians, while others are identical with the methods used by other scientists. It is because of that diversity of approaches, necessitating a complex scientific, historical, philological, and philosophical training, that those studies have been neglected, or what is much worse, carried on in an irresponsible manner without criticism, without authority, without means of verification. The recklessness of many investigators, especially of philosophers, has been aggravated by the lack of organization, by the circumstance that the new discipline "the history of science" being a sort of no-man's land at the intersection of science, history, philosophy, etc. offered great opportunities for historical shallowness as well as for scientific dilettantism.

At this point Dr. Sarton begged the audience to excuse him if he spoke of his own experience. He was obliged to do so because it was simpler to take a concrete illustration, and no single case was as well known to him as his own. Toward the end of long physical and mathematical studies at the University of Ghent, under the influence of Comte, Mach, Tannery, Poincaré, his thoughts were gradually detached from scientific technicalities and oriented more and more closely in the direction of scientific philosophy. At first his interest was predominantly philosophical, but as he realized the urgent need of a historical and humanistic preparation to complete his purely scientific one, he became more and more interested in the history of

[1] [Though written in the third person, this is part of a summary prepared by Dr. Sarton himself of a talk, "The Historical Basis of Philosophical Unification," delivered by him before the fifth International Congress for the Unity of Science, Cambridge, Massachusetts, 1939.]

science, and more convinced of the necessity of studying that history as thoroughly as possible.

By the year 1912 he was determined to devote his life to a double project:

1. To prepare a survey of the scientific knowledge available in every branch of science at each period. As that survey was to be international, interracial, interreligious, it was not possible to divide the past according to the accepted conventions; instead of which the division was made arbitrarily by centuries to the end of the fifth century B. C., then by half centuries. That survey has been completed and published by the Carnegie Institution of Washington, to the end of the thirteenth century. The part dealing with science and learning in the fourteenth century is now in the course of preparation . . .

2. To edit a journal (*Isis*) wherein other materials concerning the history of science would be published as they became available, and wherein all other publications ad hoc would be registered, classified, and whenever possible criticized and discussed. The classification of materials being the same as in the survey, it was easy to publish all kinds of additions and corrections to the latter in due order. Thus far thirty volumes of *Isis* have appeared (1913–1939), plus six volumes of *Osiris* for longer papers (1936–1939). The *Isis* volumes include fifty-six critical bibliographies wherein at least fifty thousand publications on the history and philosophy of science have been classified and many of them criticized.

Though a considerable amount of information has thus been made available the main purpose of both undertakings is less that than the diffusion of sound methods, the discouraging of dilettantism, and the final establishment of the history of science as an independent discipline with as high standard of accuracy as any other scientific discipline.

As this talk was given in Dr. Sarton's seminary room, located in the very heart of the Harvard Library, rooms generously lent by Harvard University to the Carnegie Institution, he took advantage of that opportunity to show the large apparatus which has thus far been collected and is very probably the richest of its kind in the world. He explained how students and scholars are using it, and how pains are taken not to multiply unnecessary publications but rather to conduct investigations as thoroughly as possible, in order that scientists, historians, and philosophers may be able to continue their own work on a sound foundation.

The field of the history of science is immense, for it concerns the history of every branch of science at every time and in every clime, as it was developed by people of every race, sect, and nationality and written down in a great many languages. The parts of that field which have been studied thoroughly are very few indeed; a great many have been studied superficially; others have hardly been explored. Thus it is almost impossible for a teacher of the general subject however deep and varied his experience may be, to teach it with sufficient confidence. The amount of work remaining to be done will require the devotion of many scholars for many generations to come; in fact it will never be completed. The work should be done thoroughly, slowly, patiently, in the same spirit as similar work is done by naturalists and other scientists. Above all, historians should be very humble and eschew premature generalizations, which, however tempting, would or might destroy the value of their activities.

The unity of science may be proved by the convergence of modern methods, that is, by the efforts of modern scientists approaching definite subjects from many angles and in many ways yet obtaining results which tally and developing independent theories which harmonize. The unity of science is proved also by the consideration of its growth, similar to the growth of a tree the infinite ramifications of which do not destroy the singleness; that is, it is proved inductively thanks to the efforts of historians of science. These efforts need encouragement and purification, for the philosophy of science cannot be completely developed if its historical foundation is not as soundly established as its scientific one.

Cambridge, Mass.
[1939]

[A Summing Up]

As my connection with Carnegie Institution ends August 31, 1949, it seems proper to devote this, my final, report not only to the last year but to the whole duration of my service, which began July 1, 1918.

Rereading my yearly reports, the first of which appeared in Year Book No. 18 (1918–1919), I find that my main work was not announced until the third report (Year Book No. 20) and that I began the writing of my *Introduction to the history of science* only on January 12, 1921. When I started that undertaking, I did not, and could not realize its size, complexity, and difficulties; I thought that it would occupy only part of my time and that I would be able to complete two other projects, each of which was of lifetime size. These two projects were, first, a history of modern physics (physics in all its ramifications in the nineteenth and twentieth centuries); second, a full account of the life and achievements of Leonardo da Vinci.

As this second project is not unrelated to the main undertaking, I may be permitted to say a few words about it. In 1916, I had delivered six lectures on Leonardo da Vinci at the Lowell Institute in Boston. After the completion of that course of lectures, it dawned upon me that my knowledge of the subject was very insufficient. Leonardo, sometimes called the father of modern science, was the child of the Middle Ages. In order to appreciate his thoughts correctly it was necessary to have a deeper knowledge of medieval science than I could boast at that time. It was probably then that I resolved to make a systematic and thorough survey of the progress of science, century by century; I sincerely thought that I would be able to reach our time, or at least the beginning of this century, within ten or twenty

367

years. In reality, so many were the obstacles that I did not even reach Leonardo's time, but had to stop my survey about the year 1400.

The main cause of delay was the necessity, unsuspected at first, of studying the Arabic language. This was a heavy task in itself. At first, I had been helped by my kind friend the Rev. Duncan Black Macdonald (1863–1943), of Hartford, Connecticut, but in spite of his willingness he was not always able to help me, nor could I appeal to him as often as would have been necessary, and the obligation to study Arabic could not be eschewed any longer.

It is proved in great detail in my *Introduction* that for three centuries at least (the ninth to the eleventh), Arabic was the international language of science, and that in the following two centuries (the twelfth and thirteenth) the study of it remained the shortest cut to up-to-date knowledge. We often speak of the iron curtain separating eastern from western Europe; another curtain began to separate them (that is, to separate the Orthodox, Greek East from the Latin, Catholic West) as early as the fifth century, and three centuries later it had become almost impenetrable. The Latin doctors refused to read Greek; therefore, they were finally obliged to read Arabic, a language entirely unrelated to theirs, the language not of Christians but of Muslims. That is one of the paradoxes of history. It is because of it that medieval science and medieval culture cannot be understood without a sufficient knowledge of the Arabic writings.

While I was engaged in the survey of ancient and medieval science which would bring me back within a few years (so I thought) to Leonardo, the Carnegie Institution commissioned Professor J. Playfair McMurrich (1859–1939), of Toronto, to investigate Leonardo's anatomical drawings and notes. Indeed, it is clear that Leonardo's main source in this field could not be medieval knowledge, but only his own dissections, and the value of his anatomical drawings could not be appreciated except by a man with a long anatomical experience. The results of Professor McMurrich's investigations were published by the Institution in 1930 . . .

In the meanwhile, volume 1 of the *Introduction to the history of science*, dealing with the period from Homer to Omar Khayyam, a period of two thousand years, had appeared in 1927, and volume 2 in two parts, devoted to the twelfth and thirteenth centuries, appeared in 1931. The effort made to bring these volumes to relative perfection had been so long-drawn and intense that it left the author exhausted. Thanks to the wisdom and generosity of the Institution, I was permitted to spend a sabbatical year abroad. I resided half a year in Syria, where I was a guest of the American University at Beirut and was able to extend my knowledge of the Arabic language, the Arabic people, Eastern Christianity, and Islam. Shorter times were spent in other countries which were (or had been) parts of the Arabic or Islamic world: Egypt, Palestine, Turkey, Rhodes, Cyprus, Tunis, Algeria, Morocco, Spain and Sicily. After my return to Cambridge my work was resumed and centered upon the fourteenth century. This again took far more time than had been expected — volume 3 (in two parts) appeared only in 1948 — partly because my standards of scholarship had become more severe as my experience increased, partly because the amount of accumulated materials was so much greater. Materials had been accumulating for the whole work from the beginning; the accumulation had lasted about 9 years for volume 1, 13 years for volume 2, 27 years for volume 3. Many of the documents had been published, or at least listed, in *Isis*. By the time of publication of volume 1, 27 numbers (almost 8 volumes) of *Isis* had appeared, including 18 critical bibliographies; by the time of publication of volume 2, 46 numbers (almost 15 volumes), including 30 bibliographies; by the time of publication of volume 3, 103 numbers (35 volumes), including 67 bibliographies, plus 7 volumes of *Osiris*. The materials contained in the *Introduction, Isis,* and *Osiris* are integrated by means of thousands of cross references. Thus we may say that volume 1 was built on a foundation of 8 volumes; volume 2, on a foundation of 15; volume 3, on a foundation of 42.

Reference to *Isis* suggests that the mass of information included in the three published volumes of the *Introduction* is much larger than appears at the surface. These three volumes include 4334 pages, but there is scarcely a page which does not refer to *Isis* or *Osiris*, where more information can be obtained immediately. Moreover, additions and corrections to the published volumes are included periodically in the critical bibliographies of *Isis*, the 75th of which is now in process of preparation, to appear in volume 41.

The author is keenly aware of the need of correction and amplification, but such as it is, the *Introduction* is the most elaborate work of its kind, and by far, in world literature. This statement can be made without falling under the suspicion of boasting, for it is objective, controllable, and obviously correct.

At the end of my thirty years of service, I wish to express my deep gratitude to the Institution which made it possible for me to do the work which I loved best and for which I was most fit. Thanks to its patronage Rooms 185 and 189 of the Widener Library, Harvard University, became an international center and clearing house for the history of science. These rooms were never called an "institute," but they deserved the name far more than many of the "institutes" attached to European universities . . .

The history of science is like any other discipline in the field of science or the humanities, in that the fundamental work is slow and difficult, and the results austere. It is also expensive, or at least seems to be. It requires the most expensive of all scientific instruments, far more expensive than the greatest telescopes or cyclotrons — a large library, the larger the better (try to evaluate the total cost of such libraries as the Library of Congress or the Harvard College Library). To this one may answer that though the historian of science needs such a library more than any other scholar, he is not by any means alone in using it. Each library is used simultaneously by many thousands of people. In the second place, genuine scientific work is always expensive, at any rate as compared with secondhand work which requires only enough literary ability to exploit the investigations of other people or rephrase their reports; scientific work is apparently expensive, but it alone has any chance of permanence . . .

[1949]

370

INDEX

371

INDEX

Calendar: Gregorian, 109; Jewish, 98; Julian, 109; start of year, 324
Camphuys, Joannes, 194
Canavilles, Antonio José, 259
Candolle, Pyramus de, 249n, 263n
Canon of medicine (Ibn-Sina), 68, 74–76
Cantor, George, 25
Cantor, Moritz, 25–27, 29, 34, 39, 154, 181, 226
Capua, Giovanni da, 95
Cardano, Geronimo, 107, 109, 157, 160, 174, 175, 176, 177
Carlyle, Thomas, 45
Carnegie Institution of Washington, 50, 365, 368
Caron, J. C. F., 349n
Cartesianism, 345–350
Carver, Jonathan, 202, 220–222, 226
Cassini, 216
Castelli, Benedetto, 216
Castramentation, study by Stevin, 170
Catalan, Eugène, 235n
Cavalieri, Bonaventura, 177, 216
Cayley, Arthur, 37
Celsius, Olaf, 7
Celsus, 3
Cervantes, Miguel de, 103
Charles V, 239
Chartres, school of, 72
Chasles, Michel, 176, 240
Chateaubriand, François René de, 221
Châtelet, marquise du, 350n
Chemical revolution, 340n
Chemistry: historian of, 11; Renaissance, 109–111
China, 1, 20
Choiseul, Duke of, 199
Christina, Queen of Sweden, 130
Chronicles of Modern Science and Learning, 362
Cicero, 3
Clarke, John, 347, 348
Clarke, Samuel, 347, 348
Clavius, Christopher, 109, 156
Clement V, 95
Clerget, 208
Clerselier, Claude, 346
Clusius, 113
Cochins, 198
Colomb, Maria Elisabeth von, 244n
Colomb, Michel, 245n
Columbanus, Saint, 245n

Columbus, Christopher, 4, 104, 244n, 342
Commandino, Federico, 158, 177
Compania di San Luca, 124
Comte, Auguste, 7, 28, 37n, 240, 364; and sociology, 236–237
Condillac, Etienne Bonnot de, 291
Conquistadores, 107
Copernican theory: established by Kepler, 109; study by Stevin, 166, theological opposition to, 108
Copernicanism, introduction into French schools, 343–344
Copernicus, Nicolaus, 4, 49, 107, 108, 332, 344
Cordier, Henri, 251n, 265
Córdoba, 79
Cordus, Valerius, 113
Correspondance mathématique et physique (Quetelet and Gernier), 235n, 238
Coste, François and Marguerite de la, 249
Coster, D., 277n
Cotes, Roger, 349
Cournot, Antoine Augustin, 7
Cours de philosophie positive (Comte), 7, 237n
Coustou, Guillaume, 198
Couturat, Louis, 299n, 300
Craey, Catherina, 153
Creation and criticism, conflict between, 60–62
Credi, Lorenzo di, 123
Cromwell, Oliver, 49
Curie, Marie and Pierre, 6, 63, 328
Curtze, Maxmilian, 27

D'Acquet, Hendrik, 195
Dagoumer, Guillaume, 349n
D'Aguesseau, Henri, 350
D'Alembert, Jean le Rond, 198
Damascus, 75
D'Angiviller, Charles Claude, 204
Dante Alighieri, 302, 330
D'Antonio, Pierre, 121, 122, 125
D'Armont, mlle. de Corday, 225
Darmstaedter, Ludwig, 184, 186, 358
Darwin, Charles, 59, 63, 231n
Darwin, C. G., 280
De humani corporis fabricia (Vesalius), 114
De re metallica (Agricola), 114
Democritus, 2

373

INDEX

INDEX

Fuchs, Leonhard, 113

Gachard, Louis Prosper, 240
Galen, 3, 67, 68, 73, 74, 76, 88, 89, 90, 92, 93, 95, 134; motion of blood, 137–138
Galilei, Galileo, 5, 36, 103, 109, 110, 133, 150, 151n, 178, 183, 187, 216, 297, 330, 332
Galton, Francis, 229, 231, 242
Gama, Vasco da, 104
Gandz, Solomon, 98, 290
Garnier, Jean Guillaume, 235
Gassendi, Pierre, 216
Gauss, Carl Friedrich, 239n, 247, 332
Gay, Jean Pierre, 258
Gay-Lussac, Joseph, 253n
Genius, nature of, 268–269
Geographical discoveries, 4, 104–105
Geography, 2
Geology, work of Stevin, 183
Geometry, 1; work of Stevin, 176
Gerard of Cremona, 74, 165
Gesner, Konrad von, 5, 114
al-Ghāfiqī, 90, 96n
al-Ghazali, 4, 71, 72, 83
Gheyn, Jacques de, 186
Ghini, Luca, 113
Gibbs, Willard, 34
Gide, André, 146n
Gilbert, William, 5, 110
Gioberti, 239n
Girard, Albert, 171, 216
Glogau, Johannes von, 323n
Gmelin, Johann Friedrich, 7
Goethe, Johann W. von, 225, 239n, 290n
Goichon, Amélie Marie, 77
Golden Age, 164, 165
Golius, Professor, 174
Goujaud-Bonpland, Simon, 249
Gow, James, 37
Grandin (Martin?), 218
Graunt, John, 235
Greek books, translation into Arabic, 3, 18, 69, 301
Greek classics, 112
Gregory IX, 72
Gregory XIII, 109
Gregory, James, 208, 216
Grimaldi, F. M., 216
Grimm, Jacob and Wilhelm, 191
Groot, Johan Hugo Cornets de, 151, 157

Grotius, Hugo, 151n, 157, 161, 165, 186
Guemadeuc, Baudouin de, 204
Guglielmini, D., 216
Guide of the Perplexed (Maimonides), 81–88, 89, 97
Guldin, Paul, 216
Gundisalvo, Domingo, 72
Günther, Siegmund, 27

Haan, David Bierens de, 174
Haeser, Heinrich, 30
Hals, Franz, 328, 332
Haller, Albrecht von, 5, 7
Haller, Johann, 325
Halley, Edmund, 216, 235, 240
Haly Abbas ('Ali ibn 'Abbas), 73, 74
Hamilton, William, 59
Hamlet, 63
Hanke, Thomas, 260n
al-Harizi, Judah ben Solomon, 82
Harvard, John, 100
Harvey, William, 49, 297, 330
al-Hasib, Habash, 8
Hayles, W. H., 283
Heath, Thomas L., 25, 34, 36–38, 42
Hecker, A. F., 7
Heiberg, Johan Ludvig, 25, 29, 32–33, 39, 42
Heilbronner, J. C., 7
Heliocentric hypothesis, 109
Hellenic age, 3
Hellenistic age, 3; "Renaissance of Alexandria," 108
Hellmann, Gustav, 161
Hen, Zerahiah ben Isaac, 93, 96
Henri IV, 168
Henry the Navigator, 4, 104
Heraclides of Pontos, 343
Herbals, 113, 195
Heron (Hero) of Alexandria, 33, 166
Herophilus, 3
Hevesy, G., 277n
Heyrovsky, J., 277n
Hilbert, David, 85n
Hipparchos, 109
Hippocrates of Chios, 2
Hippocrates of Cos, 2, 73, 76, 88, 90, 93, 94, 95
Hire, Philippe de la, 216
Histoire des mathématiques (Montucla), 198, 199, 203, 208, 212–217, 222–227
Historian of science: and administrators, 46–48; amateur and professional,

375

INDEX

Isernia, Andreas de, 321
Isis, 26, 40, 306, 312, 331, 355, 369;
book reviews in, 318; critical bibliographies, 296, 297, 314, 365;
language policy of, 284–285, 304;
purpose of, 365
Islam, rationalism in, 87, 99
Islamic portraits, 330n
Isma'ili, 67
Italy: Fascist, 41n; medieval, 33; southern, 79

Jefferson, Thomas, 339
Jeffreys, John Gwyn, 271
Jenner, Edward, 211
Jesuit colleges, 106; of Lyon, 197
John of Damascus, 73, 76
Jombert, Charles Antoine, 198
Jones, H. Stuart, 38
Joseph, Sa'adia ben, 84
Journal des savants, 5
Judaeus, Isaac, 73
Jussieu, Antoine-Laurent de, 249
al-Juzjani, 67

Kahlbaum, George W., 30n
Karpinski, Louis C., 353, 354
Kästner, Abraham Gotthelf, 7
Keats, John, 302
Kepler, Johannes, 5, 109, 177, 183, 216
Kessel, baron de Keveberg de, 239n
Khayyám, Omar, 4, 368
al-Khwarizmi, 4, 8, 174
Kierkegaard, Soren, 33
al-Kindi, 4, 69, 76, 83
Kirster, Peter, 75
Klebs, Arnold C., 212
Klügel, Georg Simon, 223
Knipping, P., 274
Knowledge, unity of, 15
Kochansky, A. A., 210
Kroner, Hermann, 91, 94, 95, 96
Kunth, Karl Sigismund, 245n, 260

La Chapelle, 206
La Condamine, Charles Marie de, 211, 212
Lacroix, Silvestre François, 209, 210, 224
Laffitte, Pierre, 28
Lagrange, Joseph Louis, 179, 180n, 331, 332
Lagrangian mechanics, 34
Lagny, Thomas Fanlet de, 206

Lalande, Jérôme, 197, 198, 203, 208, 224, 226
Lamarck, Jean Baptiste, 249
Lange, Hans Ostenfeldt, 33
Language: Stevin's concern with Germanic, 156, 158, 165; use and misuse of, 288–290; development of, 289; poetical use of, 291–302; spoken versus written, 290–291; scientific uses of, 291–304; international, 293, 297–301; Arabic, 368; translation movements, 301–303
Lankester, E. Ray, 270ff
Laplace, Pierre Simon, 234
La Rochefoucauld, François, 144n
Latham, H. M., 337
Latin, medieval, 23
Latin scholasticism, 72
Laue, Max von, 274
Lavoisier, Antoine, 204n, 291, 292, 340
Layard, Georges Somes, 337
Learned books: art of reading, 306–308; points of good review, 308–313, 317–318; reviews to avoid, 314–316
Léau, Léopold, 299n, 300
Le Blond, Auguste Savinien, 197n, 198ff
Lecat, Maurice, 294
Le Clerc, Daniel, 7
Legendre, Adrien Marie, 209, 210
Le Grand, Antoine, 347
Leibniz, Gottfried Wilhelm, 177, 216, 299, 332
Leo X, 128
Leopold I, 231
Lettsom, John C., 221
Leucippus, 2
Leurechon, Jean, 218, 219
Leverrier, Urbain J., 278
Levita, Johannes Isaac, 98
Lewis, Edwin R., 239n
L'Hôpital, Guillaume François de, 216
Library, 47, 370
Liger, 208
Light, wave theory of, 344–345
Lignamine, Johannes Philippus de, 321
Lincoln, Abraham, 309
Lindemann, Ferdinand, 210
Lindley, John, 260n
Linnaeus, Carl, 190, 299, 330
Lobachevsky, Nikolai, 332
Lobelius, Matthia de, 113
Lockyer, Norman, 270

INDEX

Petri, Nicolas, 156
Petty, William, 235
Philo the Jew, 287n
Philolaus, 2
Philology, Germanic, founded by Grimm, 191
Philōn of Alexandria, 84
Philoponus, Joannes, 3, 84
Philosophy, 34; Aristotelian, 69, 70, 71; Greek, 85, 100; Jewish, 100; medieval, 18, 76, 81
Physician's prayer, ascribed to Maimonides, 89–90n
Physics, 2, 33, 34; Cartesian and Newtonian, 345–350; history of, 24; Renaissance, 109–111
Physiologists, pre-Socratic, 34n
Physique sociale (Quetelet), 229n, 231, 241–242
Picard, Emile, 34, 216, 292n
Pictet, Bénédict, 23, 24n
Pictet, Marc Auguste, 247
Pieterszoon, Regnier, 182
Pilarino, Iacopo, 211
Pitiscus, Bartholomaeus, 107, 164
Pitou, Louis Ange, 201n
Plancius, Petrus, 160, 182
Planck, Max Karl Ernst, 6
Plato, 3, 83, 85, 290n
Platonism, 73
Plempius, professor, 75n
Pliny the Elder, 3, 140, 314
Plotinos, 69, 76, 83
Poincaré, Henri, 364
Political arithmetic, 234–236
Pollaiuolo, Antonio, 123, 135
Pope, Arthur Upham, 67
Porphyry, 83
Porta, Giovanni Battista della, 110, 161, 208
Post, George, 292
Praetorius, Johannes, 164
Pratz, Le Page du, 222
Priestly, Joseph, 7, 223
Principia mathematica (Newton), 5, 183, 347
Proclus, 3
Psychoanalyis, 6
Ptolemaic astronomy, 97
Ptolemaios II, 184
Ptolemy, 3, 33, 97, 140, 325, 344
Puschmann, Theodor, 31
Puzos, Nicolas, 211
Pythagoras, 63

Pythagoreans, 85

Qabbalah, 86, 99
al-Qādī al-Fādil 'Abd al-Rahīm al-Baisānī, 80, 91, 94
Qaraites, 81, 84
Quadrature of circle, 240; Montucla's history of, 198, 199, 206–210, 226; proof of impossibility of, 209–210
Quantum theory, 6, 275
Quest for truth, Renaissance, 102–120
Quetelet, Ernest Adolph, 240
Quetelet, Lambert A. J., 229–242, 247, 248; as father of statistics, 233–234; as founder of sociology, 236–237; historical works of, 237–241; roots of thought, 234–236

Rabbinowicz, I. M., 94
Rabelais, François, 239, 240
Radioactivity, 6, 280
Radium, 6, 281
Rambam. *See* Maimonides
Ramel, Jean Pierre, 201n
Ramsay, William, 61
Raphelengen, Christoffel van, 160
Rasā'il ikhwān al-safā', 83
Ratdolt, Erhart, 322
Rayleigh, Lord, 61
Raymond of Toledo, 71
al-Razi (Rhazes), 73, 74, 88, 90, 97
Réamur, René Antoine de, 262n
Récréations mathématiques (Ozanam), 202, 208, 217–220, 226
Redouté, Pierre Joseph, 252
Reformation, 20, 109
Refraction, discovery of law of by Snel, 163
Regiomontanus, 107, 322
Relativity: general theory, 6; Lecat's bibliography of, 294–295; special theory, 6
Rembrandt van Rijn, 329
Renaissance, 4, 5, 36, 68, 75; definition of, 102; geographical discoveries, 104–105; Italian, 121; new arts, 118–120; revolt against medieval and Arabic influences, 103; scientific progress during, 102–120; scientists of, 4–5
Renner, Franz, 323
Research, historical, 21, 43–44; criticism of, 59–61

INDEX

INDEX

INDEX